Dawn.

It Happened at Hopkins

A Teaching Hospital

by Augusta Tucker

Revised and Updated Edition

Library of Congress
Catalogue Card No. 73-75225

Published by
THE JOHNS HOPKINS HOSPITAL
on behalf of
THE JOHNS HOPKINS MEDICAL JOURNAL
to which all profits from this book are given.

Baltimore, Maryland

To the memory of
Dr. John Shaw Billings (1838-1913)
a graduate of
Miami University and the Medical College of Ohio,
a Lt. Colonel, Medical Corps, U. S. Army,
who, in one lifetime
built
THE JOHNS HOPKINS HOSPITAL,
THE NEW YORK PUBLIC LIBRARY,
founded
THE SURGEON-GENERAL'S LIBRARY,
and
THE INDEX CATALOGUE,
which is a bibliography of
the entire medical literature of the world.

As Ernest Hemingway wisely said, the only man whose place in the race is secure is the man who has finished his course. With the exception of members of the first graduating class of the Medical School, in this book only the dead are mentioned by name, unless it be to identify a portrait, describe a procedure, as an author, or as a past professor, dean, or an historical personage.

The text of this book is a "one-man band," and the opinions set forth herein are those of the author. A committee of three doctors, however, gave their time, read the manuscript, and their suggestions were followed. They are Doctors John T. King, Samuel P. Asper, and Vernon B. Mountcastle.

The first edition, which was published in 1960, sold out completely; and this revision was done by the author at the request of Dr. Russell A. Nelson, President of The Johns Hopkins Hospital.

The author is deeply indebted to the following for helping her with this book: Dr. Russell A. Nelson, Dr. John T. King, Dr. Samuel P. Asper, Dr. Vernon B. Mountcastle; also Richard E. Townsend, William H. Gorman, II, Dr. W. P. Stephens, Dr. John W. Payne, Dr. G. William Benedict, and Mrs. Walter D. Pinkard, Mrs. C. Bernard Brack, Amanda A. Nunley; also Gerald W. Johnson, Harold A. Williams, James H. Bready, and R. P. Harriss.

Especial gratitude is due to the School of Nursing of The Johns Hopkins Hospital for providing quarters in Hampton House during the gathering of material and updating data. The Hampton House ladies and the student nurses afforded a haven of consideration and daily amusement.

The two chapters on "The Unseen Hospital" could not have been produced without the unfailing help of Anthony J. Zolenas and Martha J. Tomlinson.

The *Johns Hopkins Magazine* and the *Johns Hopkins Journal* have been of repeated use for reference in updating this book. The real source of information concerning the last 10 years, though, has been "Under the Dome," which has supplied innumerable facts used herein.

Miss Elizabeth J. Bruen, of the Johns Hopkins Medical Institutions Public Relations Department, who worked on the Twenty Millionth Patient Research and the picture captions for IHAH-II, and Mr. Richard W. Linfield, of the Illustrations Division of The Johns Hopkins University, who took many of the photographs used in the book, deserve particular credit and thanks.

The portrait of Dr. John Shaw Billings was reproduced through the courtesy of and used with the permission of the National Library of Medicine.

The tempera portrait Children's Doctor 1949 is used with the permission of Dr. Margaret I. Handy, and of Mr. Andrew Wyeth, who holds the copyright on the photograph.

The painting "Broadway" and the pencilled sketch of Dr. Charles R. Austrian are used with the permission of the artist, Florence H. Austrian.

The cartoon "Medical Students at Play," by Yardley, used in THE SUN, the original of which was given by Mr. Yardley to the Pithotomy Club, is reproduced with the permission of the Pithotomy Club, Mr. Yardley, and THE SUN. Gratitude, herewith, is given to all three. Pictures by the late A. Aubrey Bodine, taken from the files of The Johns Hopkins Hospital, are also used.

The letters OHH which mean Old Hopkins Hands and are used repeatedly in this book refer to all and sundry who are interested in the history of The Johns Hopkins Hospital, The Johns Hopkins University School of Medicine, The Johns Hopkins Hospital School of Nursing and East Baltimore. They know, or want to know, who married whom, who is dead and who is alive, and what has changed in the ever shifting Hopkins scene.

They will be most interested and proud to learn that this revised edition of IT HAPPENED AT HOPKINS is published in commemoration and celebration of the admission of

The Twenty Millionth Patient
to
The Johns Hopkins Hospital
on March 23, 1971

As of
May 15, 1889 through June 30, 1972
there have been admitted to The Johns Hopkins Hospital
20,722,634 patients.

After this book went to press, the active presidency of The Johns Hopkins Hospital was assumed by Dr. Steven Muller, who is, also, president of The Johns Hopkins University. Dr. R. M. Heyssel is now the executive vice-president and director of The Hospital.

Once before in the history of The Hospital, the presidency was held by the president of The Johns Hopkins University. He was Dr. Daniel Coit Gilman and was interim director of The Hospital from January 22nd, 1889 to June 18th, 1889.

Former director and vice-president, Dr. Russell A. Nelson on February 5th, 1963 ascended to the presidency of The Johns Hopkins Hospital. On October 1st, 1972, Dr. Nelson became president emeritus. The Medical Board of The Hospital has passed a resolution praising him for his years of service, and Dr. Nelson remains a member of the Board of Trustees of The Johns Hopkins Hospital.

All Hopkins Hands—everywhere—extend to Doctors Muller and Heyssel their best wishes.

IT HAPPENED AT HOPKINS

Dr. John Shaw Billings after a portrait by Cecilia Beaux.

Broadway
after a painting by
Florence H. Austrian.*

*This painting was
given by the artist to
Dr. William H. Welch
during his final illness,
in Brady. It remained
at the foot of his
bed, where he could
see it, until he died.

Children's Doctor, 1949. Margaret I. Handy, AB Goucher, 1911, M.D. Johns Hopkins University School of Medicine, 1916. After a tempera painting by Andrew Wyeth, Copyright © by Andrew Wyeth, and used with the kind permission of Dr. Handy and Mr. Wyeth.

James Buchanan Brady after a portrait by George B. Shepherd.

My Recollections of the Dedication of The Johns Hopkins Hospital

By Margaret Janeway Billings

I am writing this description of the dedication of The Johns Hopkins Hospital at the request of my friend, Augusta Tucker. I have a happy and outstanding recollection of the opening of the Johns Hopkins Hospital on May 7th, 1889. It was a beautiful early spring day, sunny and mild. My father had announced, somewhat pontifically, a few days before that he was taking the entire family over to Baltimore for the day. This was a great excitement for me, age 16, because I was the youngest, and Baltimore seemed a very long way from our home in Georgetown, D. C. The others took it in stride, my oldest sister Clare being an exalted 25, the twins—Dot and Daisy—were 22 and my brother John was a freshman at college.

We girls had our new Easter dresses, little summer prints of "india silk" (now called foulard), made at home by our family dressmaker. I did not think my mother had good taste, she dressed me like a barrel. But I felt gay and excited with my beautiful new straw hat covered with flowers that looked fresh enough to pick.

Speaking of flowers, we girls were eternally fed up with wearing the many blooms from mother's otherwise excellent garden. We wanted hothouse corsages, but on this day we had nothing, not even a jonquil.

We all took the street-car from Georgetown to the B & O RR Station, a family of seven. Father, on a Major's pay, could not afford the luxury of owning or hiring a carriage. We travelled, oh wonder of wonders, in a Pullman Car, to minimize, I suppose, the ravages of coal smoke, dust and perspiration for the day was warm. Ladies rest rooms, (powder room I believe they are now called) so necessary for "repairs" after a journey, were few and far between and distinctly unprepossessing. To make matters worse, Father never allowed any of us to use cosmetics, no lipstick, rouge, not even powder. Ladies using such "artificial" aids to beauty in our set were apt to be considered "Fast". Our speed must have been barely above a crawl.

On arriving at the Johns Hopkins Hospital I felt almost overcome with emotion. Father had been working on the plans in our study at home all through my childhood years. Discussion and conferences on it filled his, and our, days. He would often come home late in the evening from a meeting with the trustees and architects in Baltimore, mother would bring him a bowl of crackers and milk and he would tell her of progress.

The dream went slowly. The dour and conservative old Quakers who were raising the money would not let anything be built until the full amount of cash was on hand. So the hospital grew slowly, almost like a cathedral. I literally "grew up" with it.

But to return to the dedication. It was held in the large rotunda with many chairs facing a raised platform on which notable men of medicine, the Trustees and other distinguished guests were seated. We had "family seats" just to the right of the platform so close that I could plainly see the faces, many of them quite familiar to me, of the speakers. Several had visited our house many times and Father had taken me to their homes. I remember Dr. Osler, Dr. Welch, Dr. Kelly, Dr. Halsted.

Opening off of the rotunda were a series of corridors, like the spokes of a wheel, leading to the various wards, operating rooms, etc. a most impressive sight. And standing at the partially opened door of every ward or room down these vistas was a starchly uniformed trained nurse, their first Hopkins nurses.

Speeches followed one another in endless succession and I don't remember a single immortal word of any of them, not even my father's. They were far above my head. There were no funny stories, at least not to me, it was all too awe-inspiring. I remember Mr. Francis King spoke, also President Gilman of Johns Hopkins University, whose speech I thought was dry as dust for a person so distinguished. (Such are the critical faculties of age 16.)

After these formal festivities we enjoyed a gala buffet lunch, typical menu for Maryland in Spring, chicken salad, cold ham, ices and fresh strawberries with cream. I stuffed myself shamelessly.

Then we went on a tour of the new hospital. There were no patients, they began to arrive the next day. We saw, had pointed out to us, many of father's ideas and theories, based on his practical experiences with sanitation, ventilation, lighting and other problems in war hospitals.

Father had won a competition against 5 or 6 others for the best design for a hospital, and then had been retained as a consultant during its construction. Every ward had outside windows, sunlight and fresh air, no dark rooms. Corners of walls and floors had been rounded so as not to provide cracks for bugs and dirt. It was a dream that had evolved slowly, thoroughly, completely, a dream to have everything as perfect as possible, built to last, and planned as far ahead as it was then possible to see.

I was "very small potatoes" that day, but I remember it vividly as a magnificent spectacle and an outstanding event.

Margaret Janeway Billings [*]

---

[*] Born November 5th, 1872, Died July 15th, 1960. Buried in Arlington National Cemetery, beside her parents.

Back view of the Johns Hopkins Hospital, 1889.

Mr. Johns Hopkins (1794-1873), whose
instructions and fortune created
The Johns Hopkins Hospital.

Come Unto Me, All Ye That Travail

IN spite of the Charles Center architectural revolution and the emergence of Baltimore as the number-one home of muscle-flexors in America, whether in base- or football, the single most important day — still — in the history of Baltimore was — and is — August 24th, 1867. Upon that date, Mr. Johns Hopkins secured an incorporation "For the Promotion of Education in the State of Maryland."

That same year, Lister introduced antiseptic surgery; the first international medical congress was held in Paris; the Suez Canal and the Pacific Railway were opened; and, on July 1st, the Dominion of Canada was established. The B. & O. acquired 7 more engines, making a total of 297; and in 1868, there arrived at Locust Point, under an agreement with the B. & O., a fine new North German Lloyd steamer called "Baltimore"; also the B. & O. Mt. Clare shops commenced building sleeping cars and parlor cars to transport passengers to their hotels at Relay and Deer Park.

Transportation-wise, life was very rapid! Then, on the 24th of July there came the terrible Jones Falls Great Flood, which wrecked much of the center of the city and destroyed the excavations of the new City Hall, too.

Mr. Peabody's Institute, which had opened in 1866, fortunately was on the good, high ground of Mt. Vernon Place and escaped. Mr. Hopkins, who many thought had been inspired in his incorporation by Mr. Peabody, moved steadily forward with his plans.

Baltimore, however, already had a long history in medical care, for in 1788 a medical society had been founded, and that same year the doctor founding it had his anatomy school wrecked by a mob; however, 2 years later (1790) he and another doctor founded a second medical school, and 9 years later the Medical and Chirurgical Faculty was formed. In 1807 the Medical School of the University of Maryland was chartered, and in 1827 the Washington University Medical School got a Pennsylvania charter, when refused one by the Maryland Legislature. In 1832 the Washington Medical College was incorporated in Maryland and in 1839 the Baltimore College of Dental Surgery — the first in the world — was incorporated. That same year, the Washington Medical College obtained powers as a university. In 1851 Washington University closed and sold for debt, and in 1867, the charter of the Washington Medical School was revived by Confederate surgeons and physicians. In 1872, the College of Physicians and Surgeons split off from Washington College; and in 1881 the Baltimore Medical College was founded, while in 1882 Woman's Medical College began.

With such a long history of medical schools, the city probably wanted to see Mr. Hopkins put out some hard money before they took his "dream" seriously. This he did, for in 1869 Dr. Fonerden died. He had been in charge of administrating the old hospital on Broadway to which the wounded from the Battle of Baltimore had been taken and where, also, pioneering work regarding vaccination had been carried on. After Dr. Fonerden's death, plans were made to move this hospital to the suburbs; and in 1870, Mr. Hopkins bought the old buildings and the grounds. The Jones Falls Flood, which had wrecked Gay Street, doubtless did much to convince him to put his hospital on high ground.

Mr. Peabody, too, had died in 1869 in London and his body had been sent back by Queen Victoria, in a battleship, to be buried, as he had requested, in Salem, Massachusetts. He had recently ordered a tomb for himself constructed in a cemetery there.

Mr. Peabody's earned world-wide acclaim and respect, evidenced at his funeral, probably convinced Mr. Hopkins to crystalize his own plans.

The year he bought the old hospital, 1870, the first Board of Trustees of The Johns Hopkins University was organized; and by 1871 he had a little sketch of his plans published. From his own fine home (now "Clifton" in Clifton Park) which then was surrounded by beautiful trees and flowers from many parts of the earth he planned a broad, shady boulevard to the Hospital on Loudenslagers' Hill — "an educational Pennsylvania Avenue unique in the history of the World." (The Pennsylvania Avenue to which he referred was the one in Washington.) The professors were to live up and down it, rather like The Lawn, at The University of Virginia.

There is an old New England saying, "When you buy a piece of property fence it. If you can't fence it, don't buy it, t'ain't worth having!"

Mr. Hopkins was 75 years old at the time he bought his Broadway site; and in his letter written 3 years later to his Trustees, he instructed them to fence the 14½ acres on which his hospital stands.

In the 84 years since The Johns Hopkins Hospital opened its doors, there has been no piece of land on earth which has been more worth having.

The man who left the money to build this hospital died on Christmas Eve, 1873, and THE SUN missed the story. To avoid interruptions by drunken loafers, the city room door had been locked; and when an ancient Negro servant, carrying a note from Dr. Alan P. Smith, the attending physician, came he was turned away by the watchman, Adolph Schuch. Bewildered, he wandered across the street and gave the story to *The American,* a rival paper.*

On December 25th, however, THE SUN devoted a column and a half, page one (they published on Christmas Day then) to Mr. Hopkins' death. The paper said, in part, "Mr. Hopkins, the merchant, banker and millionaire, whose beneficence this community is largely to realize in the future, died at 3:45 o'clock yesterday morning at his residence #81 Saratoga Street, in the 79th year of his age." On December 27th, THE SUN devoted one and a half columns, page two, to his funeral. He was buried in a rosewood casket, with a silver name and date plate. The service had been at 10 on Friday; and Mrs. Talbot, a minister of the Society of Friends from Ohio, was moved to speak, stood up, and said: "If a man die, shall he live again? It is written he shall live, again."

Mr. Hopkins was a bachelor who went to work at 17, quit when he died,

---

* The Sunpapers of Baltimore—Johnson, Kent, Mencken, Owens, Alfred A. Knopf, New York, 1937.

and is reputed to have said there were two things sure to endure: "A university, for there will always be youth; a hospital, for there will always be suffering."

To his hospital he left $3.5 million; to his university, an equal amount.

To 10 or 12 relatives, he bequeathed approximately 30 warehouses, 6 stores, 50 dwelling houses, and $50,000 in cash, while 3 servants received 1 dwelling and about $10,000 in cash.

He also gave the hospital a self-perpetuating Board of Trustees, the originals of which he had chosen himself and who were largely, like himself, Quakers.

Those original Trustees made haste with profound caution; their bequest being cosily invested at 10 to 12 per cent, they could not afford to do otherwise. They chose the President of the university by writing to the 3 most prominent men in 10 different cities and asking each to name a candidate. The name which occurred most often was Daniel Coit Gilman, a graduate of Yale and president of the then 6-year-old University of California. He was invited to become President of the newly endowed mythical university, accepted, and arrived "back East" in Baltimore in 1874. The first through freight train from the coast also reached Baltimore that year — the passenger trip took a week. The B. & O. now had 549 engines — about twice the number they owned at the time of the Civil War.

The Trustees were so successful in the choice of Dr. Gilman that when it came to selecting a man to build the hospital, they wrote to five well-known hospital authorities and asked them, without pay, to draw up what they considered suitable plans for The Johns Hopkins Hospital! Lt. Colonel, then Major, John Shaw Billings was among the five.

He was an Army surgeon with Civil War experiences in the hospitals around Washington, and Mr. Hopkins' letter of instructions regarding the Hospital plainly shows that he wished it laid out in a pavilion style. In July, 1876, Dr. Billings won the chance to build the hospital. He took his plans and with Dr. Ezra Hunt, who was a well-known sanitarian, sailed from New York in October and returned in December. The trip was paid for by the Trustees. During the intervening months, his plans had been subjected to scrutiny and criticism by the leading hospital authorities in London, Leipzig, Berlin, Vienna, Paris, and Edinburgh.

A pavilion plan means that the hospital is built so that the buildings all go off one central corridor. They are not stacked on top of each other, accessible by elevators only. As a consequence of Dr. Billings' insistence that Hopkins be so built, it has a "Main Street" up and down which traffic, composed of the most renowned and the most obscure, moves constantly. At the time the hospital opened, this main street was L-shaped, neither Harriet Lane nor Phipps buildings were then on the circuit; where they now stand were then gardens and lawns.

Another axiom adhered to in the building of this hospital was "don't spend your principal." The 17 buildings comprising The Johns Hopkins Hospital opened their doors May 7th, 1889, 16 years after Mr. Hopkins died. At the rate of $125,000 a year they were built, furnished, and the grounds by which they were surrounded were landscaped and fenced. This miracle was performed without using one penny of the original bequest, which, by judicious investment, had been increased $113,000.

Although Mr. Hopkins died in 1873, the final plans were not approved by the Trustees until April 17, 1877, and the Building Committee was authorized to proceed with the construction. The superintendent of construction entered on his

The Hospital ground being cleared in 1877; view from Broadway.

duties May 8th, 1877. Excavations were begun, the fence put up, and the grading started. In February of the next year, Dr. Billings presented a full report on his heating and ventilating plans (both marvels then and, some say, now).

The hospital architects were Cabot and Chandler, Boston. The iron work was provided by the Phoenixville Iron Works, Phoenixville, Pennsylvania; and there is still an old catalogue from them in existence in the hospital, along with the plans.

Excellence was the only thing which Dr. Billings would ever accept out of anybody, be he a carpenter, a bricklayer, a professor, or a Trustee. This Army doctor had intense energy, great decision, utter fairness, and a complete inability to countenance either in men or material mediocre performance.

Incidentally, those hospital plans are all mounted on linen, and are as beautiful and intricate as etchings; the one of the Dome is truly exquisite. They are housed in the architectural offices of the hospital, and can be seen by any qualified architect who would treasure such a perusal. To approach the Dome one climbs a steep stairway from the 4th floor into a large room in the center peak directly over the front hospital door. From this room there rises a small circular stairway which leads upward to the actual Dome itself, around which there is a catwalk; again a circular stairway leads up from south side of that to a long walk which stretches from east to west across the Dome.

The view of Baltimore is breathtaking from the actual Dome, and one can imagine the excitement which reigned in Baltimore — particularly among the carpenters — when it was being completed. The glass fitters and the iron workers, too, from those perilous heights must have viewed the city with pride and aplomb, after 16 years of laboring on this great hospital.

In those pre-concrete-block days, everything in Baltimore was built of stone,

4

marble, or red brick; everything had a chimney and everything burned coal; and a misty red glow gave the city a magnificence and beauty which those expert craftsmen rarely had time to contemplate in their intricate, exact work. First came the glass of the inner dome which rises in the center of the lower catwalk and through which, for so many, many years the sun filtered down into the lobby of the hospital illuminating the statue of Jesus. Now that dome is painted and covered with heavy hog wire: no longer can one obtain the careful laborers who can clean that multitude of little panes of intricate glass; and carpenters working on the final dome, above, if they are careless, and some are, now drop their tools on the wire, without the danger of damaging the glass.

It is a commentary on the times that the sun no longer reaches Jesus.

High in the Dome, a plaque identifies the site of the Hospital's "cornerstone" box.

When the hospital was a-building, though, William L. Woods, the chief carpenter during the construction and an employee of the hospital for 52 years, suddenly realized that the hospital had no cornerstone. So he put a small wooden box sheathed in copper behind the ironwork of the Dome with some "selected" papers therein. This was not discovered until repairs were being made on the Dome in 1959, when the contents were examined and some current material was added. The box is now replaced in its niche and a sign stating its whereabouts can be clearly read when one stands at the top of the lower Dome stairway. Among the original contents were several newspapers describing the assassination of President Garfield; a copy of the payroll for the construction of the Hospital for the week ending September 24, 1881; collection envelopes for the Church of the Holy Innocents for December 1st and 28th, 1878; an advertisement for an entertainment at

5

the Franklin Lodge No. 4, Masonic Temple; and a clay pipe.

Although the hospital has no official cornerstone, a collection of bricks, each bearing the name of a Trustee, was buried about six feet below ground at the northeast corner of the Administration Building, and are believed to be still there.

Original isolation ward topped by a multitude of chimneys, which were equipped to be part of the ventilating system through which doctors hoped to control the spread of infectious diseases. They had double-space backs and trick flues.

At the opening of the Hospital, though, the sun shone through the Dome and neither the false cornerstone nor the bricks were mentioned; but in his address, Dr. Billings did say: "As regards construction, I do not hesitate to affirm that these are the best built buildings of their kind in the world." All the floors were edge grain Georgia pine 1⅛″ thick, which had been watersoaked six months and then preserved dry for several years before being dressed for use; the gutters, flashings, and downspouts were copper; all walls were plastered three coats, after they had stood two seasons before being plastered, to permit them to settle; the buildings were brick, trimmings Cheat River Stone and moulded terracotta, and all stone was laid on its natural bed, in the same relative position it had had in the quarry; the glass in the windows of the Administration Building and pay wards was French plate, the other first-quality French double-thick; the water supply was taken from the city and filtered; buildings were gas-lit (2,285 burners), but all were wired for incandescent electric lamps, whenever it should be deemed advisable to adopt this mode of lighting; pneumatic clocks were in all wards, corridors, and kitchens, driven by pulses or puffs of air sent through small iron pipes from the central apparatus in the Administration Building, which also communicated with the general telephone service of the city; and by means of a switchboard in the clerk's office *any* building could be put in direct communication with any other building. (The telephone had been patented 13 years before.)

There was a room in the Administration Building marked Officer of the Day, for the physician on duty; and from the first Dr. Billings insisted that the hospital be organized on the Chain of Command Principle and the Director thereof be THE HEAD, and accountable only to the Trustees.

To date four doctors have occupied that position. The first was from Michigan; the second from Maine; the third an upstate New Yorker; and the fourth from North Dakota: all men of rugged backgrounds, and they have needed to be. In 1964, the term *President* was substituted for the word *Director* of the Hospital; as of 1970, there was added a Vice-President for Medical Affairs, and a Vice-President, who is the Administrator of the Hospital.

The position described by Dr. Billings as Officer of the Day, is now filled by the residents of the different services in their own buildings.

The period of the seventies and the eighties in America was a "getting away with it" time, very like the present; and Dr. Billings was infinitely fortunate in his first choice for the faculty of the Johns Hopkins: Dr. William H. Welch, who held the same belief in THE BEST PERFORMANCE, which he had. Dr. Billings had met him in 1876 in Germany, and remarked to a Trustee, Mr. Francis King, "There is a young man who would make an ideal candidate for the faculty of our school of medicine." At the time Dr. Welch came to Hopkins in 1884, he was greatly discouraged; he had returned to New York, could not interest his alma mater, College of Physicians and Surgeons, in laboratories or pathologists. He considered practicing medicine to make a living and finally persuaded the Bellevue Medical School to give him three empty rooms, furnished with kitchen tables only, in which to teach his specialty.

By 1886, the Pathology Building had been finished at Hopkins, and Dr. Welch commenced his post-graduate courses in pathology and bacteriology. His young friend, Dr. William S. Halsted, was one of those students.

Incidentally, 4 years earlier, 2 other buildings — the Dispensary and the Octagon Ward — had also been finished. Two Trustees, Dr. Alan Smith and Mr. John Garrett, thought they should be opened and the hospital could be completed by September, 1883. But due to paying for construction out of income this was *not* to be until 6 years later.

It was 1888 before the building hospital and the nebulous medical school had a second faculty member, and he was chosen by one of the shortest major interviews on record. Dr. Billings, stopping off between trains in Philadelphia, went to Dr. William Osler's rooms on Walnut Street and without sitting down, said, "Will you take charge of the Medical Department at the Johns Hopkins Hospital?" Dr. Osler, without a moment's hesitation, answered, "Yes." Dr. Billings replied, "See Welch about the details; we are to open very soon. I am very busy today, good morning." He left, having been in the room approximately two minutes; and while there, he altered the course of medical education in the United States forever.

There was now a second man, who believed in excellence, casting his fate with the Brand New Hospital. He was a graduate of McGill, a bachelor, a Canadian, a minister's son, an inveterate practical joker, and he believed the student should

7

be taught at the bedside.

When it came time to choose a Surgeon-in-Chief, the man Dr. Welch backed, Dr. Halsted, was appointed "Acting Surgeon" and chief of the dispensary. The reason for this was that through experimenting upon himself while developing nerve-blocking anaesthesia, he had become a cocaine addict, realized his plight, put himself in a hospital in Providence, Rhode Island, and remained there a year, taking the cure. All of this had been prior to his joining the group of brilliant young men in the pathological post-graduate classes, under Dr. Welch, who was his staunch friend and was positive of his cure. Therefore, when the hospital opened, Halsted was "Acting Surgeon."

The Gynecologist-in-Chief and Obstetrician to the hospital was not appointed until two weeks after the hospital opened. Dr. Osler had recommended him and he became the fourth member of The Great Four. His name was Dr. Howard A. Kelly.

Portrait of Dr. Howard Kelly as a young man. This painting now hangs in the office of the Hospital's Director of Housekeeping.

Recently, a portrait of Dr. Kelly as a young man was unearthed from the storerooms of the hospital and it shows what an alert, aware, listening, evaluating, inner-lit young man he was. Any room you hang it in, it dominates and you expect it to speak. It is now in the possession of the Nurses, whose great friend he always was, and they will hang it where they please.

He always wanted to know everything about everything and he is the only one of the original doctors who probably knew that Mr. Hopkins had purchased the grounds of the Maryland Insane Asylum, two large lots, 17 dwellings — in all 14½ acres of ground — and closed two streets to build his hospital. Doubtless he was aware that the excavation had amounted to 201,180 cubic yards, the concrete foundations to 31,000 cubic feet, the wrought-iron fence was 2,725 feet long, the numbers of trees, shrubs, and plants set out were 3,067 and that they had been planted after 9,333 cart loads of top soil were dumped on the grounds.

Dr. Kelly was in attendance at the opening of the hospital and certainly knew that the first patient was admitted on May 15th, 1889. She was Mrs. Mathilda Bauer, 53, a housewife, from Cumberland, Maryland. The first male patient was James Twomey, 56, admitted by Dr. Halsted on May 16th. Very likely, however, it was Dr. Kelly who dug up the information that the first patient treated within the hospital was in the Octagon Ward ten years before the hospital actually opened. He was the foreman of the bricklayers, John K. Bruff, and he fell 30 feet to the basement, breaking his leg. Rooms were set up for his care and construction records in the Octagon Building, and the first nurse ever to care for a patient in the hospital nursed him. That nurse was a man named Samuel H. Kerr, who received $27.42 for his services for 24 days.

The lady from Cumberland had an aortic aneurysm and a fortnight after the hospital opened, Dr. Osler scribbled a postcard to his friend Dr. Musser, " 'Spital booming. Very busy."

When the hospital opened, neither the gatehouse, nor the laundry, nor the stable were connected with the main corridor; all other buildings were connected, even the bath-house which was equipped for mecurial and sulphur baths and had movable tubs that could be filled and moved to the patient's bedside. Dr. Billings stated in his opening address that the floor of the main corridor is 114 feet above mean tide and the terrace walk above the corridor is 124 feet above mean tide.

The upper floors of the Administration Building, the center building facing the hospital from Broadway — with the cupola that Mr. Leeke, then a carpenter and eventually Treasurer of the hospital, had climbed to place the weather vane — was where the staff lived. The hospital plans show that weather-vane on its triangular portion bearing a cut-out of 1882; however, one of the architects working at the hospital recently scrutinized it through a transit and states that it has nothing upon it. Always before a 25-year anniversary, the hospital gives itself a face lifting and perhaps when the copper was removed from the three domes, leaving only the copper ribs on each, the triangular piece of the vane was altered, too.

At the time of the 75th anniversary, the elevator had just recently been installed in the Administration Building. It operates at a stately pace, as if to counteract the vibration of the air conditioning equipment now in the attic above the fourth floor south. Because of its lack of haste, the young, who never have any extra time on earth, still bound up and down the beautiful center stairway, as of old.

When the hospital opened all of the Great Four were bachelors, although Dr. Kelly was married in June. He brought his bride to live on Broadway, and he was a vestryman of The Church of Our Savior. Dr. Welch continued to live over on St. Paul Street, but Dr. Osler and Dr. Halsted lived in the Administration Building, with the interns and residents. Dr. Hurd and his family had an apartment on the 2nd floor, and his little daughters were great favorites of "the boys."

The building was most tastefully furnished, in fine Victorian manner, with thick rugs on the floors and oil paintings on the walls, and mahogany Renwick furniture. Some of the furniture and many of the paintings still survive in the storerooms of the hospital.

The youngest interns, of course, lived on the 4th floor, and one of the surviving paintings, which hung on the fourth floor, is entitled "The Sultan and

9

Dancing Girls."

Many of the most affecting things in American medicine occurred in the rooms of the Administration Building. Here Dr. Osler wrote his *Principles and Practice of Medicine,* a textbook, which has gone into 17 editions.

Following the death of Dr. Osler, the text was edited by Dr. Thomas Mc-Crae, through the 12th edition, published in 1935. Dr. Henry Christian of Boston served, then, as chief editor through the 16th edition, in 1947. The book is now edited by the Chairman of the Hopkins Department of Medicine and several of his associates.

Also, in the Administration Building, Dr. Halsted presented to his then surgical nurse, Miss Caroline Hampton, the "first" pair of rubber surgical gloves. In the little book which The Welch Bibliophilic Society copyrighted in 1939, Dr. Halsted states, "In the winter of 1889 and 1890 — I cannot recall the month — the nurse in charge of my operating room complained that the solutions of mercuric chloride produced a dermatitis of her arms and hands. As she was an unusually efficient woman, I gave the matter my consideration and one day in New York requested the Goodyear Rubber Company to make as an experiment two pair of thin rubber gloves with gauntlets. On trial these proved to be so satisfactory that additional gloves were ordered."

The very heavy black rubber glove which reposes in a special case in the Halsted Room in the Blalock Building Dr. Blalock stated had been brought from Germany, by Dr. Welch, for use in autopsies.

Miss Caroline Hampton was a graduate of the great New York Hospital, possessor of the oldest nursing school in America; she later became Mrs. Halsted. In the light of modern surgical practice, it is interesting to note that at her insistence, she got up and sat in a chair the day after Dr. Finney had done an appendectomy upon her. Her action shocked her husband's colleagues but would meet with every approbation today.

A roster of the men who have lived in the rooms of the Administration Building reads like a "Who's Who in American Medicine." Among them are Dr. Osler, Dr. Halsted, Dr. Kelly, Dr. Cushing, Dr. Bloodgood, Dr. Heuer, Dr. Reid, Dr. Finney (whose nickname was "J'ai fini"), Dr. Dandy, Dr. Crowe, and at various times Dr. Billings.

In later life, Dr. Billings developed a lip cancer and several times came down for Dr. Halsted to operate upon it. He always stayed two weeks, for it took that long for his mustache to grow back and cover the scar. His wife, then an invalid, believed that he and Dr. Halsted were enjoying periodic fishing trips, of two weeks' duration, on the Chesapeake. Miss Margaret Billings, their daughter, who nursed her, knew the facts.

At the opening of the hospital, Mr. Gilman expressed in his speech a hope that some person "might place beneath this dome a copy of Thorwaldsen's *Christus Consolator*". Five years later, Mr. W. W. Spence, a Trustee and a Scot, offered to do so; the offer was accepted and in the fall of 1896 the statue arrived and was unveiled. William Thomas, who remained employed at the hospital from its opening until his death in 1958, and who spent many years as doorman, friend, and advisor of medical men, is the authority for the statement that "Jesus came in the north door."

In 1820, the original statue was carved and stands in the Fruekirke in

Copenhagen, Denmark. Professor Stein of the Danish Royal Academy of Arts completed the Hopkins replica in 1896. The Hopkins statue is cut from a single block of Carrara marble, and is 10½ feet high and required 9 years to complete.

A million stories circle around it.

A grey-haired man in a wheel chair, gripping the chair-arms and struggling to erase the stark terror from his face as he is wheeled toward a total hip repair, sees Jesus. Instantly, he crosses himself, bows his head, then lifts it, smiling, amazed, and secure. His wife who was following, crossed herself and stood silently praying, unaware that the wheel chair had rushed on. Then she glimpses it turning left on the corridor, squares her shoulders and quickly, almost jauntily, walks after it.

A little girl, bedraggled, almost dirty, her blue eyes seriously intent upon her purpose labors up the front steps of the hospital, walks slowly forward toward Jesus, then she reaches beneath her buttonless coat and brings out a single red rose. Rising on tiptoe, she places it between His feet, smiles, then turns and skips down the steps out of the hospital, again. The rose, like the little girl, is bedraggled, but it stays, all day, where she has placed it.

Another little girl reached up to feel His feet and robe; and as she stood on tiptoe doing so, she turned her head and said to her mother, "Mommy, God sure does have big feet."

Not an hour passes, not a half hour, that somebody does not silently or openly stand or kneel before Him and ask His Help.

The custom of singing Christmas carols at the base of the statue, according to the late Miss Frances Riach, who was for many years the excellent librarian of the history room, originated as an act of gratitude, connected with a terribly burned patient. Miss Riach's memory was phenomenal, and she searched for days before she found the history, #6513, which covered the case. The facts were these: a

They sing in gratitude.

11

boy, 18 years old, filled the gasoline tank of a truck at a station on the Philadelphia Road, and somehow his clothing was sprayed with gasoline; the driver of the truck struck a match and the patient's clothing burst into flames. The patient was admitted on July 27, 1926, at 6:40 p. m. with second-degree burns on the body, neck, and face. He had every possible attention, was a patient for months, and survived. His deeply grateful mother, Kate Johnson, persuaded the choir of her church, as her thank offering, to sing Christmas carols at Jesus' feet. The name of her son was Abraham Lincoln Johnson.

Miss Riach said, "How they worked on him! I'll never forget how those boys worked on him. He was on Ward M and he was Peterson's case."

One of the finest tributes ever written about Jesus' birthday at Hopkins is a short story which was published in the *Saturday Evening Post*. The author was then a staff physician at Hopkins and is now Medical Director of Good Samaritan Hospital. Some years, "Under the Dome" reprints that story in their Christmas edition. The author and the *Saturday Evening Post* graciously permit the use of the story. The story is called "Christmas at our Hospital." Perhaps the Patients' Library can supply copies of this story.

The upper floors of the Administration Building, in 1959, were turned into offices for the administrative staff of the hospital. These are the people who run the "unseen" hospital, described in detail later in this book. And though Mr. Leeke is long dead, the Treasurer still has a "high" position. His office is on the fourth floor.

Now, nobody lives in the Administration Building. Bachelor interns, bachelor residents, and bachelor professors, if they so desire, now live in the new medical dormitory beyond Hampton House, called Reed Hall.

No professor lives in the hospital, no administrator spends the entire night in the hospital; each building has an intern in the building all the time. Do the ghosts come back and call? Does Dr. Osler call for Lafleur and Harry Toulmin? Or does Dr. Halsted call for his first resident surgeon F. J. Brockway and his assistant J. M. T. Finney?

The shortest way into the hospital is still through the front door, so the medical students living at Reed Hall and the house staff living in the Compound are now added to the other medical men who daily pass Jesus. When He was put in the hospital it was solvent. In 1970-1971 the deficit was $1.7 million. Therefore the people He must work the hardest are the Administration, so perhaps this change in the use of the building is significant. Hard times are great teachers, so obviously, the building is still being used for learning.

Among the twelve original Trustees, named by Mr. Hopkins, two were lawyers, two doctors, two Hopkins' relatives, one each an oil merchant, flour merchant, shipping merchant, railroad president, wholesale grocer, and philanthropist. Four were men in their forties, two in their fifties, the youngest a doctor, 27, the oldest a philanthropist, 67. Either by marriage, or blood, four of the twelve were Hopkins' relatives. The Quaker influence was plainly felt among them. They had no flim-flam and knew that the only thing you can ever *really* give away is your very best: a Hopkins Trustee has ever tried to do precisely that as regards his duties toward his hospital. Next to his religion, marriage, and parenthood, he regards it as the most serious obligation he bears in life; and to many of them it has been almost a form of religion.

And they have ever been subject to terrible pressures. The hospital was only nine years old when it began running a deficit of $12,000. Private hospitals were making money and some smart people thought that Hopkins should have more private patients and reduce the staff. The Trustees reported, in 1898, "If the purpose of the hospital was limited to the care of a certain number of sick, looking merely to their restoration to health or the alleviation of their sufferings while life lasted unquestionably . . . . But keeping in mind that one of the main purposes for which this hospital was established, and one which in the opinion of the founder was of equal importance — viz, the study, as well as the treatment of disease, and the education and clinical training of nurses, physicians, surgeons, and students, the Committee is not prepared to recommend any curtailment in these directions . . ."

Every effort had to be made elsewhere, they decided. Scrutinize the non-professional staff; the private patients the previous year had paid $50,000 in board and $637 for professional attendance. In other words, Doctors Osler, Halsted, and Kelly's private patients ought to pay, and from here on out they did, the hospital collecting. (Probably this was the first beginning of full-time fees belonging to the Hospital.) It was also decided that revenue could be gotten from nurse care and that the private patients could pay $20 a week for this and $25 a week for board. They thought, too, it would be a good idea for a Committee of Trustees to find out why the hospital meals were so unappetizing to the patients and to the Staff. And they decided to charge the ward patients $1 a day, make semi-private arrangements to put two or more people in a room, charge $10 to patients for medical services a week, tell the ward patients if they were willing and able to pay, please do so, and charge $4 a week board for an outside nurse, if a patient wanted to have one. Also, that the Trustees help the hospital to pay for the Bulletin. Over and over in the minutes of that meeting they emphasize that if people cannot pay these fees, let them pay what they can, BUT always remember that a teaching hospital needs every help it can get from *every* patient.

All of this sounds strangely current . . . Trustees subjected to terrible pressures . . . hospital running a deficit . . . meals are unappetizing . . . patients ought to pay more . . . and help the hospital pay for the Bulletin . . . pare the nonprofessional staff . . . and a teaching hospital needs EVERYBODY'S help.

The Board of Trustees is now composed of 25 active members and 4 emeritus members. They are unseen, unsung, unrewarded, and untiring. And there is no prouder trust, nor more challenging obligation open to a man in Maryland than that of being a Trustee of The Johns Hopkins Hospital.

In the lobby of the Administration Building as one enters, upon the left wall, is a life-size portrait of Mr. Hopkins. Across the lobby from his portrait sit the ladies who direct one where to go in his hospital. The framed flags of "Base 18" The Johns Hopkins Hospital unit in World War I, which used to be across the lobby from the Hopkins portrait, are to be folded and placed in a display case in the visiting staff lounge nearby.

The office of the President of The Johns Hopkins Hospital is in the room directly behind Mr. Hopkins' portrait. Except for the War years, the President and the Vice President in Charge of Medical Affairs have spent their entire medical lives at Hopkins. The Administrative Vice President has been at Hopkins for 16 years, and his office is at the end of the hall.

The Vice President for Medical Affairs has an office directly across the hall

13

from the President. In 1969-70, the Vice-President in Charge of Medical Affairs was the president of the American College of Physicians.

The President, a most approachable, knowledgeable man, has two most interesting historical items in his office. One is the framed letter, written in his own hand, by President Gilman welcoming Dr. Hurd to Baltimore when he became the first permanent Director of The Johns Hopkins Hospital. (President Gilman had served as a temporary Director.) It is a generous, gracious, courteous, and stately letter revealing American manners at their best.

The other thing is a complete set of all six of the medals struck to commemorate, two each time, the 25th, 50th, and 75th anniversaries of The Johns Hopkins Hospital. The present, as well as the past, is always in that room, though; for in the last ten years he has had on a table there a large picture of The Klinikum Free Hospital of Berlin, which was modelled on The Johns Hopkins Hospital and to which he had been many, many times in this period as consultant during construction.

The great hospital in Leiden, Holland, which first opened its doors in 1592, is planning a new hospital on which construction is to begin in 1972; and the President of The Johns Hopkins Hospital has been their mentor and their guide in their planning.

In October, 1971, he was made chairman of the Association of American Medical Colleges, and is the first man, not a medical school dean, to be so named. (The AAMC represents 104 medical schools and 387 teaching hospitals, with associated members in several countries.) He has also been president of the American Hospital Association and chairman of the Board of Commissions of the Joint Commission on Accreditation of Hospitals.

Further down the hall, beyond the President's office, on the same side, there is a door with a brass plate above it which says Trustees. In that room are made all the final decisions affecting The Johns Hopkins Hospital. The room is very altered in the last ten years. It now has a gold carpet upon the floor, long draperies at the windows, gold leather on the chairs, over the mantel of the fireplace is a gold sunburst wall clock and the glowing coals in the fireplace are electrically lit.

The present long table is now covered with a gold cloth for the meetings; here sit the 25 active Trustees, and the 4 emeriti may be seated at a small cross table at the far end.

A large sideboard which belonged to Dr. Osler is against the right wall as one enters the room, and upon the walls around the entire room are hung the portraits of the Presidents of the Board of Trustees of The Johns Hopkins Hospital. They are:

Francis T. King	1870-1892
William F. Dixon	1892-1903
Hon. Henry D. Harlan	1903-1941
John S. Gibbs, Jr.	1941-1947
William Wallace Lanahan	1947-1948
W. Frank Roberts	1948-1955
Walter F. Perkins	1955-1963
J. Crossan Cooper	1963-1972
William S. McGuirk	1972-

In 1963 the term was changed to Chairman of the Board and Mr. Cooper's portrait has not yet been hung.

Many momentous decisions concerning American medicine have been, are being, and will continue to be made in this room. The times that try men's souls abound here.

The old 12-men-Board of Trustees table is now in the Winford E. Smith Memorial Room, on the second floor of the Administration Building. Here, too, hangs a portrait of Dr. Winford E. Smith who for 35 years was Director of the hospital. The portrait of Dr. Gilman is there, too, as are, also, the 50- and 75-year

Dr. Winford H. Smith (1877-1961) Director, The Johns Hopkins Hospital from 1911 to 1946.

dedication plaques of the hospital. The hospital silver service is also in a locked case in this room. And nearby is the Nursing Office, which seems most fitting, somehow, for Dr. Smith and Miss Lawler *ran* the Hopkins Hospital for many, many years.

Climbing down the stairway to the lobby, again, and looking out of the front door of the hospital toward the City of Baltimore, one observes that any person who sets out to climb any ladder at Hopkins soon realizes that he or she is embarked on an uphill course, literally as well as figuratively. This is the way it should be in a teaching hospital and it is the way it always is when you are sick. Getting well is an uphill job.

Before you enter the hospital, proper, one more thing. That Treasurer who is on the fourth floor of the Administration Building states vehemently, "No patient is ever denied proper care at Hopkins for lack of money. If a man is desperately ill and needs blood and needs nursing around the clock — and can't pay for it himself — the hospital hires the nurses and supplies the blood. Every patient here gets the best care, we can give him . . . and many times it is 'give' him, too. That is one reason for the deficit."

Map of The Johns Hopkins Medical Institutions.

Speaking of gifts, as one walks past the statue of Jesus, to the right, en route to the Main Corridor, one passes a plaque given by the Lederer family regarding a fund which is the largest single gift the hospital has ever received for medical research upon the causes and the cure of epilepsy.

Regarding this fund, the Professor of Physiology and Director of that department remarks, "One of the delightful things about the Hopkins is that there has never been the uncomfortable division not to say antagonism between "preclinical" and "clinical" departments which is so obvious at so many medical institutions. When I succeeded to my present position, I was amazed to discover that for many years a good share of my own salary had been paid by the Lederer Fund! My own research has been in the Physiology of the Central Nervous System, and particularly of the Cerebral Cortex, so that what I do could be regarded as research basic to understanding the cerebral cortex, and hence of one of its abnormalities, epilepsy. This shift of funds must have been a voluntary shift on the part of the Hospital to help the Medical School, and I think is an example of the unity of feeling to which I referred above."

CHAPTER II

The Corridor, Marburg, and the Admitting Office

THE Main Corridor, which adjoins the Administration Building, is still 114 feet above mean tide, but it has changed in so many other ways that probably a résumé of those changes had better precede an explanation. The corridor still extends from Phipps around to the Wolfe Street entrance of the Woman's Clinic. The patients from Harriet Lane have all been moved to the Children's Medical and Surgical Center (CMSC); and Harriet Lane is now used for varied purposes — some clinics, mostly psychiatric, some offices, and houses on the second floor a nursery school for hospital employees' children. The plaques on its walls still remain, but the portraits have all been moved elsewhere; many are in CMSC. The tennis courts are still seen from the corridor as one goes towards the old Nurses Home (Main Residence) and Wilmer. The upper floors of Main Residence are now the hospital storage area and on the first floor are the Nurses Library, as of old, the Patients Library, Patient Staff Services and also many Florence Nightingale relics. A steady stream of people flows through that lobby from the hospital garage and lot, together they hold 1200 cars; the 8-story garage houses 850 of these. The lot and garage are connected to the lobby of Main Residence by a passageway over Jefferson Street. There is an elevator in the garage. From 7:45 to 8:30 A.M. and 4:15 to 5:15 P.M. this is a crowded passageway.

The face of Wilmer, on the Main Corridor, has not been lifted, but many of the plaques have been moved elsewhere. In the Navy there is a term for persons who spent a great part of their service time in China, before World War II. They are called China Hands. Perhaps, for persons who have spent much of their lives

The Hospital's parking lot and garage.

at Hopkins, and now are elsewhere, and who read this book, Old Hopkins Hands would be an apt designation. They knew this hospital like they know the palms of their hands and wherever they are, they desire to know precisely how it is *now*. Part of this updating of this book is for them, therefore, from time to time when OHH appears, herein, please understand the reference.

It does so now, as regards the plaques, and many other references in Chapter Two. On the walls of the Main Corridor still remain some of those plaques, which still make it a museum of memorial tablets and bas-reliefs of sorts. The Crimmins boys, who were killed in World War II and who had hoped to become Hopkins medical students, remain. Their mother gave this plaque and a fund.

Nearby is the memorial to Jesse William Lazear, a native of Baltimore County, a graduate of Johns Hopkins University and the College of Physicians and Surgeons of Columbia University in New York, an assistant resident under Dr. Osler in medicine, a pupil of Dr. Thayer's in bacteriology and infectious disease. Lazear was the medical martyr who solved the dread scourge of yellow fever. In *The Johns Hopkins Hospital and The Johns Hopkins University School of Medicine,* those magnificent and definitive volumes by the late Dr. Alan M. Chesney, he suggested that Lazear is Hopkins' greatest medical hero.

There is something touching and fine about the Crimmins' boys and the Lazear plaques being adjacent to each other.

Jacob Schmidt (OHH, now 3rd floor Main Residence) gave an unrestricted sum of over $200,000 to the Hospital. Since this book was first published in 1960, the Greenbaum family has added to the Dr. Harry S. and Rena H. Greenbaum fund, so that it now stands at over $2,000,000, thereby making it the largest family gift

Dr. Jesse W. Lazear (1866-1900).

ever received by Hopkins from a Maryland family. However, the largest single gift is that of Mrs. H. Sylvia A. H. G. Wilks, who bequeathed the hospital $2,500,000. She was the daughter of Mrs. Hetty Green of Wall Street fame. Mrs. Wilks must have inherited her mother's shrewdness, for she was in a position to leave a similar amount to ten various hospitals throughout the country. Both the Wilks and Greenbaum gifts were unrestricted.

Any OHH would want to know that Dr. Lewellys F. Barker's plaque is now in the Hurd Hall lobby. He was appointed Physician-in-Chief when Dr. Osler became Regius Professor of Medicine at Oxford University in 1905, and he served in this capacity until 1914. A grandson, his namesake, graduated from the Johns Hopkins School of Medicine in 1959, as did also his father, the late Dr. W. Halsey Barker, class of 1932.

Miss Mary Adelaide Nutting, the second superintendent of nurses, was a graduate of The Johns Hopkins School of Nursing. (OHH - Hampton House lobby).

As one approaches the doorway into the Administration Building the tempo increases. However, before leaving the corridor between Wilmer and the Administration Building, it would be well to note that the part of the corridor just traversed is the only part with windows on both sides now left, except for a short portion adjacent to the Woman's Clinic.

The Post Office remains where it always was; but the offices next to it now house the Volunteer Services. Without these two departments the hospital could not *possibly* function. They will be covered in detail in "The Unseen Hospital." Adjacent to them there is now an information desk manned by one of those pleasant ladies who rotate between here, the desk in the main lobby, the one in the out-patient department, and the one inside the Wolfe Street door of the Woman's Clinic. They, too, are a necessity; the hospital has grown so big, a stranger can be easily lost en route to anywhere!

Next to that desk is still the Memorial Room for Medical Women, named for Miss Mary E. Garrett. It is a honor most deserved, for she gave the money which made the building of the Medical School possible and stipulated in her grant that women should be admitted upon the same basis as men. They were and are; and one, still living, who is a Professor Emeritus in Medicine, made among the highest grades ever achieved by a medical student. She, too, has a son in medicine who is a Hopkins graduate, who is named for his famous father and grandfather, both of whom were on the staff at Hopkins. Another "Hopkins hen-medic" the late Dr. Florence R. Sabin, became a full member of the Rockefeller Institute.

Across the corridor, the Cary plaque, a memorial to Mrs. Jane Margaret Cary, a Baltimore educator, and her daughter, Jane Margaret Carr, remains where it has always been. In 1908, Mrs. Cary's former pupils raised a fund which they gave to the hospital in her memory. The income is used to help indigent women teachers, preferably from the South.

Dr. John Hewetson's plaque now hangs on Blalock, 11th floor. He was from McGill, a beloved member of Dr. Osler's early staff, and died of tuberculosis. Osler loved him as a son, and Hewetson's contemporaries financed this memorial.

On Blalock 10th floor now hangs the plaque to Dr. Frank R. Smith, also a greatly beloved man by his associates. He was a Britisher and a scholarly graduate of Cambridge.

Dr. William S. Thayer's plaque now hangs in the Hurd Hall lobby. He was a superb diagnostician and teacher who always wore a carnation in his buttonhole, as he still does in his bas-relief.

In the Moore Clinic library, on the second floor of the Carnegie Building, one now finds the plaque to Dr. Albert Keidel. He was an associate professor of internal medicine, cherished by his contemporaries, who died of a type of arthritis whereby he died slowly. It takes exquisite manners to make a slow farewell; he had them.

All the alterations in the corridor, from here around to Halsted are the results of the building of the Children's Medical and Surgical Center. Thayer, the service building, the doctor's dining room, the nurses' dining room, the kitchens, and other departments in the service building all were demolished to make way for this enormous building.

Also, in the abolishing, The Brady Urological Institute LOST its corridor entrance, and now is reached on its second floor, via the elevators of CMSC. (OHH, more anon.)

The corridor, too, was widened here, just beyond the Administration Building doorway, and has a number of ersatz red "leather" benches on which all and sundry loll and gossip. While doing so they gaze not only at the corridor trampers, but also at long rectangular paintings, two of which are of Amsterdam, another is a street scene and the fourth is a seascape. Three of these are by unknown artists.

One no longer enters Marburg through the corridor doors, which have in front of them a protective rail and are locked. The entrance is now around the corner, just beyond the elevator doors, and en route one passes "Abstract #4" by Donati: a modern art painting which is considered very fine.

But to go back to the benches: children with mothers en route to the CMSC clinics, old couples, medical friends, uniformed hospital employees, all sit and watch the sights. Or they shift their gaze to the people coming or going from the cafeteria, which is directly opposite.

The hospital has approximately 4,400 employees (about 1,400 more

The main corridor, with the benches located near the main entrance to the staff cafeteria.

The staff cafeteria.

than 10 years ago) and they all have the privilege of eating in this cafeteria, if they so desire, as do the ambulatory patients and their relatives.

Also, the employees of the other Medical Institutions can come here and eat, too. Therefore this cafeteria which will seat 625 people presents a complete cross-section of the various classes, colors, and kinds of people who inhabit this earth: white, brown, black, yellow, and red men; Englishmen, Americans, Canadians, Peruvians, East Indians, Chinese, Japanese, Koreans, Alaskans, American Indians, Nigerians, American Negroes, Germans, Greeks, Frenchmen, Algerians — men, women, and children from literally everywhere come to The Johns Hopkins Hospital cafeteria.

Long-haired, sloppily dressed medical students, out-of-uniform pony-tailed student nurses in blue-jeans or shorts, secretaries, some in pants suits, Roman Catholic nuns, Amish women mingle with ambulatory patients on crutches, in wheel chairs, or pushing racks containing their intravenous fluid bottles.

The one-eyed literally lead the blind, as the patients with a patch over one eye help those who cannot see to their chairs. Patients in house coats and bedroom slippers, men in bath robes, and patients in all varieties of casts are frequent sights.

Seated in and out among these patients and their relatives, usually at their peer-group tables, are interns and residents, floor nurses and head nurses, social workers and Child Life personnel, administrators and men who direct the Unseen Hospital. They are frequently accompanied by their highly competent lieutenants from the front-line offices, which abound off the basement corridor, directly below the Main Corridor.

Also present are the members of the operating room crews in their multi-colored uniforms: blue for Wilmer, green for GOR, purple for Woman's Clinic.

Now, all the persons employed by the hospital whose personal clothing would be put at a risk by their duties wear a uniform; this goes for cleaning crews, food handlers, laboratory workers, and a multitude of other people. Each department has a insignia medallion on the left arm of the uniform.

Sprinkled in and out among all of these people are the trysting couples; the

21

married couples; the Compound family, which, as a wonderful treat, have come uphill to have lunch, or supper, with their intern father, wearing his clean white coat with his name embroidered upon it. They are on their best behavior and he beams with pride and importance, for, at last, he is among people to whom *he* can give the orders.

Four cashiers, counters of food — both regular and low-calorie diet, conveyor belts to take the used trays to the kitchen below all form a part of the picture.

Over near the corridor door, through which you entered, are the vending machines, for people in a hurry who haven't time to go through the cafeteria line. Nearby sit the engineers at a table which seems to be their own; also near that door (there is another door, at the far end of the L-shaped cafeteria opening onto the corridor opposite the lobby of CMSC) sit some of the cleaning crews. Oddly enough, they also seem permanently seated by the other door, too.

Often adjacent to the engineers will be a medical student bent over his books and munching a vending-machine sandwich.

Every person who goes through the cafeteria line, except the student nurses who have chits, pays for his food; and all the food served throughout the hospital, except the special diets, is the same. This cafeteria opens from 6:30 A.M. to 9:00 A.M. for breakfast; from 9:00 A.M. to 10:00 A.M. for coffee and other beverages; from 11:00 A.M. to 2:00 P.M. for lunch and from 5:00 P.M. to 7:30 P.M. for dinner. The vending machines are accessible at most hours. Each week the "disappearance" cost of replacing silverware and plasticware is enormous. Weekly the plastic replacements cost about $421, and the silverware $182.

The trysting couples can be observed at 7:00 A.M. breakfast as well as 7:00 P.M. dinner, but one group who only appear in the morning are the young husbands who are "watching" their diet, at home, and eating an excellent breakfast in the cafeteria. They take hot cakes, sausage, eggs, sweet rolls, cereal and cream, and coffee and cream, all of which they consume with a guilty pleasure.

Breakfast, lunch, dinner, and all hours in between, the loud speaker blares here, just as it does in the corridor; and interns and residents rise and repair to the wall phones and attend to the needs of their patients.

Few of either of those groups are seen here at luncheon, though, for there is a small doctors' dining room, at the corner of the corridor, seating 125 and open

The new (since 1964) Doctors' Dining Room.

Horses, street cars, window shutters — peace — a long time ago.

only between 11 and 2 P.M. for luncheon. It can be divided into four small rooms for luncheon and dinners; but at luncheon it is open to full-time and part-time faculty and their associates, house staff and clinical fellows, and outside men, if accompanied by faculty members.

There are no portraits on the walls, no waiters, everybody goes through a cafeteria line and eats the same food served in the above described cafeteria and pays for it at the cash register. The tables are round and seat about eight or ten people and good conversation abounds.

There are still doctors about who remember that famous institution the old doctors' dining room next to Marburg, where, for many years the two well-known colored waiters presided. One of them, Ben Frisbie, took it upon himself to keep the Hopkins Unit, "Base Hospital 18" informed of events at home during World War I, and periodically took his pen in hand and told all.

There are present Great and present interns who watch them, but the portrait of Dr. J. M. T. Finney, Sr., to whom Dr. Halsted gave a job the day the hospital opened now hangs outside the GOR on the eighth floor of Blalock, while Dr. Dean Lewis, who was the second professor of surgery, is in the elevator lobby of Blalock XII. Dr. Thomas Futcher's portrait is on Osler IV; he was a great physician and teacher of fine repute. Dr. Frederick H. Baetjer, who lost his fingers in the development of X-ray and still continued to work with it, looks out upon the patients who still continue to have those treatments in the Radiology Waiting Room. The portrait of Dr. Thomas R. Boggs, whom the medical students revered, is on Osler VIII.

However cold and unattractive the present doctors' dining room may seem, from time to time one sees there an old and familiar sight. Usually seated between a doctor about 45 to 50, his sponsor, and some member of the Committee on Admission, and possibly a friend of his medical father, one will see an ever so spit-and-polished, ever so clean, ever so spruced-up, scared-absolutely-to-death young man or young woman who has applied for admission to The Johns Hopkins University School of Medicine, and has come for scrutiny: within and without. Too frightened to shake or smile or sweat, he tries to appear to eat his lunch and answer their questions while they so heartily eat theirs; and his sponsor, alert on his mental toes, defends and prompts him.

Every other occupant of the dining room has been through the same torture somewhere, some time, and wishes him well and considers him carefully while doing so.

But if this hasn't changed at Hopkins, the terms employed to denote people and things, hereabouts, are so different one needs almost a glossary to comprehend them. Ward beds are now referred to as resident staff beds. And The Professor of old, is now one of many professors — nobody seems to be either an assistant nor an associate professor. However, you still *know* who is The Professor, because he is also listed as Director of the department, sometimes, or Surgeon-in-Chief, or Physician-in-Chief, other times, as the case may be.

Now, there are nine assistant administrators, one vice-president who is the Administrator, and separate heads of the Department of Nursing and of the School of Nursing. Also, there are studies "in depth"; people are forever "in conferences"; meetings are "set-up" and "you know" has replaced, "I can't explain myself or I don't know"; "funding" means paid for (i.e. "that's a fine idea but it can't be funded", or "this study is funded by ———"); "third party payers" are talked about glibly, and that means whoever foots the bill, besides the cash you now lay on the barrelhead. Sometimes it is insurance, Medicare or Medicaid, or medical assistance (welfare). Another term steadily used is "we have a commitment", which seems to boil down to "we have promised" or "we feel guilty and our conscience is making us do this" or "we've signed on the dotted line." But to say any of these things outright seems to be the height of stupidity.

Coffee pots, mugs, sugar, ersatz cream are in every office suite; vending machines for candy, cookies, are all over the Hospital. Cigarette-vending machines are in the cafeteria, canteen and corridor cafe. "Have a cake or a coffee break" is standard conversation. People walk up and down the corridor sucking through straws attached to plastic cups and sometimes throw the cups on the floor. If you have nothing else in your mouth gum-chewing seems to be obligatory and almost as many people have false teeth as wear mini-skirts.

It all strangely resembles an airport corridor and it is a relief to turn left at "Abstract #4," go down the short flight of steps, and enter Marburg.

Before proceeding into any of the buildings in which a patient is housed, one should recall that Mr. Hopkins specifically stated that The Johns Hopkins Hospital was to be a teaching hospital. He also said in his letter, "You will also provide for the reception of a limited number of patients who are able to make compensation for the room and attention they may require."

Marburg is that building.

There is an amusing story of a Westchester matron who had gynecological difficulties and was advised by an experienced friend to go to the Professor at Physicians and Surgeons as a patient. The friend explained he was chosen to head that service at a great teaching hospital, and therefore at the pinnacle of his profession.

The Westchester matron replied, "But you don't understand. I'm already going to the best gynecologist in Westchester County. He's *through* learning."

Nobody is ever "through learning" at Hopkins, for whatever the patient gets for free, no medical rights are other than earned in this hospital. And the proud privilege of a Baltimore doctor to bring his private patients to The Johns Hopkins Hospital and to have visiting privileges there is only come by through years and years of grueling hard work in the residency system and the dispensary. And that right comes up for scrutiny and re-affirmation at the end of each separate year by the Medical Board of the hospital.

The Hopkins residency system means that there are no rotating internships. There are straight internships in medicine, pediatrics, surgery, pathology, and gynecology-obstetrics.

The internship year is followed by two or three or more years of residency experience in any one of the forementioned fields and also in ophthalmology and psychiatry and in the surgical sub-specialties such as urology, plastic surgery, neurosurgery, otolaryngology, and orthopedic surgery.

From the day a medical school graduate enters a chosen field, it takes him three or more years to go through that training, or if he be fortunate enough to be selected to be Chief Resident, the training lasts five, or more, years in all.

The system means that if a boy graduates from high school at 18, college at 22, medical school at 26, and then goes through the residency at Hopkins, he is over 30 when he finishes his formal training. Thereafter, he may either go into post-doctoral training, in research perhaps, or work toward a full-time appointment on the faculty, or set up in private practice.

All of these alternatives are open to him, for he has received one of the best medical trainings on earth and is highly sought after. This training requires, too, that from the first day he became an intern he became a teacher, as well as continuing as a pupil. For he taught the medical students observing on the wards; and later, as assistant resident, he taught the interns and medical students; and still later, as resident, he taught the assistant residents, the interns, and the medical students; and all this time he was being taught by the full-time and part-time faculty. Many of the latter are in private practice, also.

A system in which a man is always teaching and always learning eliminates stuffed shirts and accounts for the profound lack of pomposity hereabouts. No man can become truly pompous when he has a medical student always looking over his shoulder, yearning to catch his mistakes.

Once finished in the residency program, a man must make the often difficult choice between private practice of medicine or full academic position. In private practice, he must run an office, pay for his help, see his own patients, and yet devote a portion of his time, without pay, to seeing clinic patients, teaching medical students, and assisting and teaching interns and residents. Eventually he climbs from instructor, to assistant, to associate in the clinical service to which he is attached.

The term "outside" man might possibly be attributed to the Pennsylvania Dutch. It refers to a doctor who makes his living in private practice and does not receive a salary. He may bring his patients into the hospital, but he does not live on a full-time salary paid by the Hospital, or the Medical School. He may, however, be under part-time contract to teach in the Medical School. Or he may have passed through that phase and be at the zenith of his career as a famous consultant. Usually, he is a rugged individualist.

Hospital privileges are still granted at the discretion of the Professor of the speciality in question, with approval by the Medical Board and the Board of Trustees of the Hospital. They are earned by hard work and long years of qualification and no man comes by them otherwise.

At this writing 685 doctors have hospital privileges of various categories. Of these doctors 232 have outpatient privileges only, which means they can see patients in the outpatient clinics, but they cannot bring their patients into the hospital as inpatients. Of the full-time faculty 278 men can bring their patients in, while 175 "outside" or visiting or part-time faculty, whichever term you prefer, may bring their patients in as inpatients.

There is a continual hassle on this subject and always has been. The men with clinic privileges only are always trying to lower or change the standards so they can get their patients in as inpatients, while some full-time, or contract men, resent the fact that the fees from the patients they see go into the Medical School (part of the University) till and help toward paying their salaries; and the part-time men often express concern that they may be crowded out of the use of beds for their patients by the full-time faculty.

Dr. Osler was dead against full-time professors, and so was Dr. Kelly, who came to Hopkins for a salary of $3,000 a year upon which he couldn't possibly have lived and raised 9 children. Dr. Welch, a bachelor, and Dr. Halsted, childless, favored it. Both of them had been lectured on the subject since the opening of the Medical School in 1893 by Dr. Mall, the anatomist, and Dr. Abel, the professor of pharmacology, both of whom had been trained in the German universities where the system prevailed. (Incidentally, National Health Insurance was set up in Germany by Bismarck in 1882, which probably had bearing upon the system.)

For many years, however, the full-time system was a bitter, bitter fight at Hopkins, and it was not until the General Education Board in 1913 put up $1,500,000 to endow chairs in pediatrics, medicine, and surgery that the thing went through. The first three full-time professors were Dr. Halsted, Dr. Howland, and Dr. Welch; Dr. Janeway shortly became professor of medicine.

After all these years men still fume over the system, both ways, and young Hopkins men who go elsewhere to be full professors tell you, "I have a right to my private patient fees, too." Hard times may eventually settle the hassle.

In the meantime, though, when and if a patient protests fees set by either the full-time or the "outside" men, who have earned the privilege of bringing their patients as inpatients, The Johns Hopkins Hospital Corporate and Medical Staff By-laws, Rule 29, Section I - 4 reads as follows:

> "As a general policy, it is expected that the maximum fee charged by an individual physician for services rendered to an inpatient will not exceed $1,500 for any single admission to the Hospital. Fees not to exceed $2,000 may be charged under exceptional circumstances for procedures and services of great magnitude or complexity."

There are now two kinds of admissions at Hopkins. Active staff and resident staff. The active-staff patients are taken care of by the full-time, part-time, and emeritus doctors who have inpatients privileges at Hopkins. The resident-staff beds are taken care of by the resident staff. All patients are either private or semi-private.

The active-staff patients lie in either single rooms or double rooms; the resident-staff patients, in 2-bed or 4-bed rooms. However, in the recovery room there are about 12 beds all in one large area, and there is no separation between active-staff and resident-staff patients there.

The bed consist of the hospital varies, to put it mildly, for it is rather like the track use in the Grand Central Station and alters with the traffic. The great increase in semi-private insured patients has made it necessary, at times, for the hospital to divert empty beds from one use to another. However, at one time last year, there were 1,106 beds in use of which 149 were in single rooms, 347 in double rooms, and 610 in resident-staff beds (two to four in a room). On all the resident-staff floors there are single rooms for severely ill patients. Such rooms are usually charged for at the semi-private rate.

In the Woman's Clinic there are still some large areas where there are partitions between patients in a large open "ward," but this will be altered as soon as money is available.

The bassinets are the exactly same number they were 10 years ago: 66.

The only building which is all private is Marburg. From time to time the rooms in this building have been done over, the furniture replaced; but by modern plush standards, of suites for relatives attached, they are hopelessly outmoded, and they will remain so. Nowhere in the entire Hopkins Hospital is one bed wasted for well relatives to occupy, except for the rooming-in mothers in CMSC, later explained.

Make no mistake about Marburg, though: the famous of the earth are pleased to lie there when they are ill. One of the main reasons they feel that way is that Marburg is still run by the Assistant Director of the Department of Nursing of the Hospital. Her entire life has been spent nursing in the Hopkins Hospital. She is one of those ministers' daughters by whom the Hopkins Hospital has had the good fortune to be loved, served, and defended. Another such is the wife of the President of the hospital, and still another the long time President of the Women's Board. They are a hearty breed to whom "the slings and arrows of outrageous fortune" seem as natural as the sunshine.

Marburg contains 95 private beds, and has 2 essentially medical floors and 2 essentially surgical ones. All the patients are cared for by the residents and interns on the service to which they are attached, on direction from their full-time and part-time (their own) doctors.

There is a head nurse and a small staff of nurses upon each floor, but beyond that, a patient must pay for private nurses to minister to his needs.

Lucinda M. B. Benton, who was long a faithful member of its Women's Board, left the hospital one of the kindest of all bequests, over $54,000, the income from which provides, "a free room for a needy patient in the Marburg Building."

The part of Marburg fronting on Broadway was one of the original 17 buildings. The rest of it was built as a wing and completed in 1913. Albert, Amelia, Emma, Theodore, and William Marburg each gave $20,000, as a memorial to their brother, Charles L. Marburg. They gave the money in 1907, but with typical Hopkins haste, the building was opened in 1913. William Marburg continued, in his lifetime, the giving-to-the-hospital-habit, and when he died left it, also, $100,000 with no strings attached. Albert, his brother, died in 1935 and left $900,000, also on unrestricted terms.

Unrestricted, no-strings attached gifts are the kind The Hospital needs

27

Mr. William A. Marburg (1849-1931)
after a portrait by Thomas C. Corner.

most, in case you know of anybody who is thinking of mentioning it in his will.

Mr. Marburg's portrait, which has been restored, hangs in the elevator lobby on the first floor outside the Marburg parlor. The furniture in that parlor has been damaged and many of the valuable wall and mantle decorations have disappeared, too.

There is a new plaque in the Marburg lobby, which it is heartening to see, though. In 1957, the Daniel Baker, Jr., Memorial Award, was established by his widow, the long-time President of the Women's Board, for members of the Marburg house staff who were "most outstanding in providing attentive, sympathetic, and devoted care to patients in the best tradition of the art of practice of medicine at the Hospital." The annual winners' names, of which there are 19 (several times they were ties) are inscribed on the plaque and each received a check for $1,000.

To go back to the Marburg Building, while there are no treatment rooms, per se, there are cardiac arrest equipment, intravenous therapy teams, and so on always available.

The kitchen remains in the cupola, where it has been for many years, but the Marburg meals come from the main hospital kitchen, now, with the exception of the salads and desserts. These are brought round on a special cart and the building still has its own dietitian and kitchen staff.

Another feature in which the building ranks alone is that between the hours of 10 and 12 daily its corridors are known as the Peacock Alley of Prominent Physicians and Surgeons, understandably done up in their best bedside manners. One hundred and seventy-five (there were 305 ten years ago) doctors — "outside" men — have the right to bring inpatients into Hopkins, and they are seeing their patients and visiting among each other, at those hours.

Funny things still happen in Marburg, though, regarding these men. Recently a patient walked up and down the corridor, later in the day, remarking "My doctor advised me to give up women!" An interested by-stander asked, "What did you do?" "I gave up my doctor, instead," he replied.

Protocol at Hopkins is peculiar. When the King of Siam was a patient, he had a chamberlain beside his door, at all hours. And, when a gypsy queen lay fatally ill, from all over the United States her tribe arrived in Cadillacs; and for weeks the hospital oozed gypsies, and at the most unlikely places. Nothing was stolen, the bills were promptly paid; but at night, they, too, took their turns outside the fence, awaiting the death of their queen.

They were back, again, in the fall of 1970, when one of their members was a patient in the Woman's Clinic, and a child was a patient of a renal expert in CMSC.

Many a person of prominence in politics, sports, the theatre, and the arts, as well as the tycoons of the business world, have bided their time and waited their recovery in the beds of the Marburg Building. Several have given the hospital copyrights as part of their gratitude. The Women's Board would be delighted to have many more, whether they be to patents, books, plays, paintings, or musical compositions. The late Aubrey Bodine gave the copyrights to his works which appear in the hospital and so has the famous, active cartoonist of the *Sunpapers,* familiarly known as "Moco" Yardley.

In 1971 Marburg ran 95% of capacity, provided 31,972 days of patient care, average stay of patient was 11.73 days, the net revenue per patient per day was $130.59 and the expense per patient per day was $119.77. As antiquated as people say Marburg is, it is still an asset.

To the left as one exits from the Marburg Building, behind the long expanse of glass window walls, is the Central Admitting Office for all of the inpatients in the entire Johns Hopkins Hospital. It is an enormous, long, rectangular room, with swinging glass doors onto the Main Corridor. The first thing which catches one's eye are the round, low tables and little chairs to the right of those doors, covered with toys, picture books, and building blocks. Here are usually seated numerous children, completely captivated by the entertainment bonanza which has suddenly come their way. Neither the passing people in the corridor, nor their parents in the interviewing booths behind them, matter any more.

A five-year-old girl, with red gold hair and a black glass covering one eye, may be seated by an older boy with a rebuilt ear or a misplaced eyebrow. Spastic children, retarded children, obese or wan children, crutch-propelled children, all seem drawn there and manage to exist without visible fights. It is an amazing sight.

Opposite the doors, at a desk, are seated a lady or ladies as the traffic de-

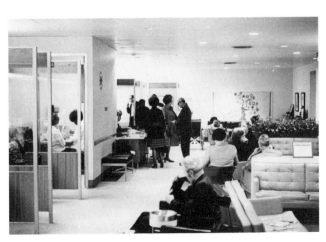

Patients wait during
the admitting
routine at Hopkins.

29

mands, who ask of all adults preliminary questions as to previous admissions, a history number, or if this is the first admission, the doctor who has arranged their arrival.

This information is relayed to the interviewers in the other booths and the prospective patients are called to those booths for their interviews, from the comfortable sofas and chairs where they are seated to the left of those center doors. The majority of the patients are what are known as reservation admissions; their illnesses require hospital treatment and their arrival was arranged for previously. They are referred to as "elective" patients. Many are surgical for since the prevalence of the "total" hip patients, due to the success of these cases done at Hopkins, people needing this procedure come from everywhere. They are predominantly well-dressed, intelligent-looking folk. Nearby are often seated referral admissions from the clinics and both groups are frequently held up in their handling by instant admissions from the Emergency Department.

The latter are often arranged for over the telephone; and one will glimpse a fast-moving stretcher in the Corridor and see an intern beside it who gives a wave and a nod to the lady at the admissions desk, which she acknowledges, as they scurry by. She passes the information on to the proper persons.

Elective patients have all completed and sent back a pre-admission form and their interviews are shorter, but they, too, have an identification bracelet (OHH, begun in 1959) made up here, and attached to their arms; a blood test is drawn from the other arm. If they are new patients a history number is assigned here, too.

Then, they settle down into the long wait. All admissions of an elective nature are asked to be at JHH between 12 noon and 1:00 P.M., and most of them comply. Usually by 2:30 P.M. they have finished all of their admitting office procedures and are waiting for the floor nurse to call and say that their rooms or bed are ready.

Sometimes the patient who had occupied that bed will become very ill and cannot be moved and the patient arriving must, therefore, be put elsewhere. Or sometimes the patient vacating didn't get away as planned and the housekeeping women have been unable to prepare the room on time.

Whatever the reason, though, the patient who sits and waits and dreads what lies ahead of him, cannot help but add to the always present tension which at all hours invades this fascinating place.

The number of inpatients in 1971 was 33,040. The number of inpatients days of care were 314,278.

All faces of man pass through this admitting office: the infant "muling and puking," the "whining school-boy," the "lover sighing like a furnace," "the soldier seeking the bubble reputation," the "justice, with eyes severe and beard of formal cut," the sixth stage, "with spectacles on nose . . . and turning again toward childish trebles," and the last stage, "sans teeth, sans eyes, sans taste, sans everything," each appear over and over each 24 hours. Patients from 41 countries were admitted last year.

There are about 90 patients a day admitted through here, and an equal number are discharged from the hospital. Although The Johns Hopkins Hospital is listed as a 1,200-bed hospital, that number of beds is never available; in February, 1972, 1,111 was the total bed capacity, although only 1,083 were open for occupancy. CMSC was cut back on account of nursing shortages and so were Halsted II

A busy moment in the admitting office.

and IV; also, there are cut-backs for construction, from time to time. (As when the hospital was being airconditioned: a coolness from which it has never been able to warm itself, financially.)

Then, too, there is frequently a fluctuating necessity of beds regarding a single patient. For instance, a surgical case occupies the bed he first lies in; the bed he is taken to in GRR (General Recovery Room) after operation; and then, perhaps, later, the bed he is transferred to in the new Intensive Care Unit, and all this time the bed he first occupied must remain unused, awaiting his return.

All of this tremendous patient load is handled by 12 interviewers, 3 to 5 of whom work on Saturday, Sundays, and evenings. These interviewers are carefully trained, highly skilled, compassionate, fair, cheerful, and cheering people; but they are not soft — far from it!

Their capacity to judge human nature is uncanny; and in an office where admission is the objective and admission boils down to bed-care, money matters. Who is going to pay for the patient? For every patient is paid for in some way, somewhat. If they are medically indigent then they come under Medical Assistance — another name for Welfare — and the state reimburses the hospital partially.

In many cases it is not enough — but it helps. If they are from out of state, then the state of their origin agencies are contacted and asked to contribute to the patient's bill. In case of patients who won't pay, stern measures are applied. For instance, one woman, from Washington, was highly insistent upon having her child admitted to CMSC *right now*. The child would not be damaged by waiting, but had been a patient in the hospital previously, so the admitting officer asked the Billing Department for a check on the account. The well-dressed woman, who was accompanied by her own mother as well as the child, owed the hospital a bill of $3,000 on a prior admission 6 months before. She had made no effort to decrease that debt, although she had repeatedly been requested to do so.

The admitting officer said she would admit the child on one proviso: that they pay the previous bill. The mother said she had no money, but the grandmother promised to return in the morning with a certified check for $1500. The admitting officer believed her and just 2 minutes before the 11:00 A.M. deadline she set, the next morning, the grandmother arrived with the check and signed an I.O.U. for the remaining portion of the previous bill.

31

Patients who want time on their bills are now asked to purchase coupon books, at the Cashier's Office, on which they redeem a $20.00 a month coupon, or some similar figure.

Two groups of patients who are admitted entirely free are those in the pediatric clinical research unit (CMSC IV) and the medical one on Osler V; both areas are designated as research floors and the Federal Government usually covers hospital charges in grants covering research work.

The costs per day to a patient differ in different locations. Per diem cost is about $103 per day, but in some private rooms it is $103 to $125 per day, while in a semi-private room it is $95 a day and a resident staff room is $95 a day. All of these prices are for room and board only. Drugs, laboratory fees, operating room fees, anesthesia, and special nursing care are extra. The average cost to the hospital per day per patient is now about $150.

Sixty to 75% of all inpatients are insured, either completely or partially. Also there are some special programs, like Workman's compensation, crippled children's funds, vocational rehabilitation, which pick up some charges. However, rich man, poor man, beggar man, thief is always asked to pay whatever he can.

The thief is here mentioned specifically, because as with all inner-city hospitals, he stalks Hopkins, constantly, and it is wise to come for admission stripped of one's valuables. Leave your jewels, your fine radio, or electric razor or money at home. These admission ladies have even had their purses stolen from the floor beside their chairs, when they went to get an additional paper regarding the case they were admitting; their coats and umbrellas have walked away from the racks on which they are kept, too. All patients upon admission are given brochures which plainly state, "the Hospital cannot be responsible for money or other articles kept at the bedside." If you do bring valuables with you, the Hospital asks you to deposit them in the Hospital's safe, and redeem them with the receipt when you get ready to leave.

Friday is the lightest day in the Admitting Office; Monday is the busiest, although the ladies say, *"Every* day is busy! And it sounds strange, but patients always come in spurts. Calm before the storm: storm before the calm, sort of thing."

There is a Child Life Worker in the Emergency Room, during the day to supervise the children. Volunteers are available to help the people to whom Hopkins is "new," and among the interviewers is one from the Department of Social Work to aid the patients who have difficulties meeting the fees.

When one considers that 10 years ago it took 10 people to "keep" a patient in bed at the Hopkins Hospital; and now, with all the sophisticated changes in medicine it takes 40 people to do so; and when one realizes that the minimum wage then was 75 cents an hour and now is $2.55; and then the interns and residents received only a small stipend, while now an intern gets $8,500 a year and a resident about $12,000 depending on the length of his previous experience, and a beginning R. N. receives $8,000 annually, one comprehends why the patient pays "so much"!

However, the average hospital stay has decreased and many medical difficulties which were considered hopeless then are routine now.

It costs money to tread the Corridor or to lie in a bed at Hopkins — particularly if you are a paying patient. But the eyes of many people are upon you, chartwise, care-wise, and hopefully, increasingly comfort-wise.

CHAPTER III

A Texan's Life Work

ANY Old Hopkins Hand who is looking for Brady these days has a terrible shock coming to him, because to get there he must get in the elevator of the Children's Medical and Surgical Center (CMSC), go to the second, third, fourth, or fifth floors, then north, when alighting from the elevator through the swinging doors marked "Brady" entrance.

It isn't the entrance; it is a ramp leading to more swinging doors which open into Brady. To put it succinctly, Brady's corridor entrance on the main floor of the hospital was completely amputated, and the part near the corridor is part of the CMSC lobby; the part near Brady is now a roadway for ambulances.

However, all OHH will remember that just to the right on entrance to Brady there used to be a small, quiet, delightful little room, with beautiful wooden window frames and glass. Many a fateful hour was spent by relatives waiting in that room for news of their loved ones who were being operated upon. When the entrance was destroyed, the present Professor of Urology and Urologist-in-Charge salvaged some of this wood and some windows, and built them into his own house in the country. So the beautiful Brady room lives on, as certainly does the Brady tradition.

The hospital roadways to the service entrances are still on both sides of Brady, where the foodstuffs and some of the medical supplies are delivered; but beyond those roadways, on each side are the ambulance roads leading to the Emergency Room and the Pediatric Emergency Room in the brand new Edwards A. Park Building; and to the south of Brady is the road-tunnel effect connecting these two ambulance roadways.

The building now is completely surrounded by noise on four sides, for though there are no street-cars grinding up Monument Street, as of yore, there is heavy, constant traffic, interspersed with frequently screaming ambulances upon it all hours of the day and night.

Once you get inside the building, the urology laboratories are in the basement, on the ground floor are O.P.D.; Genito-Urinary; Cystoscopy; and the Division of Urology. On the 1st floor are semi-private rooms; resident-staff urology; Office of the Associate Director of Nursing, while the 2nd floor has semi-private rooms, now all devoted to neurology; and the 3rd and 4th floors have semi-private and private rooms. On the 5th floor is the reproductive biology laboratory; the urological library and conference room are there, and so is what is now called the house-staff facility. The 6th floor is laboratories and urology research.

As one California Hopkins man recently wrote, "Dr. Young would turn right over in his grave, if he could see it!" One thing he would approve of, though; Brady is still clean, still quietly run, still solvent, and still run by polite and pleasant people.

It sits amputated in a roaring swirl of outside howling, yowling, banging, screaming noise. In a way, having lost its corridor entrance may be in part an advantage, because it is still isolated into being itself.

Dr. Young's portrait is still there, and so is "Diamond Jim's," only now they are hung at opposite ends of the 6th-floor lounge. Dr. Young's hangs over a desk he wouldn't have been seen dead writing on, a nondescript; and "Diamond Jim" glares at him as if he, too, considers the furnishings beneath his style.

One is still at a loss to know which to describe first, the portrait of "Diamond Jim" or the personality of Dr. Young. If it hadn't been for Dr. Young, "Diamond Jim's" portrait would never have hung in Hopkins, so he obviously deserves priority.

Dr. Hugh Hampton Young was a Texan, the son of a Confederate General and the grandson of a Confederate General; and he spent his entire medical career at the Johns Hopkins. He was a graduate of the University of Virginia Medical School when he came here and asked Dr. Halsted for a job; Halsted told him he had no place for him. Did he go home? Not at all, he stuck around doing what odd jobs he could get at the hospital until a place materialized. One of his interns, years later in the obituary he wrote for the *Journal of Urology,* after Dr. Young died, stated, "When Dr. Young was ready to take his first position at Johns Hopkins Hospital he was stymied because his father had met with sudden financial reverses, and it was necessary for him to go to work to tide over the emergency. Dr. Halsted lent him $5,000 which he passed on to his father. This is probably the reason that Dr. Young had a revolving fund of many thousands of dollars which he lent without security to his ex-students to start in practice."

Dr. Young always had an incapacity to recognize defeat, a horror of other than excellent performance and was the first Hopkins man to write his autobiography; it is *written by himself* and is a bang-up, infinitely interesting book of which any writer would be proud. He was in the hospital recovering from the shingles for six weeks and dictated it to his secretary then!

His first perineal prostatectomy operation was done, according to Dr. Crowe's excellent volume, *Halsted of Johns Hopkins,* in 1895/96; he was ever afterward refining the operation and improving his instruments therefor. He became so famous for performing it that a prominent New York urologist said, "The prostate makes most men old, but it made Hugh Young."

Dr. Hugh H. Young (1870-1945).

His operation does not necessarily preclude sexual vigor and in April, 1912, Mr. James Buchanan Brady, who considered this one of his profoundest pleasures, being a victim of prostate trouble came to Dr. Young, as a patient. He had diabetes, Bright's disease, high blood pressure, angina pectoris, and generalized urinary tract infection; but Dr. Young operated on him, successfully, from Mr. Brady's point of view.

He recovered, lived four years, and before he died, had built and partially endowed The James Buchanan Brady Urological Institute and made it possible for Dr. Young to establish the first school of urology.

His portrait, next to that of Mr. Hopkins, is the largest portrait of a single individual at the Hopkins. His institute was opened May 4th, 1915.

Mr. Brady was born on the Bowery. His father was a drunk and his mother ran the saloon and tended bar, but she made him promise never to touch liquor. At the age of 12 he was a messenger boy in the Grand Central Station. When he became Dr. Young's patient, he was a vice-president of the Standard Steel Car Company and a very rich and famous man. Not only was he a supersalesman, but also he possessed 35 jewel sets, each containing about 25 pieces, and wore a different set every day in the month. He backed many Broadway plays and gave many luxurious gifts to his friends and acquaintances.

He was very fond of Dr. Young, who says, in his book, "Mr. Brady had come to me for a check-up. I pointed out to him the great need of an institute devoted to urology that would contain not only wards for public and private patients but laboratories for clinical and research work. Such a hospital would carry Mr. Brady's name forever. From it would come a great series of clinical and scientific papers that would reach all quarters of the earth and carry on each publication the name of James Buchanan Brady. I contrasted this with the ephemeral character of the fame and pleasure he got from the plays he backed, the actors and actresses he supported, and the sportsmen he banqueted. Here was an opportunity for him to hand his name down to posterity by this institute as Rockefeller's was by the institute that bore his name and Hopkins's was by The Johns Hopkins University and Hospital. I saw that Brady was greatly impressed, and having used every argument, I left him to think it over. . . . Quitting the ward, I absented myself for an hour and then came back. Mr. Brady told me that he would do it."

In his portrait at Hopkins, he is wearing his diamond set. Mr. Henry Mencken, who wrote the best set of articles about the hospital which has ever been printed, diagnoses the diamonds "Diamond Jim" wears in his portrait, as follows: "No less than nine gorgeous diamonds, one of them precisely three-quarters of an inch in diameter. This monster is in Jim's white satin necktie. Another, almost as large, is in a ring on his left hand. Two more appear in what is to be seen of his watch-chain. The remaining five glitter from the buttons of his waistcoat, which bulges beautifully over the noble arch of his equator."

The Brady housemen lived on the top floor of the Brady Institute; they never had the extra time, during Dr. Young's days, to walk around to the Administration Building. Dr. Young demanded, and got, expert, constant care for his patients, who were desperately ill for days after their operations. He required of himself an equally perfect performance and daily, morning and night, made himself perform finger and arm, shoulder, chest muscle, and abdominal exercises, simultaneously, to keep his hands supple. No ballet dancer ever worked more religiously on the bar.

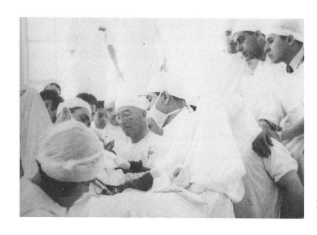

Dr. Hugh H. Young in the operating room (center, without mask).

If his interns weren't keeping the patients alive, they were working on their papers, and by papers, Dr. Young did not mean case histories (they kept them up to date, absolutely up to date, as they breathed). The papers they worked on were their research projects, of which he required each man to have one.

A Hopkins graduate (OHH:JHMS, 1910) states, "I went to World War I. When I came home from France I was a house guest of Dr. Thomas Cullen, and he persuaded me to go over and look at "Young's set-up". Dr. Young was glad to see me. At our second meeting he asked how long I was going to be around. I said, 'A week or ten days'. (I had been doing general surgery, mostly gynecology.) He said, 'I have a beautiful paper on the trigone. Didusch drew the pictures of the operations, etc., but I have no embryology. It will only take you a day or so to look up the embryology.' There was none. The largest serial sectioned embryo was one in the Hiss collection of 50 mm. I took that report to Dr. Young, and he said, 'That will be of no help; go over to Welch's Laboratory; get the diener to get you some embryoes; take them over to Streeter (Institute of Embryology) and have them cut.' Then he turned on his heel and scurried away. I was nonplussed for a minute. I called him, but he pretended not to hear, so I took after him. He could walk faster than any man I knew when he wanted to. I did not catch him. The result was I stayed three years at Hopkins and came out a urologist."

People liked Dr. Young or hated him, and the men he trained liked him. He said to one, who is now a full professor, as he was leaving, "Never defend me in any medical meeting or before any of numerous people whom you will meet and get to know better. I like to think that I have more friends than I have enemies, but you'll be surprised how many people have no use for me. I have chosen to ignore and forget them. It won't be to your advantage to argue with them, for they won't change their minds."

Many a conformist stood by in stubborn hatred when Dr. Young passed, then, later, turned to him in his travail to save his life. He was a great favorite with the medical students, though, and always spoke to anybody he suspected of being one, as "Doctor." No man he ever taught will forget that he said, "The capacity of the human bladder is the same as the hip pocket—one pint."

Not only was the Brady Institute solvent, but he ran it on the Robin Hood principle; and when World War I came along, and he went to war, he first rented out his radium to pay the way his fees would have provided for the Institute. He was undoubtedly the Father of Modern Urology and every man who served in the Armed Forces in World Wars I and II and the later "Police actions" is indebted to him for the G.U. methods he set up. As long as he lived, men came from around the world to stand in line and wait for a Brady bed. There is another portrait of Dr. Young on Brady V and also a photograph of him in the library there. In that library, too, is the plaque to Dr. William A. Frontz (OHH, this was formerly in the Main Corridor), one of the men he trained, who died a bachelor and left his estate of $84,786.58 for "the care and support of patients in Brady."

Brady now takes female patients on any floor, but long before it did, the name of a woman was memorialized there. She was Mary Agnes Goldthwaite and she graduated from the Johns Hopkins School of Nursing in 1916 and for many years had charge of the X-ray room in the Brady Institute. After her death, her friends and relatives endowed the room in her memory and put a plaque on the door of the X-ray room, where she had so long done such meticulous work, in her memory.

Brady has always been a training institute from which many of the men have gone on to become full professors elsewhere; and since Dr. Young's death in 1945, 10 of the residents have become full professors, elsewhere, and many have become associate professors.

No Brady interns now live on the top floor of the building; however one room on Brady V is called "an on-call sleeping room, for house officers who remain through the night." The rest of the staff live over in the Compound, or out in the city. What was the porch on the 6th floor has been made into a library as a memorial to Dr. Young. There is now a training grant, providing three fellowships for Brady men and research is still in progress to discover the cause of simple enlargement of the prostate and of cancer of the prostate.

Brady now has 66 beds, 12 of which are private, 33 semi-private, and 21 resident staff. The second floor is devoted entirely to neurological patients. Brady inpatient days for 1971 numbered 19,788.

Brady was built in the days before the concrete block had boxed-in American architecture; it was the work of loving, careful artisans, and it still shows it. It was also built in the days when a supersalesman of a now declining industry could become a millionaire. Incidentally, to quote Dr. Young again about Mr. Brady's jewel sets: "Another remarkable one he called his transportation set. Here almost every form of locomotion was illustrated. The stickpin was an airplane; the waist-coat buttons, carwheels; the cuff links, cars of various types; his watch was decorated with an automobile, his wallet and eyeglass case with other forms of locomotion, many of considerable size. When he burst forth with his "transportation set," he created a sensation."

Brady was built in the days when men had reverence for their appearance, too, and it is the only section of the hospital which still remains where long-haired interns and residents are not sanctioned.

Something else of which both Dr. Young and Mr. Brady would approve is that the son of Dr. Young's lifelong confrère, the late Associate Professor Emeritus of Urology, Dr. J. A. Campbell Colston, is a urologist, too, and his name is often heard on the loud speaker at Hopkins.

While on the West Coast, Dr. Young's namesake and grandson also practices urology.

CHAPTER IV

Neurology at Hopkins

IN 1889 when The Johns Hopkins Hospital opened its doors, Dr. Osler was appointed Professor of Neurology, as well as of Medicine and the Diseases of Children. Pediatrics soon became a separate department, but neurology remained "an appendage" of medicine. However, as Dr. Osler's medical duties became increasingly heavy, in 1896 Dr. Henry M. Thomas, Sr., was appointed clinical Professor of Neurology. He remained so until his death, in spite of being an invalid from tuberculosis, for a number of years. In this period clinical neurology was taught as an outpatient activity exclusively. It had no beds, no house staff, nor teaching program; though extensive clinical and basic research relating to neurological problems was pursued in Anatomy, Medicine, Surgery, Physiology, Psychiatry, and Pharmacology.

In 1925, the Rockefeller Foundation offered Hopkins the money to make neurology a full department and to endow a chair of the professorship. A study with this is mind was commenced. Certain departments did not care to give up their own predominance in certain neurological specialties; and in the ensuing 5 years, although at least 3 European neurologists were under consideration as chief, only one was offered the post, and he declined.

By 1930, no appreciable progress had been made, and the aim was altered somewhat as it was thought wise to found a neuropsychiatric divison with neurology and psychiatry as sister departments, into which neurological surgery would be merged, the whole being closely united with the School of Hygiene, through mental hygiene clinics and laboratories. The design of such a clinic was begun and a famous British neurologist was offered the professorship, which he declined. It was then offered to a German neurologist, but the hard times arising from the 1929 depression caught up with the financing and the whole matter was again dropped. However, 35 years later a renowned British neurologist wrote he was of the opinion that the Rockefeller money had gone to found the Neurological Institute in Montreal.

By 1934 the fate of neurology was still unsettled, but it was decided to use the City Hospital for clinical ward work, The Johns Hopkins Hospital Dispensary for outpatient clinics and the various labs, some in Phipps, to develop four young men per year, who hopefully would grow into the type of neurologist needed.

The program was partially successful as it produced 11 neurologists and one neurosurgeon. So the matter rested until 1949, when a new plan to make neurology a subdivision of Medicine with offshoots in Pediatrics and the basic neurological sciences was put forward. By 1952, the Division of Neurological Medicine consisted full-time of 2 professors, 2 fellows, each at Hopkins and Baltimore City Hospitals, and 1 research fellow at Baltimore City Hospital. Beds were always hard

Dr. Frank R. Ford
(1892-1970).

to come by, and one re-occurring plan was to make Osler I into a complete bed floor for Neurology, but this repeatedly fell through, as there was no where else to put physical therapy.

So things rocked along over the years, and curiously enough because of the failure to get together, in their various specialities several neurologists at Hopkins became world-renowned. Dr. Dandy, in brain surgery, and Dr. Frank R. Ford, in neurological medicine, were among these. Dr. Ford is reputed to have said in the thirties, "I can either make a Department of Neurology, or I can make a neurologist of myself, but I cannot do both, and under the circumstances now existing, I prefer to do the latter." Incidentally, his text book on neurology is revered throughout the world and he had just finished a final revision upon it before his death in 1970.

For many years, he could always be found on Saturday mornings attending the packed conferences which the present Professor Emeritus of Ophthalmology conducts in Wilmer upon the neurology of the eye. His textbook, of 3 volumes, has also just been revised.

Dr. Ford's comments were always requested by him, and the chair Dr. Ford sat in is now left unoccupied each Saturday, unless the Professor Emeritus invites some famous visitor to use it.

During these same years above reviewed, 2 renowned laboratories were founded, in Phipps. The first, the Laboratory of Psychobiology, has contributed much distinguished work in the nature of the rhythm timing devices (the so-called biological clocks) in mammals, and in man. The second, the Pavlovian Laboratory, now works on problems of visceral conditioning with special reference to cardio-vascular responses. It is one of the major laboratories pursuing classical condition

The Kennedy Professor of Neurology.

techniques outside the Soviet Union.

The first was founded in 1922, the second in 1929; and they have continued their brilliant findings under the two professors who originated them, both of whom are now emeritus.

In spite of these individually renowned men, in 1964, Hopkins was rated as 27th out of some 85 medical schools in its contribution of specialists in neurology; . . . and on the basis of graduates since 1951 going into neurology it ranked 42nd. A number of professors at the Medical School and the Dean were profoundly upset about the situation.

However on July 27th, 1966, the Dean received a letter from the National Institutes of Health (HE&W) stating that the Teagle Foundation of New York had requested recommendations from them of a limited number of medical schools at which they might endow a chair in honor of Walter C. Teagle. The Teagle offer was made on the tacit assumption that Hopkins would take decisive steps to improve its situation in neurology; it also was suggested that Hopkins apply to the Firestone Foundation for a Dwight D. Eisenhower Professorship in Clinical Neurology, which is oriented toward the neurological diseases of children.

Great excitement reigned in the medical circles of Hopkins all summer, and a committee chaired since 1964 by the very wise and quiet Professor of Physiology commenced work upon the matter.

As that Chairman recently remarked, "Of course we did not get the Teagle chair! We were not quite ready, and it went elsewhere. But the offer of the Teagle chair did, I think, bring Dr. Turner around to the point of view that Neurology was something important, with very new and important developments for the future of

40

man. It helped generate the internal support which is so necessary at Hopkins if one wishes to succeed in such a new venture. By the time the new department opened, we had succeeded in getting this support on all sides, and this genuine feeling has had much to do with the immediate success of the department, I believe."

The outcome of all this is a very happy ending, for now there exists at Hopkins a full-fledged Department of Neurology which has 2 endowed chairs. (Incidentally, it takes a million dollars to endow a chair for a senior professor.) The Kennedy chair is financed by the Joseph B. Kennedy Foundation, which also supplies $25,000 a year for fluid research and salaries of at least $150,000 annually.

The Kennedy professor is Director of the Department of Neurology and Neurologist-in-Chief. Both he (38) and the Eisenhower professor, also 38, are men most carefully chosen and with brilliant research records, and much is expected of them and their "new" department.

The department now consists of one Director, one administrator, and has its own house staff, and currently has the following beds: Brady II, 19 adult neurological beds and CMSC, VI, 8 pediatric neurological beds; one research floor of the Traylor Building is devoted specifically to it. All neurology in the entire hospital is under its jurisdiction.

Its influence is growing by leaps and bounds, and the set-up under which it now operates is for a five-year duration, at the termination of which it is expected that more space will be available. It has now become understood that Neurology is much more than neurological medicine; for while it concerns the brain, it is also the science of human behavior and covers a very broad field which encompasses much more than neurological medicine. Thanks to these recent developments, now, the Medical School will attract many young men who are drawn into this fast-changing, expanding discipline.

The Eisenhower
Professor of Neurology.

CHAPTER V

To Tend the Child

PRESIDENT BUCHANAN had a favorite and handsome niece, Harriet Lane, who married, at a time then considered late in life (she was 36), Mr. Henry E. Johnston of Baltimore. They produced 2 sons, one of whom died when he was 15 and the other died at 13.

The second son had been dead a year when Mr. and Mrs. Johnston, who was a banker, decided to build the Harriet Lane Children's Home. They incorporated it in 1883, and Mr. Johnston died the next year. Mrs. Johnston died in 1903 and left $90,000 to the university to endow three scholarships in memory of her husband and sons. Certain people had living trusts in the residue of her estate; and, for various reasons, it was not until 1905 the Trustees of the Harriet Lane — it has a separate Board of Trustees — decided to locate their home on The Johns Hopkins Hospital grounds.

From the beginning of the hospital, Dr. Osler had steadily insisted that there must be a separate building devoted entirely to the care of children, with a separate professor in the diseases of children.

And from the day the Harriet Lane opened its doors in 1912 and Dr. John Howland was appointed Pediatrician-in-Chief (he was made a full-time Professor in 1914), Harriet Lane was a citadel of American pediatrics. It distinguished itself in brilliant research, in excellent care of countless children, and in wonderful service to the outpatient sick child.

To date there have been 6 full Professors of Pediatrics: Dr. Clemens von Pirquet of Vienna (1908-1911); Dr. Howland (1912-1926); Dr. Edwards A. Park

Each year, on May 9, the head nurse places flowers on the grave of Harriet Lane Johnston, for whom the Harriet Lane Home was named. Until 1969, the Home housed all of Hopkins' children's services. May 9 was the birthdate of Mrs. Johnston.

(1926-1946); Dr. Francis F. Schwentker (1946-1954); Dr. Lawson Wilkins, Acting Professor (1954-1956); and the present Professor. He is a graduate of Yale Medical School and was 36 years old when he became Pediatrician-in-Chief.

Portraits of 4 of these were moved to the Children's Medical and Surgical Center, when it was dedicated in 1964, at the time of the 75th anniversary of the hospital. For OHH they are placed as follows: Dr. Howland, 2nd floor hallway; Dr. Park, stairway wall between 1st and 2nd floors. (This will be moved to the Edwards Park Building, which adjoins CMSC from Monument Street and opened in the summer of 1971); Dr. Schwentker, CMSC II; Dr. Wilkins, CMSC II.

Certainly, physically speaking, the brightest jewel in the crown of the Hopkins Hospital in the last 10 years was the opening of the Children's Medical and Surgical Center. The Dedication Address was given on May 13th, 1964, in a large tent erected in the backyard of the hospital, by the then and now Given Fund Professor of Pediatrics and Pediatrician-in-Chief, who is also Director of the department.

In that speech he said, "Indeed to my mind the greatest single advantage which the species Homo sapiens possesses, from the standpoint of exploitation, is to be born immature and remain immature for a long part of his life.

"Yet, somewhat paradoxically, the immature is more liable to death, to damage, to crippling disorders. His resistance to infection is low. He is totally dependent upon the caprices of his environment for his survival."

To accomplish that survival, he couldn't have a better environment than has been created for him at CMSC. On the tour, conducted at the 75th anniversary, of the new $15,000,000 building, one saw in the main lobby, 3 very impressive plaques from whose funds approximately one half of the money to construct the building had been derived and the Trustees of whom had all sat on the platform during the Professor's speech. Those groups are Eudowood Sanitorium, Harriet Lane Children's Home, and the Robert Garrett Fund. The remainder of the money was supplied by The Johns Hopkins Hospital and special gifts. The 3 donor funds each has a beautiful Board of Directors' room upon the upper floors of the new building and many of their mementoes from the past are on their walls.

The history of each fund is very interesting. That of the Harriet Lane money is already known to the reader. The Eudowood Sanitorium money was the many gifts of many people over many years to help care for tubercular patients, at the sanitorium located, then, in Towson, Maryland. When tuberculosis became amenable to present forms of treatment and disappeared as a disease requiring such space and treatment facilities, it became apparent that Eudowood's accumulated money must go into some current fight against disease. CMSC seemed the best of all possible causes and their board "came" in with the project.

One person who was greatly helpful in the creation of the Robert Garrett Fund was Dr. Henry Barton Jacobs, who as a young physician had lived with the Garretts and cared for the invalid banker. He later married Mr. Garrett's widow. In his youth Dr. Jacobs had done much outstanding work in tuberculosis, and sat on both the boards of the Robert Garrett Fund and Eudowood Sanitorium. (There is a memorial room to him in the Welch Library containing his very valuable medical library, including his excellent collection of volumes relating to tuberculosis.) In 1885, Mrs. Jacobs maintained a general dispensary on Caroline Street, near Monument; in 1888, she opened the Garrett Sanitorium for Children at Mt. Airy,

The Chapel.

Maryland; and in 1889, the Robert Garrett Dispensary was functioning on North Carey Street.

Dr. Jacobs died long before the idea of CMSC came into existence; but the members of the Garrett Board, some of whom are now members of the Board of Trustees of The Johns Hopkins Hospital, voted to "come" in with CMSC, also.

This is a capsule explanation of the three plaques placed upon the walls of the main lobby of CMSC. To the right of these plaques and set obliquely behind the Harriet Lane Plaque is a small chapel, shaped like a pie, and referred to on its entrance plaque as a "room of meditation."

Encompassing the entire curved rear wall is a very beautiful mosaic in memory of James R. Edmonds, Jr., F.A.I.A., the architect for this and many other Hopkins structures. Inset in the mosaic are the four lines from the 23rd Psalm:

> The Lord is my Shepherd I shall not want
> He maketh me to lie down in green pastures
> He leadeth me beside the still waters
> He restoreth my soul

The kneeling cushions at the altar prayer rail are all needlepoint, carrying the seals of Eudowood, State of Maryland, The Johns Hopkins Hospital,* Harriet Lane, Garrett Fund, and Children's Medical and Surgical Center. The seats of the chairs against the circular rear wall are also needlepoint. Six people can be seated in the chapel and it is clearly nonsectarian in its concept and provides an oasis of peace in the midst of movement and surrounding anxieties. It was given in memory of Margaret Metcalf Warfield.

The Chaplain of the hospital states that the lady's daughter told him she wanted to have some place, when her mother was dying, where she could go and cry and pray and be by herself. She could find no place in the Hopkins Hospital to do this, so she gave the chapel, in her mother's memory.

CMSC is a 255 bed hospital of 11 stories with 6 floors devoted to inpatient

* Whereabouts unknown: stolen.

44

services. Two floors, at present, are devoted to outpatient services, and 2 are for the study of mental retardation. In the main lobby are the 2 elevator tiers, of 4 shafts each. They are busy, indeed, for one not only goes up in them to all of the floors of CMSC and the Brady ramps, but also down to pediatric X-ray, the basement corridor and the sub-corridor leading under Monument Street to the Kennedy Institute and Traylor Building and Turner Auditorium. Children, parents, medical students, research workers are wedged in. As the cars progress, one sees many fascinating sights, including children in bathrobes talking in telephone booths — actual booths — seated on child-size seats in front of low-hung phones. Another thing which impresses one on the different floors is the enormous amount of space per child. The Director of the department states: "Here there is more actual space per child than in any hospital in the world. Nothing in the U. S. compares with the openness, the amount of space."

The building is shaped like an L, the long portion extending into the hospital's backyard being the floors devoted to patient care, except on the 2nd and 3rd floors. On the 2nd, that portion houses the Helen B. Taussig Cardiac Center and until the Edwards Park Building was opened, the Comprehensive Child Care Clinic. While on the 2nd floor, the wing extending toward Marburg houses administrative offices. Above the 2nd floor this wing is devoted entirely to research areas; 3rd floor: endocrinology; 4th: biochemistry; 5th: cardio-vascular-angiocardiography; 6th: cardio-vascular-pediatric surgery; 7th: pediatric surgery; 8th: neuro-pathology-plastic surgery; 9th: orthopedic; 10th: chemistry-enzymology; 11th: virology-cytogenetics.

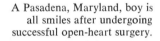

A young patient calls home from a special phone in the Child Life area on his floor.

A Pasadena, Maryland, boy is all smiles after undergoing successful open-heart surgery.

Whereas in the backyard wing, on the 3rd floor are the Pediatric Consultation Clinic; on the 4th are the child psychiatric cases of short duration and the special Pediatric Clinical Research Unit, called PCRU, which are in-and-out long term cases — dwarfs, kidney patients, etc.; on the 5th floor are the infants from birth to 2 years of age, and the premature nursery. (The "preemies" are all born in the Woman's Clinic and generally within an hour of birth are wheeled via the Main Corridor, in their private, electrically heated, oxygen-equipped bed-basket, domed over against the germs of the general run of people, at double-quick pace up to the nursery in CMSC.) The word "Preemies" brings precedent over all other traffic, at all times, throughout the hospital. There are 26 isolettes, but usually they average 18 to 20 occupants. Normally born babies, who are healthy, remain in the bassinets in the Woman's Clinic. There are still 66 of these. However they are also under the care of the pediatricians from CMSC. A busier bunch of men do not on earth exist. Now, instead of running across the backyard from Harriet Lane, they run up and down stairways, through corridors, using all short-cuts between CMSC and the Woman's Clinic.

On CMSC VI is the intensive care unit of 14 beds plus a 48-hour unit for children with minor surgery and in the rear are the neuropsychiatric and neurosurgical patients. CMSC VII houses the children from 2 to 12 who are going into surgery or recovering therefrom. CMSC VIII is for children from 2 to 12 with medical problems, while CMSC IX is for teen-agers, 13 to 19, with medical and surgical problems. Floors X and XI house the Kennedy Research Laboratories. Their foyer was beautifully furnished, but one night the thief came and removed everything; now it is equipped with nondescript rickety chairs no one would ever steal.

Much of the equipment in CMSC was of new design including 5 high-humidity rooms for respiratory relief, where "made" fog can become so thick it is impossible to see across the room; also there are two-sided linen cabinets, open to the children's rooms, as well as the hall, and an intercom system between the nurses' station and all patient rooms is on all patient floors. A dream building come true!

To keep it all going medically, there is a Chief Resident, usually in his 7th year; a Chief Resident of the Outpatient Department, usually in his 6th year; and 18 interns, who serve one year as interns and two more as assistant residents. All OHH will be interested to know that as of July, 1971, Chief residents receive $12,500; 3rd year assistant residents, $11,500 a year; 2nd year assistant residents, $10,500 and 1st year assistant residents $9,500 while interns get $8,500 annually. There is no supplement for wife or children; uniforms, laundry thereof, and malpractice insurance are free. The salaries are paid by the university and hospital jointly; but when the shouting is over, the hospital pays 75% of them. As yet, nobody pays a medical student a salary. They still take pediatrics in their 3rd and 4th years and work on the floors with the inpatients under staff supervision, and in the dispensary or outpatient clinics under the same supervision. One student said, recently, "Every time I think I can't stand medicine anymore and am too discouraged to continue, I go over to CMSC and get knee-deep in kids and they revive me."

Also, he is forever welcome in the Pediatric Library (CMSC II) where there are 400 textbooks and 4,000 bound journal volumes, and the Surgical Library (CMSC VII) where there are 200 textbooks, and 100 bound journal volumes. Another thing, all the pediatric case histories are kept in this building, and as the house staff eventually rotates from floor to floor there is much to learn, at all hours.

The Robert Garrett Professor of Pediatric Surgery reassures his young patient's parents.

Then, too, one of the first things which impresses a visitor to CMSC is how many good looking, *young* nurses one sees. Children respond to TLC, especially if it is applied by a good looking person; so do medical students.

Add to all the above advantages a group of full professors, who are approachable and many of whom are brilliant. The first fully endowed chair in Surgery at Hopkins is that occupied by the Robert Garrett Professor of Pediatric Surgery, who is Children's Surgeon-in-Charge. There are now 10 to 12 endowed chairs at Hopkins, but there is no Federal money in this chair and no J. H. H. money. It is paid for entirely by the Robert Garrett Fund which had accrued to $21 million. This dynamic, young Robert Garrett professor says that children are not small adults; they are different people. Therefore the surgery differs, because the patients are different. Hence, to develop programs relating to the child in surgery, he meets regularly with neurosurgeons, urologists, orthopedists — all the disciplines — to discuss the child's needs in *their* fields and their skills.

Children accept life "as is" and therefore they do not seem to be upset by the fact that this charming, witty, young man has no hair — a consequence of scarlet fever at the age of two months. Recently, when he was conducting rounds with 20 to 25 people in tow, he felt a pull on the tail of his long white coat, and deciding that he had it on crookedly, shrugged his shoulders, straightened the contents in his coat pockets, and continued his description of the condition of the patient he was studying with his students and the accompanying faculty. Again, he felt another pull at his coat-tail, in fact, this time, a definite tugging.

Looking down — way down, too, because he is very tall — he saw a four-year-old little boy, whose eyes were busily travelling the entire distance up to the doctor's face; and when he asked, kindly, "What's the matter? What do you want?"

The child replied, "Aren't you Mister Clean?"

The whole entourage roared with laughter, and the tall professor stooped down and said, instantly, "Yes, I am. But I forgot my earring today."

Another amusing story regarding this man is that of a person who telephoned a hang-out near Hopkins frequented by doctors, gave a vivid description of his appearance, and asked the answering waitress if he were present. She replied, "I don't know. I can't tell. Every man here has his hat on."

The ratio of surgical children at CMSC runs a majority from the Baltimore area; remainder from Maryland, D. C., and Southern Pennsylvania. Few of the children are from foreign countries. The surgeons at CMSC are generally busy correcting serious congenital heart defects, newborn emergencies, intensive abdominal obstructions, windpipe or esophagus difficulties or brain tumors. Any patient brought here who is a true emergency is always admitted, regardless. Recently, a child had a bill for $34,000 resulting from bringing up part of his intestine to make a new esophagus. The parents couldn't pay it, so the Robert Garrett Fund picked up the deficit.

As the Professor remarked, "This is an expensive motel! But when a child gets out of here it has to be ready to roll — well enough to do anything. There are no hypochrondiacs in children; that is a disease of late adolescence!"

Pediatric surgery is one place where the insurance gap is woefully evident, as most health plans do not insure children under 14 years of age.

One of the things which children have taught these Hopkins surgeons is that one must be utterly honest in pre-operative instruction if one wishes to alleviate fear in the patient. Therefore pre-operative briefings, particularly for the open heart operations on children with congenital defects are routine now. Recently it was decided that it might be the better part of wisdom to have an anesthetist prepare such a child as to what he might expect in the operating room from him.

To do so, a very worried anesthetist approached a little black boy, aged seven, the night before his operation and after a few friendly sentences, he said, "Johnny, I want to tell you how it will be tomorrow, when we come to get you so that we can put you to sleep, before your heart operation. I want to give you a briefing, like the astronauts have. You ready?"

Johnny fastened his eyes upon the doctor, who had decided to describe the fantasy dreams which the child might experience while under the influence of the anesthetic. Before doing so, though, he picked up the mask and explained that Johnny would be connected with an oxygen tank, "Just like the astronauts", then he put the mask over the child's face and said, "Now, Johnny, take a deep breath, just like the astronauts do."

Two little hands came flying up and snatched the mask away and Johnny said, swiftly, "WAIT a Minute! What are your plans for re-entry?"

The anesthetist gave up fantasy and got down to fact, immediately. He should have known better, in the first place, for one thing a whole hospital full of sick children teaches the attending adults is that children are honest and they expect you to be so, too.

Before we leave this building let's take three tours: one of the patient floors, again, one of the research floors, and one of the past in the present.

A portion of the basement under this building houses the new hospital kitchen, directly beneath the new cafeteria, while another portion nearer the elevator tiers, is the X-ray department. It is spacious, wide halled, big-roomed and painted yellow with here and there a pale sky-blue room; and the result is over-all space, sunshine and sky, which is hard to accomplish underground.

All pediatric X-ray is done here and there are 4 machines, while on an average day 60 patients pass through these rooms which are open 7 days a week. The X-ray pediatric case histories are housed here, too, and are available at all times. There are also viewing rooms, with viewing machines and consultant rooms.

The waiting room has benches and chairs with red-leather-type cushions for relatives; and on the walls of all rooms and the corridor, repeatedly, wheel-chair and stretcher patients (none are ambulatory) are comforted by what might best be called "peer" pictures. These are done by the Child Life Department (more anon) and pinned or pasted on the walls. Mobiles hang overhead, white elephants ride herd on blue walls. (They are in the pediatric cardiology X-ray room, where an oversized boot-shoe also has an escaping child tumbling from its top.) Art For the Hospitals of Maryland has travelling libraries of framed colored paintings and pictures, appropriate to the age groups, hanging throughout this hospital.

All of the most modern X-ray equipment which could be thought of or desired is here. Again, a dream hospital!

Here, too, as everywhere in this hospital, everyone awaits verdicts, including the prone child in whom fright has already been alleviated by preparatory talks from doctors, nurses, volunteers, and Child Life Ladies. The patients expect, instead of dread. Even the ones whose X-ray indicate heart surgery.

The next patient floor, of course, is the 2nd floor, but the patients one sees here are usually ambulatory. Here are the outpatient clinics for cardiology, Comprehensive Child Care, rheumatic fever, dental; the Pediatric Laboratory; EKG and Hematology Laboratories to service them are here, too. In the center island are the doctors' offices and the administrative offices.

(These children, here, are all patients of the Comprehensive Child Care clinic which has registered in it 17,000 children under 18 years of age from the East Baltimore area. Their number will be increased to 32,000 when the Edwards Park Building is completed and their quarters are moved to there. The project started as a Government experiment in 1966, and the patients appear by appointment and are treated FREE OF CHARGE, the bill being footed by the U. S. Government.)

For the information of OHH the outpatient department is still housed in Harriet Lane and is still referred to as "The Pit." It still functions on a 24-hour-a-day basis, 365 days a year, as will the new outpatient department in the Edwards Park Building when it is opened; and it will assume the functions of Harriet Lane, although a clinic in the new building will be called Harriet Lane Clinic.

Through Harriet Lane dispensary are now clocked about 50,000 visits a year. The fee in the emergency room there is now $22 and in the general clinic, the first visit is $20 and each visit thereafter is $13.

All of these patients, as well as those of the Comprehensive Child Care group and the Pediatric Consultation Clinic in CMSC are cared for by the CMSC staff.

In addition to the 50,000 visits just referred to, are the 26,000 visits to the CCCC, for which there is no fee. Monday through Friday, the general, congenital heart, rheumatic fever, and psychiatric clinics take place daily on the 2nd and 3rd floors of CMSC. And on listed days, previously known to the parents of patients and for which prior appointments have been given, chest, chronic diseases, dental, dermatology, diabetic, seizure, tumor, hearing and speech, and pediatric urology clinics are all held and the patients seen, advised, and helped. The fees for private patients in CMSC Pediatric Consultation Clinic is $10 upwards according to the doctor. Other patients pay $25 for a first visit and $13 each succeeding visit.

There are so many veterans, under five, of innumerable "needles" for diphtheria, typhoid, smallpox, measles, cold shots, cholera — and if their parents are travelling outside America, many other added needles — that the patient load in these diseases has virtually disappeared from a large segment of ill children.

Nutrition standards and preventive medicine have commenced to pay off in the care of the "middle-aged" child, and in other groups, too. Today, also, there is increasingly effective therapy for a variety of congenital anomalies, on which reparative procedures are now possible. In addition there is today an effective antibiotic against "staph" pneumonia. Infants, however, in all age groups are liable, though, to meningitis and traumatic conditions like subdural hematoma.

All staff rotate at CMSC, so eventually every man gets to see and treat all these different illnesses. However, the purpose of the Comprehensive Child Care Clinic, on the 2nd floor of CMSC is to nurture healthy children, without ailments and it is also busily involved in teaching mothers of children with ailments how to combat their difficulties.

While they and the children are waiting, the children come within the care of the Child Life teacher. In 1944, the Child Life Program was started as a volunteer effort by the Women's Board of The Johns Hopkins Hospital. It has since proved so very successful that it has become a necessity and the hospital, now, pays the major portion of its cost.

It has a director, an associate director, and 14 Child Life teachers; and it is accredited as a school by the State of Maryland.

The aim is to provide educational, recreational, and social outlet for children while they are at CMSC, and on each patient floor there is a playroom under the guidance of these — again — pretty girls. The teachers are on the inpatient floors as well and the outpatient areas. Daily at 9:30 A.M. all children who are well enough are brought to the recreation room on each floor. They come on foot, in beds, or wheelchairs. Here, the teachers devote their mornings to pre-school activity and group teaching. Afternoons are generally used for free play time and tutoring in individual rooms.

The Women's Board also sponsors a Child Life Community Program, which is a branch of the Child Life Program. This, too, has a full-time director and tries to increase educational-recreational facilities outside of the hospital for the use of Hopkins neighborhood children. Essentially, it is an effort to get the neighboring community interested in meeting the needs of its children and helping to increase neighborhood programs.

This little girl from East India plays in the Child Life Room.

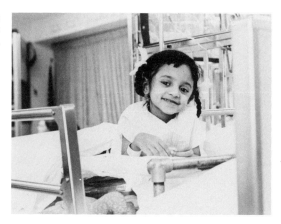

50

Dr. Helen B. Taussig.

To go back to the 2nd floor of CMSC: here the playroom is geared for the small child, and the young "middle-aged" child, under 10. They draw pictures, seated at little tables, make skirts out of ricconi, which they string, cook at a miniature stove, and play with assorted toys; and the highly trained, intelligent worker can keep as many as 30 of them occupied at once!

Next to her playroom one enters the Taussig Cardiac Clinic, named for the Professor Emeritus of Pediatrics whose name is known wherever a heart beats. She is the only Hopkins woman doctor mentioned in *The New York Times Index of Medicine since the 12th Century.* The other Hopkins person mentioned in that index is the late Dr. Alfred Blalock, the Professor of Surgery, who was her co-partner in developing the Blalock-Taussig "blue baby" operation.

In Harriet Lane, her clinic was in the basement; and it was the work she saw there which convinced her that something could and must be done for "blue babies." Hers is a typical example of the interplay between a physician (in this case a pediatrician) and a surgeon in modern medicine. The physician saw the situation, and being a woman decided something must be done to rectify it, then she figured out how something might be done and went to the Professor of Surgery and convinced him that something COULD be done. Together, they did it!

The Cardiac Clinic was officially named for her in 1970 and there is a plaque mounted there which reads "in recognition of contributions to Pediatric Cardiology and the children throughout the world."

One of the finest gifts which CMSC has ever had was that of the Hoffberger family; and on this floor there is a whole section devoted to the Hoffberger Research Wing, where many interesting things are always "in the works." At the entrance to this wing are portraits of both Mr. and Mrs. Charles Hoffberger. Another portrait which hangs in CMSC concerning a gift is that of Master John Mifflin Hood III, who died in Harriet Lane and his family left a bequest in his memory to be devoted to research.

51

The portrait the children love best, though, is that of "Anna," which hangs on the 6th floor, in the cross hallway beyond the elevators. "Anna" was the dog used in the research for the first successful open heart operation.

In fact much of the work which was done in the jam-packed, overcrowded, overworked clinics in Harriet Lane Home shows up again, pursued further in CMSC, including the studies of the association of the thyroid gland with dwarfing and the knowledge of the relationship of the adrenal gland to hermaphrodiest, on which the operation to correct this abnormality has been based.

Outside of Wilmer, no portion of the hospital has more grateful patient bequests than CMSC; and it is also interesting to learn that their autopsy rate is 80% of their deaths. To memorialize a dead child and to learn "for living children" are both strong emotions with American parents. When one remembers that the Faculty of the Department of Pediatrics, exclusive of the Given and Garrett Professors, numbers 73 men, one begins to comprehend all that may be evaluated and learned from their patient autopsies.

As stated previously, on the 3rd floor of CMSC are the private outpatient clinics, now known as Pediatric Consultation Clinic. (OHH - part of POPS.)

Among the patients seen on the 4th floor, the first inpatient floor, are the dwarfs and the kidney patients. Many patients of both groups from all over the country come to Hopkins for help.

The same year that Dr. Lawson Wilkins, who pioneered studies of endocrine disorders in children and organized the pediatric endocrinology clinic at Hopkins, died, the National Pituitary Agency was formed at Hopkins. By then it was known that a hormone extracted from the pituitary gland at autopsy could provide the key to a normal life for a "hypopituitary dwarf" of which there are 7,000 to 10,000 in the United States. Then being treated (1963) at the Hopkins were 13 of these children; of these one boy who was 30″ tall at the age of 7 grew 7½″ during a 15-month period of treatment.

The hitch to the whole program was that it took 2 to 300 pituitaries to treat a single child for one year. The same hormone from animals wouldn't work on humans, hence the formation of the National Pituitary Agency, in hopes of obtaining more pituitaries from autopsies.

Many things have been learned over the years about the children so treated; and now, most recently, the artificial synthesis of this human growth hormone has been achieved and the "little people" have become a most familiar sight at Hopkins.

One of the most beautiful sights at Hopkins within recent months was the young nun from Milbrook, New York, who was accompanied by a very little boy. He had first been placed in a foster home, and three years ago, when he was two, the nuns got him.

He has brown eyes, brown hair, weighs 18 pounds and has an IQ of 102.

He is quick as a humming bird and darts to and fro with lightning speed. He has been a patient of this clinic for all the time the nuns have had him, and the sisters love him dearly and have delighted in making him tiny clothes and miniature suspenders. Usually, he comes to CMSC accompanied by an older nun, but they all loved him so dearly they could not bear to accompany him this time. It had been arranged that he was to be adopted and they couldn't face parting with him, hence they sent him with the "youngest sister." Somehow, there was a hitch in the adoption papers, so the young sister was to take him back to Milbrook for a final reunion, first, but during this present examination he did have an opportunity to meet his new and permanent father.

And Johnny, the little boy, adored him. He adored him, especially, because Mr. Johnson, who is adopting him, is also a dwarf. Both of them are under treatment from the same doctors in the same clinic. Mr. Johnson is a checker at a large warehouse in Atlanta, and when Johnny stands beside him and puts his hand in his, everything in life, his life, comes into proper focus and he feels secure. And so does Mr. Johnson; and their happiness is shared by his wife, too, who is also a dwarf, for the doctors have assured them that Johnny will grow at least as tall as they are, or may become. A shining beauty encircles all of them and the only person who watches and wipes a tear away is the young nun, for she, too, has learned to love him dearly.

The Associate Professor Emeritus of Pediatrics, whose patients are also housed on the floor with Johnny, has spent practically all of her waking hours, during her entire medical life, in or adjacent to the Hopkins Hospital. She is available to her patients at a moment's notice. A world renowned authority on renal difficulties, she has the great wisdom to remember how desperate the plight of these children was before the use of cortisone. This method of control has been used for approximately 20 years, now; but in the last 10 years the profession has known how to use it better and now it is more economical, available, and many of its side effects are now known and can be controlled.

The children who are liable to kidney disorders have a queer and unexpected ratio. Gypsies come first, then white children, and the least susceptible appear to be black children. But some are still poor, forgotten little souls and it is a long laborious procedure to care for them. Some clear up within a couple of years, while others go on for 10 years or more before they can forget about it. This stalwart small fortress of a doctor never ceases to fight for her devoted patients; she never says, "That failed"; instead she says, "We must try something else."

Dr. Harriet G. Guild.

She believes that it is vastly better to catch up with a renal difficulty before it comes to a renal transplant and any child with any kidney malfunction should be immediately brought to a doctor, while there is still time to do something.

Children with this malady have changed in the last ten years. They no longer "perch in their ward beds, like sitting ducks, bloated, too weary to move much, and look at you with faces which bear a marked resemblance to those they would — or if they recover, may — have when they are very old men and women."

This small, quiet, subdued, blue-eyed, almost frail pediatrician has done much to bring about this happy difference. And in these days, when doctors do not always elicit admiration, it is splendid to realize that she can merit a paragraph like the following from, of all papers, *The Wall Street Journal:*

In May 1970, they carried a first-page story about a child who, four years ago, at the age of two-and-a-half, was stung by a bee. The sting triggered a disorder in the little girl's kidneys and to date the child's illness has cost her parents $57,794, to which the Hopkins Hospital has contributed, through restricted endowment funds, repeatedly. The child's case history weighs 5 pounds, and the father, the mother, and the three sons 16, 14, and 9 do everything they can to save and make money to keep the little girl alive.

Her principal doctor is the little lady above referred to. Of her *The Wall Street Journal* said: "she had made it her practice to charge her patients only the amount that she can collect from their insurance. And so she has marked the . . . . . . account as paid although in four years of intensive care she has collected only $763."

She is an ornament to her mentors, her profession, and her sex. Her greatest honor, though, is when she walks down the Main Corridor, and some husky, blonde, blue-eyed, tough looking little boy, about the age of six, looks up and says in a sturdy, merry, hail-fellow voice, "Hi, Doc!"

When the Edwards Park Building is completed, the Harriet Lane plaques

Dr. Mary Ellen Avery, professor and chairman of the Department of Pediatrics at McGill University in Montreal.

will be brought over and placed in it; then the famous old building will either be used for offices, or torn down to make way for new construction. So this seems a proper place to mention two more of the "Harriet Lane girls." One of them, the late Dr. Hattie E. Alexander, who was one of the speakers at the symposium on "The Child" during the opening of CMSC at the 75th anniversary celebration of the Hospital in 1964, was Professor of Pediatrics at the College of Physicians and Surgeons of Columbia University. The other is now Professor of Pediatrics and Chairman of the Department of Pediatrics of the Faculty of Medicine at McGill University in Montreal, as well as Physician-in-Chief of the Montreal Children's Hospital. Dr. Margaret I. Handy's portrait also appears in this book. Dr. Handy practiced for years in Chadds Ford, Pennsylvania and Wilmington, Delaware.

To return to CMSC: this is the only building in the Hopkins Hospital where a sick person may, if the condition warrants, have a relative stay overnight. Some children are greatly helped by the nearby presence of their mothers, who live at the hospital for no charge, sleeping on chairs which fold out into beds. (Fathers can also live in, although this is not a frequent occurrence). A Registered Nurse is in charge of co-ordinating the activities of the live-in mother, who can learn to care for the child, frequently, and relieve some of the burdens from the nurses.

Both the Given and Garrett Professors believe in treating the whole child, and entering the home through the child. This is a particularly vital part of the child's recovery in cases of open heart surgery, where the child came an invalid and leaves a well boy. Such a change necessitates re-preparing the mother to view him as he "is" and NOT as she has learned to do since birth. These very ill children are usually in the hospital 10 to 14 days, so there is sufficient time for the nurse to have many long talks with them about their future duties. Children who have renal dialysis or kidney transplants need re-educated mothers badly. So do delinquent and deficient mothers who must have careful instruction as to the long-term care and improvement of home conditions and home sanitation.

The renal transplants were begun in 1969, and a child has to be conditioned to face his body image when it is altered by surgery, too. The bathing, feeding, toilet needs of surgical children must be carefully taught to the parent involved by this most comprehending of nurses.

There are a maximum of 68 bed chairs; however, there were 1,329 live-in mothers last year and some of them occupied the 8 rooms on the first floor of Hampton House set aside for their use, too. All of these mothers sleep free, but they pay for their food.

There is a children's library on CMSC VII, which has well over 1,000 volumes, and they are a great aid to all of the children, whether they have live-in, read-in mothers, or not.

Speaking of intelligence, it is interesting to know that one very astute professor does not think children are brighter than they were ten years ago; he also thinks that television is helpful, to a point. The "more" they know is not always beneficial, particularly if what they've learned is related to violence.

The 5th floor of CMSC, which is devoted to infants from birth to 2 years, including the preemies, always has a number of live-in mothers and one room is devoted to 3 mothers and 3 preemies. That room is adjacent to the pre-mature nursery, in the rear. The nursery is equipped to handle 26 babies, and they are cared for by a wonderful group of sensitive, comprehending, colored nurses' assist-

A nurse checks an infant in the premature nursery.

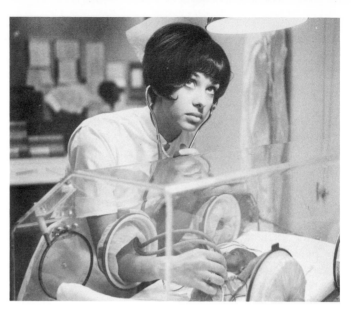

ants. The mothers of the "graduated" preemies, in the room nearby, whose babies are almost ready to go home, can learn much from them; and so could the career mothers "working on a close schedule" at the shopping centers who jam a bottle nipple into their babies' mouths. For these women seem to have all the time in the world; they use their rocking chairs as a seventh sense and expect the preemie they are now feeding to advise them, in the silent language of utter comprehension of their needs, desires, and demands. All the time, these women are as aware, quick, and ready to alter course as a butterfly. Truly they are attuned to life.

Consequently, these wonderful, intricate mechanizations which man has never been able to duplicate — human beings, minute though they may be — learn to trust, to feed, to love, to live, through the kindness, patience, and generosity of these truly gentle women. All day long, they burp, they rock, they pat, they croon, and they defend.

For frequently, nearby, an intern and a nurse will be bending over a desperately ill preemie trying frantically to save his/her life, while the nearby feeding baby rests in the safe security of warm arms.

Because of the long association of the Garrett Fund and the Eudowood Fund with tuberculosis, one question which arises in the reader's mind is the whereabouts of the tubercular child in CMSC. They are kept in the general pediatric wards, in isolation rooms if necessary, until their diagnosis is established. Once a good therapeutic response develops, they are discharged and managed on an ambulatory basis in the Pediatric Chest Clinic. Other infectious disease cases are similarly kept in the general pediatric wards.

All throughout CMSC the idea that children belong with children is stressed repeatedly, and most plainly seen in the way children in all stages of illness are brought into the playrooms both in the mornings and after the 1 to 3 P.M. rest periods in the afternoons. Many things bear out that this is a therapeutically wise attitude. One very touching example of this was the little girl on the 6th floor, with a beauty as fresh as a buttercup, who is 7 and because of spinal difficulties has

56

spent a great portion of her life in the hospital. She had been operated on many times and cannot walk, never has, and probably never will; but she remains cheerful and gay. Recently, when she was returned from a serious operation to a room where she lost her previous roommate, she was highly provoked and wanted to know where her 4-year-old roommate was!

She was teaching that other child to talk, and she shrewdly knew that without her repetitive help, the non-talker would lose confidence and forget words. "Children help children" and "Children need children" are frequently heard in CMSC and there are even people here who believe that babies talk, too.

Before concluding this chapter, perhaps it would be wise to give a quick résumé of the Edwards Park Building. It will cost $3 million, be 4 stories high and provide facilities for complete preventive, screening, and treatment services, including rehabilitative and psychiatric services. It will eventually serve 35,000 children of East Baltimore. Some of its unique features will be the 1st emergency room for children in a general hospital; the 1st outpatient building expressly for the comprehensive care of children in a large poverty area; the 1st building built experimentally to study acceptability, efficiency, and economy in child care.

And as nutrition is one of the subjects which will be most repeatedly stressed in it, it is most interesting to remember that live men stand on dead men's shoulders. One wonderful example of that is the history of vitamin D at Hopkins, where it was discovered. In 1918, Dr. Howland asked Dr. McCollum at the School of Hygiene if anyone had produced rickets experimentally in an animal.

Dr. McCollum, a biochemist who had been interested in nutrition, showed Dr. Howland some rats whose diets had been controlled to produce a condition which seemed like rickets. It was. Dr. Howland cabled Dr. Park, in France, requesting he return as quickly as possible; Dr. Park had studied the pathology of rickets and was very interested in the disease. With the aid of Dr. Paul Shipley, an expert histologist, Park, Shipley and McCollum proved the existence of Vitamin D.

The Edwards A. Park Building.

In 1964, the Given Professor at CMSC cited excess use of Vitamin D. as a possible association with mental retardation and other serious birth defects. He pointed out that Vitamin D. has a cumulative effect, and in excess amounts sometimes results in hypercalcemia or too much calcium in the system.

Due to his extreme interest in mental retardation, the Joseph P. Kennedy Jr. Foundation built and endowed the 2 research floors on CMSC. Also, the first hospital built with Government funds for the study of mental retardation after President Kennedy got the legislation passed allocating those funds was built across Monument Street from Hopkins and named for President Kennedy. Many of its faculty are on the faculty at Hopkins and all of its surgery is done in Hopkins GOR.

In the last 10 years, the Given Professor feels that many things have been accomplished; he points out that the middle-class child rarely needs hospitalization, except for corrective measures or surgery, while the poor child needs it with much greater frequency, due to serious anemias, inferior early life, and faulty nutrition. However, anemia has been remarkably reduced in the Hopkins area, and there are very few iron-deficiency ones seen now.

He considers another advancement of these years the extension of pediatrics to the handicapped child, so that functionally he is an integral part of CMSC. The handicapped child now has some status in medical thinking, and medical students now clamour to take the elective first-year course to be given at the Kennedy Institute.

Much of the recent research work has greatly affected child future, such as the improvement in metabolic disorders, specifically PKU. Twenty different problems have been detected early and managed in recent programs on pre-natal birth defects; it is now possible to diagnosis in the uterus, with the collaboration of obstetricians and gynecologists some of these difficulties. Also, the changes in growth retardation have been spectacular.

There is an entirely new concept of the "child" as a whole — not just the illness which brought him here, but *everything* affecting him: his ancestry, his home life, his learning abilities — and all are evaluated and correctable difficulties are aided in CMSC.

A child is indeed fortunate who can be brought here as a patient, for brilliant men study him, kind people care for him, and he has such a continuous good time he is loath to go home.

And they come back at Christmas to see the manger in the lobby of CMSC.

CHAPTER VI

Hopkins to Hopkins via Vanderbilt

IN Culloden, Georgia, in 1899, a man had a son. In 1912, the son was 13 and the man was a patient in The Johns Hopkins Hospital. The father recovered and the son decided right then to become a doctor. He graduated from The Hopkins Medical School in 1922, was at Vanderbilt until 1941, when he became the Surgeon-in-Chief, J.H.H. And he graduated into the medical archives of the world, forever, in 1944. In 1949 he was named by the International Society of Surgery as the world's outstanding vascular surgeon; in 1960 he received the Rudolph Matas Award in vascular surgery, which is one of the world's great honors for surgeons of the heart and blood vessels. It meant particularly much to Dr. Alfred Blalock, too, because it was the very famous Dr. Matas, of New Orleans, who wrote the introduction to those treasured volumes of Dr. Halsted's surgical papers, which he had leaned on and perused all of his medical life.

Early in 1964, as part of its 75th anniversary celebration, The Johns Hopkins Hospital renamed the Clinical-Science Building the Blalock Clinical-Science Building, and the portrait of Dr. Blalock now hangs in the lobby. The resemblance may not be what might be desired by OHH, for the portrait, damaged many times by vandals, has been rebuilt and is now covered with glass. The slashes have been repainted and the indelible pencil smears painstakingly and carefully obliterated. That so kindly a man, who did so much for humanity, should be so savagely treated is

Dr. Alfred Blalock, left, receives the Hospital's Distinguished Service Medal from Board Chairman Walter F. Perkins in 1964.

one of the horrible indices of these difficult times. It is particularly ironical when Hopkins now spends $500,000.00 annually for uniformed guards around the clock that desecrations still occur. This is an enormous item in a hospital whose annual deficit now runs about $2 million.

At the time of Dr. Blalock's death, 2,000 blue baby operations had been done.

Also in this lobby is a portrait just recently hung of Vivien Thomas, who came from Vanderbilt with Dr. Blalock in 1941 and whom Dr. Blalock put in charge of the Hunterian Surgical Research Laboratory then. He worked with all the animals which Dr. Blalock used in perfecting his blue baby operation, and knows and knew about as much about the operation as any man alive. He is now supervisor of the Surgical Research Laboratory, and was always part of all the advances of surgery, in their experimental development, which are credited to Dr. Blalock. As long as Dr. Blalock lived he "scrubbed" with Dr. Blalock in the experimental surgery lab. Dr. Blalock depended upon him, relied on him, trusted him, and he is a man who is an ornament to his race.

Also, in the lobby are the large mural blow-ups of Maryland scenes, particularly those of Chesapeake Bay made from photographs which were taken by the late Aubrey Bodine; he was one of the most remarkable and gifted photographic artists in the United States, and the winner of innumerable prizes and honors.

He always worked for the *Sunpapers,* and went to work when he was 14, taught himself all the photography he knew, and was a master of international repute in the art. Three beautiful books of his photographs can be purchased in Baltimore now; they are expensive, exquisite productions. A biography of Aubrey Bodine, with pictures, tracing his artistic development appeared in the fall of 1971.

Aubrey was a lifelong and completely devoted friend of The Johns Hopkins Hospital and probably, over the years, took more—and certainly better—photo-

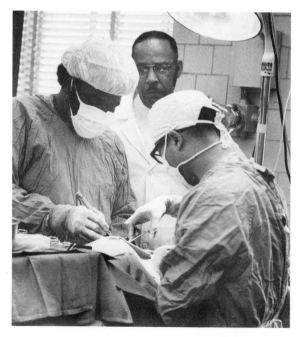

Vivien Thomas, center, keeps a watchful eye on the execution of a new technique under development in a surgical laboratory.

60

graphs of the place, one way or another, than any man who yet has lived. In the early sixties one of his most beautiful views of the hospital was used as the Christmas card of the hospital, and many people who received it have it framed and hung on the walls of their houses.

He was a very terse, usually silent, lean, perceptive red-head, who would wait endless hours to catch the right light for the picture.

In October of 1970, he died, in the Hopkins Hospital, and even that has a story attached to it. Aubrey was in his dark room at the *Sunpapers* when he had a stroke (he'd had diabetes and heart trouble for years).

When the ambulance came and he was put on the stretcher, some reporter standing by, said, "Where you going to take him?" The driver replied, naming the nearest hospital. Ill as he was Aubrey heard, made a colossal effort and said his last words. They were, "NO. Take me to THE JOHNS HOPKINS HOSPITAL!"

His editor asked the ambulance men to do so, but they pointed out that it was a city regulation that they must always take the patient to the nearest hospital, so the *Sunpapers* called a private ambulance company, which came promptly and Aubrey, in charge of his life to the end, died several hours later in Marburg.

Also on the right wall, when one enters from the Main Corridor, in this lobby is an inset case, containing the names of people who gave money for use in this building, either for laboratories or for completion of rooms.

The marble set in the opposite wall comes from the old surgical amphitheatre, which was opened in 1904, and later torn down when the Blalock Clinical-Science Building was built. It is interesting to note that all of the surgeons and nurses trained in that old surgical amphitheatre, as well as the three men already mentioned in this chapter, never lived by an eight-hour day, nor a five-day week; as long as there was work to do, they did it.

When this book was first written, Dr. Blalock who was also Director of the Department of Surgery, said, "The best help I know of you can get anywhere is Dr. Crowe's *Halsted of Johns Hopkins.* I have a copy I'll lend you. It is a strange thing about that book. The last two weeks of his life Dr. Crowe would work on it all the time. We couldn't stop him. He seemed to know he had to finish it then, or he never would. As a matter of fact, we had to take it afterwards and pull the stuff together, in some places. But it gives the best surgical picture of the Hopkins, in a few words, I've ever seen."

This conversation took place in the Halsted museum, later described in this chapter, of which Dr. Blalock was very proud; and he discussed the treasures there and pointed to the rubber glove he had in a case there and remarked, "Most people think that Dr. Halsted invented rubber gloves for his nurse who later became his wife. But he didn't. They already were using them in Germany some years before and Dr. Welch brought back several pairs from Germany. That is one of the ones Dr. Welch brought back. It is very clumsy and thick, you see. I think it must have been used for autopsies."

Then he gave permission for the author to attend an open heart operation, went across the hall and got his copy of Dr. Crowe's book, locked the museum door and said, "If there is any way I can help you with your book, just say so, and I will."

Several days later, during an open heart operation, by some form of grapevine, word was transmitted beyond the operating room that things were not going well. Presently a door opened and the slight frame of Dr. Blalock moved unobtru-

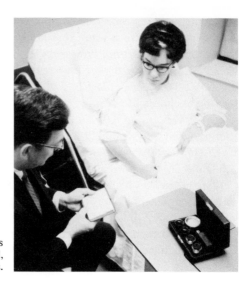

The Chaplain of The Johns Hopkins Hospital goes throughout the Hospital, all hours, all days, all nights.

sively into the room and took up a watch behind the "backest" intern. Nobody moved aside; no man's intensity altered, but every man on the operating team felt more comfortable and capable. Shortly, Dr. Blalock said to the "backest" intern, "Have they tried so and so?" The intern said, "No sir." Dr. Blalock replied easily, "Tell 'em to try it." Then he stayed a few minutes more to see if the procedure was going to work, went over and scrutinized the heart-lung machine and watched it begin to succeed and quietly slipped through the door through which he had come.

Dr. Blalock was very proud of his men and he had every right to be. He "raised up" 10 Chairmen of Departments of Surgery now at UCLA, Vanderbilt, Pittsburgh, New York University, Duke, Johns Hopkins, University of Virginia, Cornell, National Heart Institute and the present Director of the American College of Surgeons. Also, there are now scattered throughout America 12 Chiefs of Surgery "raised up" by him.

One of the most touching tributes he ever received occurred at his funeral, held on a stifling hot summer day, at the Church of the Redeemer, which is out Charles Street, a long, long way from East Baltimore. A very attractive, pretty young woman in the congregation asked if this was the right church, and was this Dr. Blalock's funeral.

When she had been reassured and asked if she worked at the Hospital, she replied, "No. But my father, who is a pediatrician in Louisville, is a classmate and friend of Dr. Blalock's and I thought I ought to come. My husband is an Episcopal minister and we live in Essex, out on the edge of Baltimore. Once when I was at the Hospital, as a patient in the out-patient clinic, I went by afterwards to speak to Dr. Blalock, but he wasn't in his office. So I just left a message and said I was sorry not to meet him. And I never saw him. But the next day, I received a whole page letter from Dr. Blalock saying that he was sorry not to have met me and talking about my father and when they were young together. It's a long way from Essex, but I just thought I *had* to come. And I'm glad I did."

Perhaps it is fitting that the single office opening onto the lobby of the Blalock Clinical-Science Building is that of the Chaplain of the hospital, for he, too, is a man who works without hours. He may be seen at 7 A. M. in the cafeteria, talking with the student nurses before they go on duty, or as late as 10:00 or 11:00 at night, having just come from some very ill patient. He is now in his 9th year here, having come to Hopkins from the North Church of the Brethren in Baltimore. On the staff, there are now 23 clergy, who work a 6-hour day, once a week. Of these 13 are Protestant, including the Greek Orthodox Church, 6 are Roman Catholic priests, 4 are rabbis and 3 of the Protestant clergy are colored. The clergy now make 30,000 patient visits a year. Any members of any faith may be visited by their own clergy upon their request.

Every Sunday the Protestant service is conducted by the Chaplain in Hurd Hall at 9:30 A. M. while the Roman Catholic masses, held in Hurd Hall, too, are at 7:30 A. M. and 12 noon and conducted by a priest of that faith.

The Chaplain teaches in nursing school on problems relating to the dying patient and the unmarried mother. However, 80% of his time is spent in inpatient care. Among these patients are critical emergency patients, who need daily care, as do many cardiac patients; also he does psychotherapy with adolescents, and helps with the drug abuse program. His teaching consumes 15 to 20% of his time. There are workshops, too, advising clergy, in general regarding hospital work, to which 230 to 250 come each year.

The last poem in the *Oxford Book of English Verse* still covers their duties better than many paragraphs could. It contains the verse:

> When the will has forgotten the lifelong aim,
> And the mind can only disgrace its fame,
> And a man is uncertain of his own name —
> The power of the Lord shall fill this frame.

All faiths, all hours, all days, all nights, these 23 clergymen go throughout the hospital conveying His power.

When one passes a large generator station, the air is full of vibration; everything extra in it seems to have danced away.

This tempo-quickening at Hopkins is obvious as one moves down the corridor toward the blue light (denoting the emergency or accident room, which lies beyond the swinging doors leading off the elevator corridor in the Blalock Building).

Down the main corridor beyond this building are Halsted and Osler, toward which are more people, moving faster, all intent upon a definite progress, performed in haste, toward a definite goal. These 3 buildings with the great expanse of the Dispensary or Carnegie Building behind them, mesh and intermesh, corridor-connect and services-exchange much as the fingers of a giant pair of hands might interlace

The ambulance entrance
of the emergency department.

63

and move together.

The people who turned off into Blalock, hastening toward the two swinging doors, with their two glass moon-shaped insets, move at even a swifter pace, for they are enroute to the Emergency Room. This waiting room is equipped with stretchers, wheel chairs, waiting bench accommodations for about 50 people, an admitting officer, and several clerks.

Although this department operates in no more space than it had 10 years ago, its work load has increased enormously. Ten years ago it handled 160 patients in an 8-hour period; now it clocks 220 for the same period of time and on a busy Monday it has handled as many as 400 in 8 hours.

The tremendous increase has been occasioned by the fact that two hospitals then in East Baltimore, Sinai and St. Joseph's, have moved to the suburbs, leaving behind them large patient loads. Also, the practising physicians in East Baltimore have decreased to the point where they are woefully inadequate to care for the population. Furthermore the outpatient boundaries which used to exist in Baltimore hospitals are ignored or abolished. Ambulances do take patients to the nearest hospital, but ambulatory patients go where they please.

By re-studying their space usage and greatly increasing their Emergency Room staff, the patient load has somehow been handled. There is now an administrative staff of 2 coordinators, 6 clerks, 1 drug abuse counsellor, and 1 social worker. The Emergency Room also has an alcoholic counsellor. The nursing service consists of 1 supervisor, 1 assistant head nurse, 2 medical nurses, 1 surgical nurse, 1 ob-gyn nurse, 1 Emergency Overnight Unit nurse, 1 nurse in the dispensary area, plus 5 other nursing personnel. These are the number of people in these positions during an 8 hour shift. The total personnel of the 2 staffs is 77 people.

The doctors' staff has 3 surgical assistant residents, 4 surgical interns, 4 assistant residents in medicine and 5 medical interns. Also, there are 1 ob-gyn intern and 1 psychiatric assistant resident. This staff covers the duty 24 hours a day, 7 days a week.

In the same square footage where 10 years ago 30,000 to 40,000 persons were seen annually, they now care for 110,000 persons, each of whom arrives accompanied by 2 or 3 people, usually. Non-emergencies wait 4 to 5 hours while emergencies are handled in less than half an hour. Non-emergencies, and sometimes, emergencies in the office of private practitioners, particularly if they are orthopedic or ophthalmological patients, wait a similar period, too. Ophthalmologists make their patient-engagements 6 months to a year in advance, so such a case throws an entire day's schedule out of kilter. However, the people who are seen in the Hopkins Emergency Room have no knowledge of this exasperating and uncomfortable truth and consider themselves vastly put upon by the time-lag between their arrival and their treatment.

The patients' relatives are not themselves, either; and the Emergency Room staff is hand-picked to hold their tempers, be polite, and courteous at all times. In fact, they are crisis-oriented. Every female is called a "lady"; every male, "sir."

The grateful patient who was actually poverty-stricken has disappeared from the modern accident room. All these people are well-shod, and many are demanding or resentful. Almost nobody passes through this accident room for whom somebody, eventually, does not pay something: Medical Assistance (welfare) insurance, Workman's compensation or private hospital insurance companies, Medicare or Medicaid, or in case of out-of-state patients, similar agencies in the states of their origin are asked to pay.

Therefore, with the exception of the medical students and student nurses working here as part of their training, the 13th chapter of I Corinthians applies to no patient and no employee in any accident room any longer. Perhaps the reason the medical students and student nurses love to work here so is that they receive that intangible reward which that chapter promises to all who obey it.

All ambulatory patients, on arrival, are interviewed, in turn, and asked their vital statistics, whether they have been here before, and "third party payer." The fees are as follows: $1.50 for a triage visit; $3.50 for someone from emergency to Outpatient Clinic, where the triage fee is deducted from the fee charged there; $10.00 through the system into triage to be seen by a doctor. After seen by a doctor in a designated area, the patient goes on elsewhere or is discharged. Clinic fees vary. $22.00 covers a complete examination in surgical, medical, gyn-obs or psychiatric service. At triage, in the dispensary, every night until 10:00 P. M. one of 4 rotating doctors assigned there, gives them a quick evaluation, decides whether they are medical, surgical, etc. and whether they need immediate or deferred attention. If they need deferred attention, arrangements are made for them to come back later, at a given time, to the proper clinic in the Outpatient Department of the Carnegie Dispensary. If they need immediate care, they are sent back to the proper place in the Emergency Room to wait. They are also asked to pay $22.00, from which the original $3.50 is deducted. This medical sorting system is closed from Friday at 5 P. M. to Monday at 9 A. M. and the work is done on the medical side of the Emergency Room.

The entire Emergency Room at Hopkins is excellently equipped, there being on the surgical side a laceration room, adjacent to a special room for infected cases, 7 cubicles with beds, for cases which must be watched overnight, or for a few hours before a decision is made, regarding hospital admission. Also, there are 2 rooms for psychiatric patients under observation. Directly behind the surgical rooms are 2 rooms devoted to urgent problems of delivery and women's diseases. Next is a complete laboratory with an up-to-date technician to carry out basic diagnostic tests.

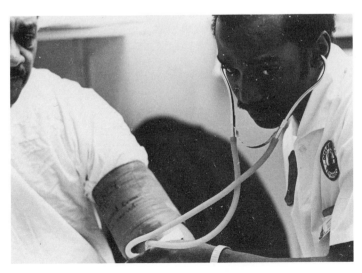

A technician who is a former corpsman, assists physicians and nurses in aiding emergency department patients.

Then come 2 large, complete up-to-date X-ray rooms, along with a new X-omat unit which dries and develops X-rays within 90 seconds. (The X-ray staff on a normal day consists of 1 radiologist, 4 staff members assisting, and usually 2 or 3 students.) Between the 2 X-ray rooms is the multiple trauma room, where the serious and urgent trauma cases are attended.

The other pair of swinging doors, in the Emergency Waiting Room nearest to the Blalock doors, leads into the medical area, which has a poison control unit, 10 examining rooms, plus a cardiac resuscitation room and a room designed for the treatment of asthma patients.

Next to the medical section is the psychiatric section with an office for the psychiatrist and an area for the psychiatric nurse and the psychiatric clerk.

At the end of the corridor, near the Halsted Lobby, is a new unit, called the Primary Care Unit. This has 4 examining rooms, and is manned by senior physicians and nursing and nursing aid personnel. This Primary Care Unit is supported by a triage section in the Emergency Department, already described.

Down the long halls of both the Surgical and Medical portions of the Emergency Department are numerous benches, with supplmentary folding chairs, when necessary for those waiting patients who have passed through from the waiting room they first entered, and are awaiting attention in the unit to which they were assigned. Because all of the adjacent doors are opening and closing with people coming and going, they have an idea they are being neglected. They are not. If they are repeats, they have to wait for their case histories to be brought up to the doctors; and if they are slated for X-ray, they have to wait until the machines are free and the doctor treating them has a chance to study their films with the radiologist, also — and this will forever be true in the Hopkins Emergency Room — they have to wait until the life-and-death cases which came in after they did have received whatever care medicine and surgery can offer them at the emergency level.

A case in point was that of a blue-eyed, short-haired, blonde young man from a nearby chain store, whose elbow had been injured in moving some crates. He walked that inside corridor in bitter pain for over an hour after his X-ray had been taken, before a doctor could get time to come from the laceration room and splint his injury.

Several minutes after he arrived in the Emergency Room, long before he "made" it to the inside corridor, 4 ambulances arrived with 4 men who had been joy-riding in a stolen car which was demolished in the accident and had left them severely injured, too.

When the nurses and co-ordinators rushing to and fro say to such a person, "You are bumped by priorities, we'll get to you soon as we can," it doesn't help his blood pressure, nor lower his pain.

Sometimes, in the midst of a busy wild night or an endless day, there will be call on the Red Phone, and that even makes things more hectic. Immediately it comes, the senior doctor present on that service grabs his bag and rushes for the ambulance dock. Almost before he can get there, a police car arrives, he jumps in, and they start down the ramp with all sirens blaring.

Nobody talks; the driver has already replied in answer to his original query, "Man trapped beneath a concrete wall. Mobile surgical unit meeting you there."

Baltimore City Fire Department has a fully equipped operating room, permanently staffed, which reports to all such emergencies; and three hospitals,

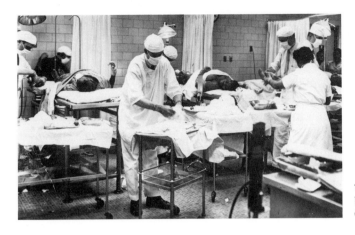

Weekend evenings are busiest in the emergency department.

depending upon their geographical nearness, supply the doctor, who may or may not, depending on his own judgment, send back to his hospital for a back-up team. This magnificent service goes to all emergencies which cannot be moved and must have instant aid to live. The doctor stays as long as the patient needs him. It is a grueling, exciting, exhausting experience — and a *gratifying* one.

Another use of the Red Phone is to alert the Emergency Room that an ambulance is enroute there bringing a super-emergency — perhaps a coronary.

As soon as the ambulance picks up such a case, the crew radios the Ambulance Dispatcher at Fire Headquarters and states the patient's condition and which hospital they are heading for. Dispatcher then alerts that hospital on the Red Phone, thereby giving them a couple of minutes leeway to prepare room and equipment to receive the patient.

All the old stand-by things still come in to the Emergency Room: like the baby who swallowed the jacks his sister was playing with and who must be broncho-scoped, or the Chinaman accompanied by his very pregnant wife who, he says, is "velly, velly sick." She is hustled off to the Woman's Clinic, her case history is sent for, and the intern cursed with it sees, it is two inches thick. A man with a white curtain ruffle wound around his head sways in and says he got "cut behind the ear." The wonderfully wise nurse unwraps the home dressing, gets him onto a table, and the policemen on whose beat the cutting occurred appears. The assistant resident's gentle, knowing fingers touch, push about the wound which is the size now of a hen's egg, and he consults the interns as to whether the man is bleeding internally. The policeman questions the victim, who is a puddler in the steel mills. He'd been paid off, had his money in his pockets and was "rolled." The nurse says practically, "Where is the rest of your money?" He answers instantly, "In my left shoe." She yanks this off, removes $40 and puts it away in his name in the hospital treasury.

On the medical corridor, the suicide case arrives. Seventeen, redheaded, in a green dress; she has tried to kill herself four times. She has "buried four of her family in two months." She wears red bedroom slippers with pink pompoms, and a waiting relative insists that her green suede pumps, which match her dress, be taken to her! The police go searching the bars for her no-account husband who must sign the papers to commit her to a mental institution.

Over the tables in the laceration room, the teams work steadily, and remember, somewhere in the backs of their heads, that outside it is a warm April night. The cheek-slashings, slit throats, and stabbings continue to pour into the Emergency Room. The wife of a Harvard professor, who is visiting in Baltimore and has been hurt in a collision, is brought in. She has slight abrasions, but no broken bones, so they lay her on a stretcher and the teams concentrate on the gory, near-death army descending upon them. Finally, her husband protests to a nurse, with long Emergency Room training, and she replied, "We'll get to your wife as soon as we can, Mister. She'll be all right. But it's mating season in East Baltimore and these others are going to die if we don't sew 'em up — and quick!"

All day, all night, all Saturday, all Sunday they come, for there are no eight-hour days in illness, nor in the desire to escape pain.

On the wall, over the scrub-up sinks in Room #101 of the Emergency Department, which is the General Laceration Treatment Room, is a large wall plaque which reads:

In Honor of
Samuel Stockton Miles
Class of 1940
Killed in Action Aug. 7th, 1942, while
serving as medical officer with
First Marine
Raider Battalion.

The doctors scrubbing up at these sinks must glance at this plaque many, many times, for they, too, are in the front-line trenches.

The man who knows more about the Emergency Room than any employee has worked here 8 years and says he'd rather work here than anywhere in the hospital. He is administrative assistant for the ER and after working all day, often comes back and works 3 evenings, too. He says, "It makes you feel happy to see a life saved, or to get a cast on a broken leg, or just to feel you are *helping* people." He is everywhere, all over the place, doing anything which needs to be done, and the hospital is fortunate, indeed, that he is here.

One last word about the Emergency Room: the plaques there are listed below in detail, because there are more of them than anywhere else in so small a space in the hospital; also, because of the restricted nature of the area, you will not be allowed to wander around and see them. Factual data is listed: no sums of money are mentioned on any of the plaques.

Richard D. Hahn, M.D., given by William K. Douglass
Hennie and Julius Gutman given by Julius Gutman & Company
In memory of Emanuel Chambers
In memory of W. Graham Boyce
In memory of Elmer Burkitt Freeman, M.D.
In memory of George Homer Cornwall and Benjamin Franklin Cornwall
In memory of John Davis Gambill, M.D., my friend
In memory of Evelyn Marie Hughes, daughter of Mr. and Mrs. Raymond Hughes
In memory of Charles E. and Ida S. Dohme
Donated by S. and N. Katz Foundation in memory of Philip Katz
The gift of Dr. and Mrs. C. A. Clapp (hall of wall section adjacent to bed plaque
    cubicles)

In memory of Henry Brooke Gilpin (bed-wall plaque)

In memory of Louis L. Katzner (bed-wall plaque)

In memory of Ella A. Lesem (bed-wall plaque)

In memory of Walter Hopkins — 1876-1945 (bed-wall plaque)

In memory of Frank West Iredell (bed-wall plaque)

In memory of Harry White — 1849-1922 (bed-wall plaque)

In memory of Hilda Blum (bed-wall plaque)

In memory of Douglas Gordon Carroll (bed-wall plaque) (beside door to psychiatric bedroom)

In memory of Helen Earnshaw Cook and Albert Samuel Cook (bed-wall plaque)

In memory of Catherine Milligan McLane, given by her sister, Elizabeth C. McLane (wall plaque beside treatment room)

The gift of the Hecht Company (wall plaque)

A visit to a grim place should end in a final laugh. One of the Emergency Room interviews who was talking to a stevedore with an infected finger, inquired his name, his insurance card, where he lived, and was he married, and his telephone number.

Then the interviewer continued, "Your wife living at the same address?"

The stevedore replied, "Was a few minutes ago when I called her."

If you bear in mind the simile that Halsted and Osler are the lungs, Blalock Clinical Science the air moving in and out of them, and the Dispensary is the heart pumping the blood, and Pathology is the head, evaluating all of these separate processes, you will come upon some idea of what this group of buildings means.

The Oxford Dictionary says that clinical means "of or pertaining to a sick-bed"; science means "systematic and formulated knowledge, the pursuit of this"; surgery (Halsted) means "manual treatment of injuries or disorders of the body". from the Greek *kheir,* hand, and *ergo,* work. While medicine (Osler) comes from Latin word *medeor,* Heal. Dispensary is a place where medicine is dispensed, whereas pathology means the study of disease. The functions of Blalock, Halsted and Osler, the Dispensary and Pathology become clear when one applies these definitions to each.

This building is an excellent example of the interlocking of the many disciplines at Hopkins. Nowadays, men in all specialities may be seen anywhere at any time. Psychiatrists are throughout the hospital, and so are radiologists, to mention two such groups. As a consequence of this intermingling, ideas jump from floor to floor in Blalock. On the second floor are the surgical and urological clinics.

One little boy, about ten, wearing his cowboy boots and other paraphernalia of the mythical west, watched his mother scrutinize the building directory whereabouts in the lobby, and said, "Mamma, let's go see an InChief!" The Neurologist-in-Chief, the Physician-in-Chief, and the Surgeon-in-Chief are all listed on the board.

He was very disappointed when he only got to the 2nd floor and his mother took him to minor surgery to get his infected finger dressed. On that floor, too, is the dental clinic, which has been in existence at Hopkins for many years and was originally manned by men who were graduates of the Baltimore College of Dental Surgery (1840), which was the first dental college in the world. In 1920-21 it merged with the University of Maryland and is now called the Baltimore Dental College of the University of Maryland. This complicated name resulted because of

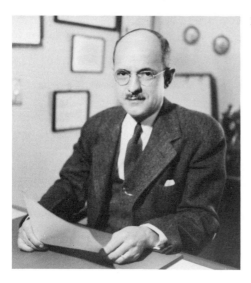

Dr. Grant E. Ward (1896-1958).

a bequest left to BCDS which stipulated the above title always appear in its mast-head. The late Dr. H. Hayward Streett, who was for many years the Dental-Surgeon-in-Charge at Hopkins, was one of these men. His son, who still practises in Balti-more, worked at Hopkins for many years, in the clinic, and went to the Pacific in World War II with one of the Hopkins units.

A rundown of the number of visits paid to the clinics on this floor last year will give you an idea of how busy things are hereabouts: Genito Urology, 5,585; Dental, 5,558; Surgical: Neurosurgery, 1,059; Plastic, 3,387; General, 1,376; Surgical Dressing Room, 9,609; Surgical Follow Up, 2,607; Vascular, 833; Pediatric Surgery, 1,052; Pediatric G. I., 65. It takes so little time to say them, and so long to see them, and help them!

When this book was first written, the clinic next referred to was in this building, although now it has been moved to the Carnegie; however, what occurred regarding it happened *here,* and therefore is included here.

It was in the Tumor Clinic that so many people now living were cured in their minds and their bodies by association with, and treatment from, a man they did not doubt was a medical saint. His name was Dr. Grant E. Ward and he died in 1958 of cancer, following several desperate operations, one of which destroyed his power to raise his right arm. After that operation he lay in bed, taught himself to use his left hand to pick up the skills of his right, and with the help of engineers devised a harness which would make his right hand again valuable to him in an operating room. It was built, and so great was that man's joy in being able to operate that the fact that the harness was bitterly cumbersome was never mentioned by him. He worked as long as he could move or stand. There are not many buildings which have their benedictions given to them so early in their lifetimes. The men he trained continue in his footsteps and the spirit he instilled in them calms many a frightened heart.

One of the finest tributes he ever received was this: there used to be an excellent parking garage in the alley behind the 800 block North Charles Street. One of the most accommodating persons who worked there was a colored man named Brooks, who always wore a railroad fireman's cap. He was very polite and a favorite with all the doctors who parked there, among whom was Dr. Grant Ward.

One day a medical lady chided Brooks so about never taking off his cap and ruining the circulation in his head that he took it off and showed her the growth, about the size of a small orange, which it concealed. He was a tall, sparse man; but even leaning over, so that she could observe it, she saw the condition, immediately became very perturbed, and demanded that he go over to Hopkins, *now,* and ask Dr. Ward to examine the growth. Reluctantly, Brooks did as she insisted and Dr. Ward removed it, then and there. He was very good to Brooks, checked him regularly, and watched over him carefully. Brooks adored him, as a consequence, and discarded his cap — for good.

Dr. Ward died during the great snowstorm in 1958; and when Brooks heard the sad news, he went out, bought a brand new snow shovel and walked — there was no other way to get there — from Charles and Eager Streets to Dr. Ward's home on West University Parkway and spent uncountable hours digging out the driveway and all of the walks, including the sidewalk.

He was a tall man and the snow was as high as his shoulders. He would take no pay for the colossal task and afterwards, when the medical lady told him what a wonderful thing he had done, Brooks turned on her and said, "After what he'd done for me *nothing* was too much to do for Dr. Ward! I wanted things to look 'just right' for him — and they did."

Blalock III houses medical specialty clinics — arthritis, chest, cardiac, G. I., dermatology, allergy, endocrine — and they see 28,000 patients a year. Nuclear medicine, outpatient radiology, and the radioisotope lab are here, too, as well as the medical record room.

On the 4th floor are the co-ordinators of the Private Patient Clinic; their patient records; the Private Patient Clinics and the Private-Outpatients. As before stated the POPS' name has been changed to Patient Consultation Clinics.

One of the most exciting floors comes next for it is there, among other things, that the health-care programs for Columbia, in Howard County, and East Baltimore are being prepared. The Director of the Outpatient Service has his office on this floor. Columbia is already in operation and mentioned elsewhere, but the clinics in East Baltimore, for which 13 different agencies have contributed, will ultimately serve 25,000 East Baltimore residents. They are to be staffed by Hopkins men and will be built some blocks from the hospital at Eager and Ensor Streets.

The Halsted Museum is located on Blalock VII and houses many personal belongings and professional mementos of the first Professor of Surgery.

The cardiovascular division has space on this same floor. The heart sound laboratory, E.K.G., respiratory lab, Wellcome Research lab, and myocardial Infarction Study Center are here, too.

The 6th floor is the private property of the Department of Surgery. The division of anesthesiology and surgical-radiology research lab are here, too. Also, the "In-Chief" and the Halsted Administration Offices are on this floor. The magnificent portrait of Dr. Finney hangs in the corridor, and one can begin to feel the tension and excitement of GOR invading the atmosphere. So many of the men still working here knew Dr. J. M. T. Finney and have trained under his sons, or his grandsons. The name Finney has probably been more constantly on the loudspeaker at Hopkins longer than that of any other medical family. This floor is also head-quarters for the transplant surgery division.

The Halsted Museum has been moved to the 7th floor and is directly across the corridor from the visitors lounge where the relatives and friends of patients either in surgery or in recovery wait. In this room are housed some of the various objects which Dr. Halsted held of value.

Among them are several sofas and chairs, a breakfront, with many early medical pictures displayed therein, including "Welch Rabbits"; some oriental rugs from Dr. Halsted's collection. In that breakfront is also a Halsted clamp and one of the pair of rubber gloves which Dr. Halsted had made for Miss Hampton; nearby under glass in a recessed table is a scarf he gave Mrs. Mont Reid and Dr. Reid's watch, which Dr. Halsted had given to him. Drs. George J. Heuer and Reid operated on Dr. Halsted in his final illness. Among the various mementoes is the gold medal which, a few months before his death, was given Dr. Halsted by the American National Dental Association. This medal was presented in appreciation of what nerve-blocking anaesthesia had done for dental practice. In the room are two of Dr. Halsted's high silk hats, numerous pictures, bound volumes of his articles; also, there is an oil painting of dahlias, done as a gratitude gift by the grandmother of a blue baby, which was presented to Dr. Blalock and which he treasured.

On this floor is also the GOR information desk, the Broyles Endoscopic Clinic and the dressing rooms and dining room for the house staff and private staff GOR doctors. Here, too is the office of that very valuable lady, the Assistant Director of Nursing. In fact the 7th and 8th floors are devoted to anaesthesia and operating rooms. In the corridor on the 8th floor are the portraits of three famous living surgeons. Dr. W. F. Reinhoff, Jr., was the first surgeon to remove a lung; Dr. W. M. Firor, who, OHH will be pleased to learn has had $800,000.00 left in 1969, to endow a new chair in surgery in the Medical School, in his honor. The bequest was left by Mrs. Alice Larson Fink, who was a Hopkins nurse, whose husband built and operated the Southern Hotel. For many, many years before he became emeritus, he bore the unique honor of being the surgeon the medical students always chose to operate upon them, when and if they needed such aid.

Commenting recently upon his portrait (Dr. Firor's) the Professor of Physiology said, "Ah, Dr. Firor, that wonderful man! When I was an intern in Surgery, we used to call him "boss", and he called me "rebel", I think because I came from Virginia. How much he taught in quiet ways! One night I shall never forget, when he, Dr. W. F. Littler (now the country's leading hand surgeon, New York) and I stayed up all night in a room in Marburg trying to save a dying patient. We failed, but we learned from Dr. Firor a great deal. One thing was acceptance."

Dr. A. McGehee Harvey, Professor of Medicine from July 1946 to June 1973.

The third portrait is of Dr. A. Earl Walker, neurosurgeon in charge, who follows in the footsteps of Dr. Dandy.

The research labs on the 9th, 10th, and 11th floors belong to the Department of Medicine, although the offices of the Resident Surgeon, the Resident Cardiac Surgeon and Resident Transplant Surgeon are on the 9th floor, too.

These are the basic and clinical research laboratories; for instance, hematology tests done as research a few years ago are now everyday lab tests, done here. Clinical rheumatism is done on Blalock IX, but that basic research is now conducted at Good Samaritan, one of the Hopkins' affiliates.

Microscopes are still as prevalent here as babies in a supermarket, and what one sees via them, too, is always changing. Medical students, too, are prevalent in the summer, but the rest of the year research fellows abound.

In the 9th floor lobby, by the elevators, is the portrait of the late Dr. Warfield T. Longcope, who was the "In-Chief" and very learned Professor of Medicine. The physician who holds those two positions, now, has his office on the 10th floor of this building. He has been Professor of Medicine and Physician-in-Chief longer than any man in the history of Hopkins, and lived through more years of drastic change at Hopkins than any of his predecessors, both medically and sociologically.

Nothing can emphasize this more than the fact that the rebuilt portrait of Dr. Osler, which hung for so many countless years opposite the elevators in Osler, now hangs in his private office, for safe-keeping. Thomas Corner's beautiful portrait of Dr. Osler was vandalized. It might be wise for all OHH who loved Dr. Osler, for all who asked him to *tell* them what to do for their dying patients, upstairs, each time they saw the portrait, never to see him, again. For Dr. Osler is not himself; those among you who relied upon him, may find your eyes so clouded with tears that you cannot observe what remains.

The restoration is good craftmanship. His eyes were not damaged. The nose was slashed and has been rebuilt, and the portrait was reworked across the bottom and up to the left side, where it was cut, too.

There is nothing replacing his portrait on the Osler lobby wall. Between the elevators is a small bronze silhouette of his head, in profile.

The medical library is on that 10th floor and so is the portrait of Dr. Frank

R. Smith whom Dr. Osler knew and enjoyed, also there is a beautiful Chinese portrait of Shen Nung there, too. And daily looking at Dr. Osler's portrait is a disciple of his, who with the exception of himself, probably knows more about the diseases and the difficulties — and how to fight both — among the Baltimore poor than any man here trained.

On the floor above where the infectious diseases are studied and where the biological division and some animal rooms are is the plaque to Dr. John Hewetson.

As Dr. Osler insisted that they be, many medical students are still members of research teams and already at work on problems long before they graduate; some even during their first year are busy in Blalock. Although not a bed patient lies in this entire building, there is not a doctor working in it who is not concerned with their improvement, their treatment, and *any* new advance which will benefit them.

Doctors search in the clinics, examine in the clinical labs, re-search what is suspected, but may be unknown in the research labs, for as Dr. Halsted said many years ago, "We're not afraid to try things."

The 12th floor of Blalock clearly exemplifies this, for here are the animal surgery supervisor, the surgical labs, and a memorial library. Also, here is the portrait of the second Professor of Surgery and "In-Chief"; Dr. Dean D. Lewis. He, too, has a memorial named in his honor from a grateful patient.

He would be so interested, too, to know what was going on in the Finney-Howell Cancer Research Laboratory, which was the gift of a urologist, the late Dr. George Walker, a bachelor, who died of cancer, and left his life savings to found this lab, endow it and name it for two of his colleagues whom he admired.

The brilliant Director of it, Dr. George O. Gey, died in 1970, of cancer. He began the culture of the He La strain — human cancer cells used by researchers all over the world — and was also active in the research on the preservation and transplanting of human glands. His whole medical life was spent at the Hopkins and devoted to cancer research.

On the top floor of this building is the engine room, which affects the welfare of every man below it, and ironically enough here, too, is the "In-Chief" office and Director of the newly formed Neurology Department, which starts at the top of a man's head and studies everything in him, which the engine room makes comfortable.

Dr. George O. Gey (1889-1970).

CHAPTER VII

The Third of the Great Four

LYING to the east of the Blalock Building is Halsted, with its 8 floors of surgical patients, and then Osler, with its equal number of medical patients; and behind, constantly feeding more patients into all 3 of these buildings, is the Dispensary. Brady is connected with Blalock by a glassed-in bridgeway; and standing beyond the Dispensary and connecting therewith on certain floors, is the proud, venerable Pathology Building, waiting with judgmatical calm to set any of these enthusiastic operators in the treatment of disease and surgery straight, with its long record of the study of disease.

To put it succinctly: Halsted and Osler are the draft horses of the hospital, pulling the great load of the Dispensary, and having in their mouths, always, the bit of the Pathology Building's decisions and just criticisms.

When the hospital opened, although it had an acting surgeon in the person of Dr. William S. Halsted, it had no operating rooms as we now know them. Money to build them had been set aside, but it was felt that surgical methods were altering so radically and swiftly that these rooms should be designed according to the wishes of the Professor of Surgery. As a consequence, the surgical building was not opened until October 5, 1904; but it was the very model of its kind when it did open.

In 1889, the acting surgeon was employed at a salary of only $1,000 a year. The table upon which Dr. Halsted operated was a wooden one he brought from Germany, which had been used in the Franco-Prussian War. It is now in the room in GOR on Blalock VIII (OHH) called the Cardiac Gallery.

During the first seven and a half months the hospital was open, 316 patients were admitted to the surgical wards. Nine had inguinal hernia and 5 had carcinoma of the breast. Dr. Halsted was in the operating room at 8 A.M., and after lunch made ward rounds, gave a formal lecture or clinic at 3 P.M. in the amphi-

Dr. Halsted's operating table is now in display in the gallery of operating room 12.

theatre to the graduate students, and then worked in his experimental laboratory. He had two full-time assistants. Unpaid, of course, board and keep furnished.

By March, 1890, Dr. Halsted was made Surgeon-in-Chief to the hospital and Chief of the Dispensary.

It was some time during that year that he had the rubber gloves made for Miss Caroline Hampton; the harsh antiseptics used in the operating room had caused a rash upon her hands. She became Mrs. William S. Halsted upon June 4, 1890. In those days there were no married nurses at the Hopkins Hospital. No interns were married, either, and no residents were married until they had finished their training and were ready to strike out in private practice. Oft-quoted phrases were: "He travels fastest who travels alone" and "Medicine is a mistress which requires attention 24 hours a day."

Propinquity persevered, though, and a surprising number of Dr. Halsted's spartanly trained men survived to marry Hopkins trained nurses.

In April, 1892, the Medical Board of the hospital petitioned the Trustees to elevate Dr. Halsted to the position of full professor and their action was tantamount to saying that they considered his cure as a cocaine addict permanent, and the Trustees elevated him. It had taken a long time for this courageous man to convince others — seven years, in fact.

Among Dr. Osler's papers in the custody of McGill University to which he left his library were some pages called "The Inner History of The Johns Hopkins Hospital"; and it was understood that his intention was that they remained sealed until the 100th anniversary of the hospital in 1989. However, through a set of circumstances too lengthy to be described here, this was not done; and they were received for publication April 17, 1969 by The *Johns Hopkins Medical Journal* and published by them in their October issue of that year.

They describe many interesting people and days at the early Hopkins including the courtship of Miss Hampton and Dr. Halsted. Dr. Osler continues, regarding Dr. Halsted: "About six months after the full position had been given I saw him in a severe chill, and this was the first intimation I had that he was still taking morphia. Subsequently I had many talks about it and gained his full confidence. He had never been able to reduce the amount to less than three grains daily, on this he could do his work comfortably and maintain his excellent physical vigor (for he was a very muscular fellow). I do not think that any one suspected him — not even Welch."

Eleven years before this, in 1881, Dr. Halsted's sister collapsed from a postpartum hemorrhage, and her brother, after checking the hemorrhage, transfused her with blood drawn into a syringe from one of his own veins and injected immediately into hers.

This was probably the first successful direct blood transfusion in America.

A year later, his mother was ill with jaundice and severe tenderness in the region of the gall-bladder. Famous consultants did not advise an operation, but she grew worse; and her son, then thirty years old, did operate, "found the gall-bladder distended with pus, incised it and removed seven stones." His mother recovered.

Halsted's accidental cocaine addiction came about because of his experiments from which he showed that surgical anaesthesia can be obtained by injecting the nerve to the affected part. This principle of nerve blocking is the foundation

Dr. William S. Halsted (1852-1922), after
a portrait by Thomas C. Corner.

on which all neuroregional anaesthesia is based.

This story relating to Dr. Halsted and cocaine is told in detail here, because in our distraught society it is wise to remember that people, with difficulties from drugs, *do* fight and *can* contribute.

There are persons who in an aloof, quiet way, forever capture the imagination and the will to do one's very best in their subordinates, and through a fierce fineness in themselves fire other men to brilliant accomplishment. Dr. Halsted was such an individual and he aroused this response in all of his residents. Harvey Cushing, Dr. Bloodgood, Walter Dandy, Hugh Young, "Billy" Baer, Dr. Baetjer, and Dr. Crowe all felt it. And each of those men, in his separate way, made for himself a name which is immortal.

Dr. Cushing was a brain surgeon, who before he left Dr. Halsted's service to take the senior chair of surgery at Harvard had refused seven full professorships elsewhere.

Dr. Dandy, who never left Hopkins, devised the operation for Méniere's disease, a form of vertigo which is most debilitating. In 1917, he realized that some method should be found to make brain tumors more clearly visible on X-ray plates, and eventually devised what is called "ventriculography," a system of pumping air into the liquid-filled cavities in brain, then X-raying it, thereby making the tumors plainly seen. He also did the first operation for a ruptured intervertebral disc. Dr. Halsted, before he died, stated, "I know of no contribution to surgery, since the opening of The Johns Hopkins Hospital, which might rank with Dandy's."

Dr. Hugh Young also learned his trade under the Master; and Dr. Baetjer, at Dr. Halsted's suggestion, organized the X-ray Department. On May 27, 1902, he was authorized by the Executive Committee of the Board of Trustees, "to do photographic and X-ray work of the hospital at a salary of $900 a year." By the time he died in 1933, he had lost an eye, most of his fingers, and had malignant metastases in the axilliary glands from the rays. In Dr. Baetjer's time, the danger of overexposure to X-rays was not understood. You tread a hallowed hall when you walk this Hopkins corridor!

Dr. Joseph C. Bloodgood, one of Dr. Halsted's earliest and most famous residents, brought back from Europe in June of 1893 a microtome for cutting frozen sections and a firsthand knowledge of how to stain them.

Undoubtedly, Dr. Bloodgood participated in the pathological analysis which was done at Hopkins on the growth which had been sent there from the White House after it was removed from President Cleveland's mouth. The analysis showed it to be cancer, and a hush-hush operation was done on J. P. Morgan's yacht, anchored in the Hudson River. The country had just passed through a panic and President Cleveland was thought to be the only man who could avoid another one. Dr. Keen of Washington pulled the tooth around which the trouble was centered and removed most of President Cleveland's upper left jaw. He, again, sent what he had removed to Hopkins and the answer came back he had not removed all the cancer. In the second operation, he removed a quarter of an inch more of the jaw.

A rubber replacement for the jaw bone was made, teeth were fit into it, and two months later, when the President spoke to some congressmen, none could tell he had had the operations.

As long as Dr. Bloodgood lived, two-thirds of his life was spent in his laboratory.

Among those famous residents of Dr. Halsted, Dr. Samuel J. Crowe, through a very strange experience regarding a sick horse which Dr. Halsted treated for him in the North Carolina mountains, returned to Hopkins for his second year, when he was about to quit, and fired by Halsted's great magnetism, remained to climb to his residency. At Dr. Halsted's invitation, he later organized and headed the Department of Otolaryngology at Hopkins.

Many people still alive owe their ability to hear to his discovery that irradiation of lymphoid tissue growing around the eustachian tubes can prevent certain kinds of deafness.

Any mention of Dr. Crowe and his department automatically awakens memory of his nephew, Dr. John W. Baylor, who will forever rank among Hopkins' Best. When a young man, about 30, he had an operation of such a nature that for the remainder of his life he had to sleep sitting up in a chair; the company insuring him offered to pay him full disability, provided he would cease to practice and become an invalid. He refused, and for 25 years or more continued his meticulous, comprehending care of many still living and deeply grateful patients. He always personally dressed his patient's wounds for three days after operating, and he always gave every patient his complete attention. John Baylor lived up to his Hippocratic oath with a gorgeous courage.

Since the invention of the blue baby operation, there have been performed at the Hopkins 2,000 of these, and the children so operated upon have literally been brought from around the world. From 1964, (when Dr. Blalock died) only 105 blue baby operations have been done. (Explained later.)

One thing which Dr. Blalock always did and is still done most meticulously at Hopkins, is to explain as much as possible to the patient of the situation he faces. It is axiomatic at Hopkins that "we try nothing experimental upon a patient, without the patient's knowledge and permission. If it has been proven in the research labs, conclusively, we use it; but if it be unproven but the only hope of the patient, we explain, request, and usually the patient is grateful to have the procedure used. For instance, if a baby has a heart malady for which no operation has been devised; but the surgeon has one he has tried repeatedly, in animal experiments, and believes might work on a human, the parents' permission is asked, and if they concur, the operation is tried. In such a manner, the blue babies' operation began."

On the anniversary of the blue baby operation, in 1944, THE SUN carried an interview with Doctors Blalock and Taussig which has some very interesting statements. One thing Dr. Taussig said was, "I was working under Dr. Edwards A. Park, who was a believer in special clinics. He gave me a fluoroscope, with which to X-ray my patients, and said to me, 'Now you will learn about congenital malformations.' "

The first child operated upon was a girl 16 months old, who lived 9 months afterwards, and the article later states, "The third patient operated upon, critically ill before operation, lived to the age of 26."

Since July 1, 1958, to June 30, 1970, 3,814 cardiac operations have been done at Hopkins, and as already stated from 1964 to September 9, 1970, only 105 blue baby operations have been done. The reason for this is that the Blalock/Taussig shunt is rarely used now because newer, quicker methods have been introduced.

The first edition of this book included a description of an "open heart" operation, which many people requested be included again. It is now included, "updated" by the Professor of Surgery, who kindly looked it over.

As one looks down upon the "open heart" procedure from the glass-domed ceiling gallery over the operating room, one sees that a skilled female technician stands in front of a continuous blood-pressure electrocardiogram machine and calls readings during the entire operation, much as a sailor calls soundings at sea. Once the heart is entered, one of the specially trained technicians operating the heart-pump machine calls seconds in true count-down fashion; and all the time these two processes are continuing, the surgeons proceed with the operation.

Looking down upon the group, the incredible beauty of man sweeps into the mind: the silver of the lung as the patient breathes, exposed, peeping in and out, of the cavity in which they are working on the patient's heart, and shining, as the scales of a fish will shine. As the heart is given the injection which stills it, the concentration of the Turk and the lady from Ceylon with the cast mark watching from the gallery increases and they lean forward, raise the chained binoculars, and gaze down intently. The nurse who will have the care of the patient in the Recovery Room has come in and is watching, too, as the needles fly over the screen of the continuous electrocardiogram machine. Someone murmurs to her, "He's 46. Must have smoked a lot. Look at how black that lung is there (to the uninitiated it looked silver). You'll have your hands full with him." The operating surgeon now has his fingers inside the heart, releasing the adhesions; even stopped, the pointed tip flaps occasionally, like a fish might flap; the patient, on the heart-lung pump, breathes on, slowly. There is no lightning swift haste, just steady lack of waste in motion which is really the finest form of haste; and presently the surgeon becomes convinced that there are no more leaks in the heart and puts the man back on his own circulation — a process which requires only minutes, it seems to the watching layman — and the slow laborious work of getting out of the chest cavity commences. It takes a long time to get out; it took a long time to get in. These patients are anaesthetized about 8:00 A.M.; they have split the chest and are in to the heart about 9:00 A.M.; and depending upon how things go, they are ready to commence coming out by about 20 minutes later, if they go well. The patient nowadays rarely has to be put back on the heart-lung pump again, or the heart massaged with electric

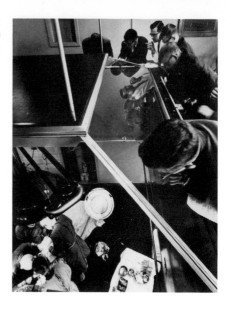

Visiting physicians watch an operation from a gallery in the Carnegie Building operating theatre.

stinger paddles. The whole operation now lasts about four hours. After it is over, the patient is taken immediately to the General Recovery Room, and this carefully trained, aforementioned nurse and her reliefs, plus a couple of interns, watch him constantly for three days and three nights, all of which time he is hooked up to the continuous electrocardiogram and blood pressure machine, fed by transfusions and glucose, and carefully checked manually by a stethoscope, too.

It takes a team of 6 doctors, 2 technicians, 2 nurses, 2 orderlies to perform this operation, and a team of 2 doctors, and 3 nurses in the Recovery Room for 3 days afterwards, before the patient may be returned to the bed whence he came and complete his recovery.

The amazing capacity of man to fight for his life, his utter and everlasting resistance is plainly visible during this most wonderful of operations, as a result of which a person who would certainly be dead in a short period may live for years instead.

The blood for the heart pump must be fresh-drawn the morning of the operation, and it requires two to three pints of fresh blood for the pump; after each operation the plastic tubing necessary to man the pump must be thrown away, and this costs better than $300 for the tubing and blood, combined. To perform a single one of these operations, originally, cost in the neighborhood of $1,600. The Women's Board provided the first $18,000 for Hopkins to get a lung pump and commence assembling the other equipment necessary to this operation. The operation now costs $7,140, and this breaks down as follows:

hospitalization of 30 days at $95 each day	$2,850.00
catheterization laboratory fee	150.00
blood, 21 pints at $50	1,050.00
average for special duty nurses	315.00
recovery room, 4 days at $25.00	100.00
operating room charge	250.00
cardiopulmonary bypass (pump)	300.00

Preparations for surgery are underway.

miscellaneous charges: IV therapy, oxygen, drugs, medications, X-ray, EKG, etc.	1,500.00
Professional (surgeon) fees: resident surgeon	400.00
(average fee for staff is $1,000)	$7,140.00

An average of nine such operations are performed weekly at Hopkins now. (Ten years ago they did four weekly). A 22-year-old woman, a man of 46, a girl of 12 have all been done; heart difficulties are no respecter of age nor of sex.

The operating room just described is one of 6 glass-ceiling ones where people from far and near come to look down at the surgeons at work upon the open hearts, blue babies, and total hips (about which more later). It is also one of the 17 operating rooms which occupy the seventh and eighth floors of the Dispensary and Blalock. Here is performed ALL of the surgery for the entire hospital except the gynecological, obstetrical, eye and the emergency surgery done in the Emergency Room (lacerations, simple fractures.) Major emergency surgery — gunshot and automobile accident — is done in GOR.

Attached to these operating rooms is the Recovery Room, added in 1953, in which there are 22 beds and every type of modern apparatus to aid a patient in fighting for his or her life. It is described, at length, in the chapter on "The Unseen Hospital." The open heart cases remain in the Recovery Room for 3 to 5 days, as do the brain cases; while children now go to the new Intensive Care Unit in CMSC, on the 6th floor.

Twenty-four hours a day this section — General Operating Room (GOR) and General Recovery Room (GRR) — is ready to go on a moment's notice, and 12,153 operations were performed in GOR in 1971.

The last 10 years in surgery might well be referred to as the "Decade of the Transplant." It didn't just spring out of nowhere, though, for 5,000 years ago the Egyptians and Hindus were doing skin grafts to replace noses destroyed by syphilis; in 1908, Dr. C. C. Guthrie transplanted a dog's head, and in 1912 he reported he had transplanted heart, lungs, kidneys, thyroid, and ovaries in animals.

In 1938, Dr. Alexis Carrel and Charles Lindbergh developed an extracorporeal pump for human organs, attempting to preserve organs within and without the body. In 1954, at Peter Bent Brigham Hospital in Boston, the first kidney transplant was done and the patient survived and married his nurse. The first heart transplant — as all the world knows — was performed at the Groote Schuur Hospital, in Capetown, South Africa, on December 3, 1967.

The first heart transplant at Hopkins was done on November 25, 1968, commenced at 2:30 A.M.; and the patient, Sydney Seidenberg, 56 years old, was in the Recovery Room by 8:30 A.M. The donor was Wilson W. Lieske, 26 years old, who was brought from Havre de Grace with "irreversible brain damage," and died at 4:09 A.M.

Mr. Seidenberg recovered sufficiently to become ambulatory, was frequently seen walking about the hospital and lived 70 days.

To date at Hopkins there have been more than 150 kidney transplants. A Division of Transplantation was created in the Department of Surgery, July 1, 1969.

A detailed description of their set-up appears later in this chapter.

During the transplant surge, Hopkins-trained men have contributed greatly. At UCLA, where both the Professor and Chairman of the Department of Surgery, and the Professor of Surgery and Urology and Chief of the Division of Urology are Hopkins men, the latter wrote the author in May of 1966, "My greatest scientific interest centers around kidney transplantation. (We now have a series of fifty-one cases here at UCLA.)"

In June, 1969, *This Week* magazine, in an article on the work of the Hopkins heart surgeon in Houston, stated, "he has performed almost two dozen transplant operations". On April 4, 1969, a mechanical heart was substituted by him in a man 16 months after he did the first cardiac transplant upon a patient in Houston. Now they use a relatively new operative technique down there called "bypass surgery," which he prophesies will be "the cardiac surgery of the 1970's."

At Hopkins they are now doing 2 by-pass operations a day and expect

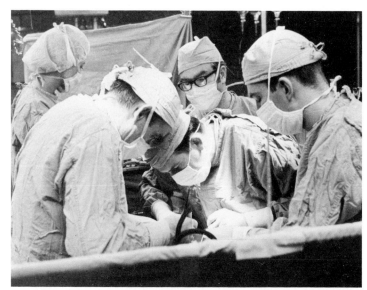

Hopkins surgeons perform a heart transplant, November 25, 1968.

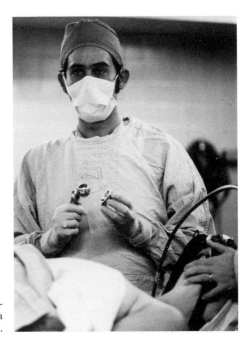

An orthopedic surgeon holds prosthetic devices which will serve as a total hip replacement for the patient.

to go to 3, shortly. It takes 5 hours, and consists of removing a section of a vein from the patient's leg, opening his chest and employing the heart-lung machine to perform the functions of the heart, while the vein is attached to the artery or arteries, by-passing the section which is blocked.

This operation is done in patients who have angina pectoris due to a partial or complete blockage of a coronary artery.

In other words, if a man can use himself to help himself, he is better off than with any substitute plastic contrivances. Incidentally, one operation which is performed repeatedly is replacing the plastic tube which didn't grow when the heart did. Hopefully, in certain cases, this can be done with by-pass.

Since 1969, one straight "hardware" operation being done at Hopkins is known as "total" or "artificial" hips. Patients who suffer terrible pain from arthritic hips are given vast relief, and Hopkins surgeons were among the first in America to perform the operation. The patient's hip joint is removed and replaced with a two-part device made either entirely of metal, or of metal and plastic. The operation usually takes about two and a half hours, and Hopkins hopes to do 70 a year; one patient received two artificial hips. The metal ball is anchored to the thigh bone by a stem which is placed in the bone cavity and cemented, there. Then a metal socket is cemented to the pelvis, or hip girdle.

Also at Hopkins they are thinking about replacing diseased knees and other major body joints.

Hopkins belongs to an "organ-pool" which is especially valuable in kidney transplants, where much of the success is believed to lie in the typing, prior to operation; with a good match, there is very much less chance of the recipient rejecting the transplanted organ. The pool or Typing-Lab as it is technically called, is connected to a computer and hence to transplantation centers as far south as Atlanta and as far West as Indiana. Every potential donor can be matched within

30 minutes with every possible recipient in the region. City Hospitals and Good Samaritan are also part of the set-up; Good Samaritan can maintain 20 patients a week through its dialysis laboratory, who are waiting for kidney transplants, whereas Hopkins has a Renal Dialysis Unit set-up on Halsted III to care for 8 patients at a time or 16 a week. Hopkins has a trained staff who are very knowledgeable in approaching relatives of possible dying donors. When the kidney is flown in from elsewhere, there is advance-time notice and the operation, at Hopkins, may be prescheduled for a certain time. But when a donor and 2 recipients are operated on simultaneously, 3 surgical teams are required. One removes the kidneys, one prepares the iliac artery and vein for anastomosis to the renal artery and vein, and the third team does the subsequent suturing of these vessels and the ureter.

Interestingly enough, three things for which Hopkins has received considerable acclaim in the last ten years all have a yes-and-no relationship to surgery, but they were all developed through the Department of Surgery and this seems a proper place to mention them.

For many years in the Hopkins accident room, all with stab wounds were laid aside and carefully watched for swelling to try to estimate whether they had organs which had been penetrated and were bleeding internally. If they began to swell they were rushed up to GOR and the surgeons set to.

Now there is a method of examining those 8 or 10 weekly abdominal stab wounds by X-ray. A Chief Resident in Surgery devised the technique of pumping a solution into the stab wound and then X-raying the patient. If the cavity is not penetrated, the fluid is trapped under the skin and the X-ray shows a superficial wound. In that case you just sew the patient up; but if the cavity is penetrated, he goes to GOR, and in a hurry, too.

The second is that of all the American hospitals, because of its famous Breast Cancer Clinic and the reverence for and admiration of its long-time Chief, Hopkins has been chosen by the World Health Organization to participate in a ten-country study on the prevention, diagnosis, and evaluation of treatment methods, post-operative care, and rehabilitation of these unfortunate women.

The third has to do with a man whose brains had been trained in one discipline, using them to aid men working in other disciplines who had no training along

Dr. William B. Kouwenhoven.

the lines in which he was so knowledgeable. The heart-lung pump was developed in 1953; and in 1954, on his retirement as Professor of Electrical Engineering and Dean of the School of Engineering of the Johns Hopkins University, Dr. William B. Kouwenhoven (his name would have to be mentioned in the end, as you will see) was given a laboratory in The Johns Hopkins Hospital, in which to continue his research. In that laboratory he developed the basis and practical means of defibrillating the heart externally. Also, in conjunction with a very brilliant young heart surgeon, no longer at Hopkins, he devised the technique of closed chest cardiac massage. In 1969, the American College of Physicians, at their 50th annual meeting, presented him with an award. Also, the American Heart Association gave him their Award of Merit for his collaborative work with James R. Jude on closed chest cardiopulmonary resuscitation. The Institute of Electrical and Electronics Engineers honored him with the first Power-Life Award, and in 1970 The Johns Hopkins University School of Medicine gave him an honorary M.D. — its first such presentation.

And he is alive and well, thank you, walking up and down the corridor, lecturing on surgery to medical students and always available to any of them who wish to consult him! Truly, a living legend.

More than that, too, because you never see an ambulance pass whose crew does not know how to apply his method of restoring the beat to a stopped heart. And you never see a heart patient rigged for monitoring that his knowledge isn't contributing to that patient's welfare.

Dr. Blalock died in 1964, but the young Hopkins surgeon who took his position may well find that when his reign is over the most brilliant contributor to his era never attended medical school!

The new Intensive Care Units, 21 surgical beds on Halsted VII, and 21 medical beds on Osler VII, are the most advanced example of the marriage between surgery, medicine, and electricity.

There are now 195 beds in Halsted. General surgery is still on Halsted I, and has 12 private and 6 semi-private beds. The 2nd floor has general and plastic surgery and the 28 beds are resident staff beds. Halsted III, houses orthopedic active staff beds (OHH this means full-time, part-time and emeritus men) and the

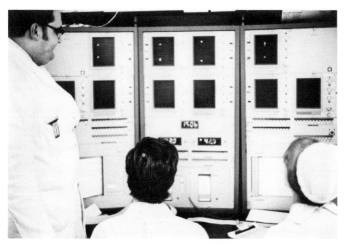

Intensive Care Unit staff members keep watchful eyes on central patient monitoring equipment.

Dr. William S. Halsted holds a "corridor" consultation with Dr. Richard N. Follis.

27 beds are semi-private. Halsted IV is general and plastic surgery and the 29 beds are tended by the resident staff. Halsted V is given over to orthopedic and otolaryngology beds of which there are 32 resident staff. On the 6th floor are neurosurgery and cardiac patients of which 9 are active staff and 19 resident staff beds; the floor also has 4 beds in an acute cerebrovascular research unit. The patients on Halsted VII are all in intensive care, while on Halsted VIII are the general and cardiac patients of which there are 33 active staff beds.

The surgical library is on the 4th floor and the bronze bust of Dr. Dandy and the standing portrait of Dr. Halsted are both in it. Down in the Halsted lobby are still the profile portrait of Dr. Halsted and the surgical residents pictures. The surgical residency is still six- or seven-year training, and when one counts the number of men whose faces are shown in those pictures, one finds that they now number 92, or have served the hospital approximately an aggregate of 644 years.

To date at Hopkins, there have been four Professors of Surgery: Dr. Halsted,

Monitoring patients in the Intensive Care Unit is also done at the bedside.

Dr. Dean Lewis, Dr. Alfred Blalock, and the present Professor. The first and third Professors have been honored by having two of the four surgical wards at Oxford named for them. The first ward was named for Dr. Blalock; the second for Dr. Halsted.

In his book, Dr. Crowe states: "Of seventeen of Halsted's resident surgeons, seven became Professors of Surgery at Harvard, Yale, Stanford, Cornell, Virginia, Pittsburgh and Cincinnati. Six went to other university medical schools or teaching hospitals: One as a Clinical Professor, three as Associate Professors, one as Instructor in Surgery and one as Surgeon in Chief to the Henry Ford Hospital. Four went into private practice."

Dr. Blalock was equally a great trainer of professors: Pittsburgh, University of Virginia, UCLA, St. Louis University, Duke, are only a few of the schools in

Some of the 92 residents are pictured herewith.
Photographic limitations make it impossible
to picture all of these men.

which the Chairman of Surgery was a former Blalock Chief Resident.

When one sees all of the modern equipment, one cannot help but think how much it would have meant to Dr. Halsted, or Dr. Cushing, or Dr. Dandy to attend an "open heart" or observe the patients in the four research beds, upstairs.

Perhaps, though, in the face of so much equipment and knowledge, this story about Dr. Halsted is still applicable. Once in the North Carolina mountains, where he maintained a summer home, he was called to attend a little boy who had a piece of steel embedded in his eye. Dr. Halsted had no surgical tools and no time to lose and set about sterilizing the kitchen knives with which to operate. The country doctor, who had also been called, arrived, examined the patient, sauntered over to the upright, crank telephone, unscrewed the mouth-piece, took the magnet therefrom, brought it over and used it to draw the splinter from the child's eye. Dr. Halsted took delight in telling this story to medical students, concluding, "You see, we don't know everything at Hopkins."

CHAPTER VIII

Dr. Billings' Second Choice

WHEN Dr. Billings stopped off in Philadelphia in the spring of 1889 and asked the then Dr. William Osler, who was his personal choice and candidate, to become Professor of Medicine and Physician-in-Chief of the about-to-be-opened Johns Hopkins Hospital, he provided the opportunity for a method of teaching which has circled the globe and created generations of superior physicians.

Let no man dispute you: the physician is still the Captain of the Medical Ship. Man cannot function without a heart, and until he is dead it is the physician who evaluates and cares for the heart. Even in the present machine medicine age, the physician is still the final arbiter in any consultation, and if he says, "No, I don't agree to that operation," it isn't performed. This is highly logical, too, for among other things, you can't transplant a heart unless a physician says it is *worth* transplanting.

In a curious way, the two portions of the hospital which probably have contributed more to the advances of the last ten years than all others keep out of the headlines. Medicine is a listening profession and its final judge, pathology, is an almost silent one. Even after the physician has said the heart is worth transplanting, the scrutiny of the pathologist authenticates his judgment.

Space medicine has, in a sense, turned a man inside out with machines, but Hopkins still aims to train medical men who can practise without, as well as with, the aid of technology.

It takes one's breath away, though, to remember that when Dr. Osler, eventually Sir William Osler, arrived at the hospital he lived on the 3rd floor of the Administration Building, in a room which was lighted by gas. He was a bachelor of 40 years and the youngest son among the nine children of a Canadian

Dr. Osler works on his textbook, "The Principles and Practice of Medicine," in his room in the Administration Building.

Episcopal minister, and he considered those quarters magnificently modern.

All of his life he had the superb gift of being able to walk into a room and by his mere presence convey to a patient that he believed to be alive was the greatest joy any man could ever have, no matter how much he might be temporarily discommoded by the fact that he was! The pomp and circumstance of this wicked world never awed him, and any honors he received in it, he worked diligently to deserve. Always, he did his *very* best, and it never occurred to him that other people wouldn't too; under his influence, they did.

He was an indefatigable worker who didn't bicker and who loved to destroy the dignity of people who did; his practical jokes got under the hide of many folks, and he was highly capable of paying back, with interest, any shenanigans which others perpetrated upon him. Once, while he was writing his famous textbook, he got from Dr. Welch some misinformation (concocted on the moment in Dr. Welch's head) and which had been presumedly read from foreign medical journals. It confused Dr. Osler considerably in his mind and in his writing, but presently Dr. Welch confessed to his hoax.

A few nights later, Dr. Osler rang the doorbell of the rooming house where Dr. Welch, also a bachelor, lived. The lady who ran the place came to the door; and Dr. Osler, holding a fine bunch of flowers in his hand, said, "Good evening, Madam. Is Dr. Welch in?" She shook her head and replied, "Won't be back till 11. Never is." "Then is *Mrs.* Welch in?" Dr. Osler persisted. "There is *no* Mrs. Welch," the lady said, emphatically. Dr. Osler extended his hand, handed her the flowers, and replied, "That is what *you* think, Madam." Then, he turned on his heel and walked away.

The lady took the flowers into the parlor, put them in a vase, and sat immobile with her elbow just inside the fluted edge of the marble-topped table looking at them, until Dr. Welch returned home. He tried vainly to persuade her that his statement, and not that of his convincing friend, was the true one.

As you already know, Dr. Osler's portrait no longer hangs in the lobby of

The portrait of Dr. Osler by Thomas C. Corner. The photo was made at the time of the 75th Anniversary of the Hospital, when the portrait still hung in the Osler lobby.

the Osler Building. A photograph of it, as you remember it, is included in this book for your pleasure; also included is a photograph of the portrait done in Paris in 1909 by S. Seymour Thomas, which is here reproduced through the courtesy of Doctors Elmer Belt and Willard E. Goodwin. Dr. Belt's photograph of the original painting is here used. The author first saw the portrait in a paper which Dr. Goodwin wrote about the friendship between Dr. Osler and Dr. Kelly, a description of which is in the bibliography of this book.

For many years Dr. Belt has sent hundreds of copies of this portrait in his Christmas card to medical students and enclosed a most interesting sheet, which reads, in part: "In the winter of 1908, Dr. Hugh Hampton Young and Dr. William Osler were in Paris together. Dr. Young and Mr. Seymour Thomas had been boyhood friends in San Antonio, Texas, where Mr. Thomas' artistic talent had become manifest. He had continued his artistic career in Paris. It was Dr. Young's idea to have Mr. Thomas paint the portrait of his friend, Dr. William Osler. So he arranged to bring the two men together and directed Dr. Osler to the Paris studio of Seymour Thomas.

"Seymour Thomas' studio was among a cluster of such studios at No. 11 Impasse Rousin in a closed off French court. When Dr. Osler finally found his way to this court on a winter afternoon of 1908, the court was a scene of intense police activity. In one of these studios Madam Steinhiel, a famous French beauty, had just strangled her artist husband. Pictures of the beauteous murderess filled all the French papers. Her sensuous features which later won her freedom in the French courts were known to everyone. Upon Dr. Osler's knock at Mr. Thomas' studio door, Seymour Thomas in his artist's frock threw the door open and welcomed him in. Within the studio, near the door, stood a full-length portrait, "The Lady in Brown," Mrs. S. Seymour Thomas, painted by Mr. Thomas, as she appeared on her wedding day. Osler's devil got hold of him — 'Ah,' said Dr. Osler, 'I didn't know you had painted Madam Steinhiel.'

"With Seymour Thomas and Osler, friendship was instantaneous. This

The portrait of Dr. Osler by S. Seymour Thomas.

perfect portrait with which Osler was delighted was finished in less than two weeks, nine hours painting time and nine sittings, a premier coup. . . . So cooperative was Osler during the sittings, so full of pleasant conversation, that Seymour Thomas found this portrait the easiest he had ever painted. To Osler he said, 'You have painted your own portrait.' Osler said: 'This one makes chromos of all the rest. As long as you keep this portrait you will always have a good doctor with you.' Mr. Thomas never parted with it to the day of his death. Then it was found that he had willed it to Oxford University in England."

In Dr. Goodwin's brochure, under the portrait, he uses the quotation from *Religio Medici,* which reads: "For there are mystically in our faces certain characters which carry in them the motto of our souls, wherein he that cannot read A B C may read our natures."

Dr. Osler was the first man in the United States to insist that the medical student belonged in the hospital, in his 3rd and 4th year, learning by *doing* and *seeing.* He believed in thorough physical examination and in using his tongue while he used his hands, for he had a magic way of drawing facts from the patient, while he was going over him, which left the boys breathless with admiration. The men he taught to the very ends of their lives never stopped looking, seeing, listening, particularly listening: for he believed as did the old patient who said, "When you talkin' you ain't learnin' nuthin'." People trusted him and as a magnet drew steel, he could draw confidence. His listening was kind, attentive, comprehending. (Today the young call it "levelling" with the patient, and they think they invented it.)

Fifteen years after the hospital opened, Dr. Osler left to become Regius Professor of Medicine at Oxford. In 1890, though, his post-graduate courses had begun and he was already training Dr. Lewellys F. Barker, another Canadian and another minister's son, who followed him as Professor of Medicine; also he was training Dr. William S. Thayer who became Professor of Medicine after Dr. Theodore Janeway, who was appointed the first full-time Professor of Medicine in America, succeeded Dr. Barker in 1914. Dr. Thayer became Professor upon the resignation of Dr. Janeway and resigned in 1921, when Dr. Longcope succeeded him. The present Professor is the first graduate of the Hopkins Medical School ever to hold this chair. He has updated Dr. Osler's famous book *Principles and Practice of Medicine* twice and is now working on the 3rd updating under his editorship.

In 1896, the clinical laboratory was erected and Dr. Thayer was put in charge, for Dr. Osler required that blood and urine tests be done on all of his patients.

The two professors whom Dr. Osler trained, Dr. Barker and Dr. Thayer, have both left records of life as it was in those days. In Dr. Barker's *Time and the Physician,* which is a fascinating book, he says that while he was first living in the Administration Building, next to Dr. Osler, he was so poor that he had to have his pants re-seated repeatedly, and his coat-elbows patched also. As a consequence, he developed a great sympathy for the Dispensary patients with patches in their clothes, too. Dr. Osler put in Dr. Barker's way many writing duties whereby he made "spending money"; in those days housemen received board and keep only. They felt themselves to be tremendously lucky, too, just to be "chosen" to receive their advanced training at "The Hopkins."

From the beginning, the Department of Medicine has always been a full-

On leaving Baltimore, Dr. Osler gave his chair to Dr. Henry M. Thomas, Sr. It descended in that family to his son, the late Dr. Henry M. Thomas, Jr. and was bequested by him to his wife Dr. Caroline B. Thomas, professor emeritus of medicine. She is the only woman who has ever attained this rank at Hopkins.

dress performance, both literally and figuratively. After Dr. Osler lived across town, he used to arrive at the hospital wearing a frock coat, top hat, and brandishing his cane. Dr. Barker, when he later became a consultant, also rode in hansom cabs and also garbed himself in the Oslerian manner.

Dr. Thayer came down from Boston equipped to look like a gentleman and so conducted himself throughout his entire lifetime that "a verray parfit gentil knight" seemed the most natural of all epithets which could be applied to him; except the one which Dr. Welch gave him of being the "doctor's doctor." This phrase was also applied to the late Dr. Charles R. Austrian with equal reason. He said to a man, who wished to abolish the Main Corridor of the hospital, several years ago, "If you did so, you would rob me of half of my practice. I cannot walk more than a few feet here that some doctor does not stop to consult me about some patient."

A conference teaching room on the 8th floor of Osler is named in Dr. Austrian's honor and a portrait of him done by his wife Florence Hochschild Austrian, who is a famous Baltimore artist, hangs in the room. It is an excellent likeness; and one expects him to look up from his reading and say to the nearest medical student, "Do you believe what this lecturer is saying? I don't!"

His only son, a Hopkins Medical School graduate, is now a Trustee of The Johns Hopkins University and a Professor of Medicine at the University of Pennsylvania. (OHH:JHMS, 1941)

Speaking of medical students, in the light of Dr. Thayer's lifelong sartorial elegance, Edith Gittings Reid tells a story in her charming biography of him which may in part explain Dr. Thayer's great popularity among medical students. Here is a capsule of the story. He went to a burlesque show in Boston while a student at Harvard and saw a dancer do the "splits." The next night accompanied by some of his confreres he returned to the show; and when she, again, did the "splits" all the boys tore in two, stiff white collars which they held between their hands. This created a hideous rending sound which frightened the performer and the audience profoundly. Harvard did not think this was a humorous escapade and requested the young man to give them a temporary rest from his presence, and his father sent

Dr. Charles R. Austrian
(1885-1959): the doctor's doctor.

him abroad to study for one year as a consequence.

In 1897, graduates of the Medical School were appointed as house officers and the Hopkins Residency system commenced. When Dr. Barker took over, in 1905, the laboratories in biology, chemistry, and physiology were established in the Department of Medicine.

Of all the subjects which a medical student studies, medicine is still the most time-consuming, even in the present machine-medicine age. All the brightest medical students, too, will tell you with infinite emphasis, "Osler is the place to be!" In response to the question "Why?" they always answer, "Because the *action's* there! Those patients don't have *one* disease, they have half a dozen: diabetes, coronary occlusion, tuberculosis, syphilis, kidney involvement, and asthma; and they are dying from half of 'em, simultaneously, all the time.

"You don't have time to think when you're working over 'em! Get one thing; bring another; begin the transfusion; watch the blood pressure; hang on to that pulse! BOY, it's wonderful. I just love it there. No wonder the boys on the Marburg service asked to rotate with Osler!"

Again, when you question, the answer is, "Sure they get sick in Marburg, but usually they are dying of just one disease, or maybe two. But in Osler — that is where the excitement is!"

The student nurses concur with these sentiments, although some of them rate Halsted as a close second.

Out of an annual class of Hopkins medical students of 110, there are 30 applicants for medical internships and usually of this number about 12 Hopkins boys succeed in getting admitted to climb the Osler ladder. Last year, however, only 2 or 3 obtained that privilege.

The Osler Clinic, opened in 1931 and built with funds from the General Education Board and an anonymous donor, has the third largest bed capacity of any building in the hospital, 196 beds; however when you add the Marburg beds to it, the figure rises to 291, which brings it again to the second largest bed capacity, exceeded only by CMSC. Last year, (1971) Marburg ran 95% of capacity, while

Osler ran 84%; the patient days of care rendered in Marburg amounted to 31,972, and in Osler to 58,148. In Marburg the patient paid $130.59 per day and it cost $119.77 to keep him there; while in Osler the patient paid $135.14, and it cost $134.66 to keep him there. The average days per patient stay in Marburg were 11.73 and in Osler, 12.66.

Marburg patients were paid for by insurance or themselves, with few exceptions, while Osler patients were paid for as follows: approximately one half, paid for by Blue Cross and Blue Shield; 40% by Medicare and Medicaid; 10% by the city and Federal government; ½% possibly paid for by nobody. The patients run approximately 50% white, and 50% colored.

Osler has the second largest number of (OHH, ward) "resident staff" beds of any building, there being 137 of these. (CMSC has 155). All these resident staff patients are examined by the medical students, under the supervision of the interns and the residents, and the building is always filled with earnest men, seeing, listening, looking, learning.

Twice weekly staff rounds are held in Osler, but on Saturday Grand Ward Rounds are held in the Turner Auditorium at 9:45 A.M.; and many a Baltimore doctor sees to it that he, as well as the medical students, attend. Times have changed though (OHH) for some of the full-time faculty, and part-time, too, chew gum, smoke cigarettes — still — wear striped shirts and loud ties, and look as if they are about to take bets on the second race at Pimlico.

The men in private practice, though, on the whole, still look trustworthy and reliable and they attend these rounds in droves. The Turner Auditorium will hold 750 and is described in detail elsewhere in this book. Usually on Saturday mornings 300 to 350 men are present.

There is a TV paging system which does not interrupt the case presentations, and the day is half over before these men are through with the rounds and discussing them. In many, many instances, as OHH remember, over the past years,

The main Turner Auditorium is used for major lectures and Saturday grand rounds.

they also spent Saturday afternoons working in the free clinics in the Dispensary.

In these days when doctors are considered America's number one gold-diggers, it is worth realizing that Saturday is a learning, seeing, hearing, discussing day, in which they make no money. Medicine, with her silent step, in many ways is still far ahead of practise methods and these dedicated practitioners come to "catch-up" and "keep up." Any M.D. is welcome.

Doctors from the Veterans' Hospital and Army, Navy, and Air Force and Public Health, too, are often present. Much is to be seen and learned. Recently a young officer there, when queried, replied that he was a Duke graduate, stationed at Fort Meade, who when his military time is up, has a billet as an intern at Massachusetts General lined up. "In the meantime, though," he said, "I'm a learning-listener and I get here every Saturday morning, no matter WHAT!"

The interns, the medical students, the residents, and the outside men who have treated these patients and worked up their cases are on the griddle during the whole performance and have to be completely on their toes to answer an obscure, but perhaps pertinent, question from their elders. No patients, anywhere, have better medicine practiced upon them than do these resident staff-ward patients at Hopkins.

A 35-year-old doctor who had climbed a Hopkins ladder was recently asked what he'd do if he got sick. "Demand that I'd be put on resident staff patients in Osler," he said emphatically. "Why?" "Because," he replied, "Every man who worked on me would have pushed ten other men of lesser quality away from the chance to do so before he ever got near my bed — and that goes for medical students, as well as interns, residents, and professors. The medicine at Hopkins STILL holds up, regardless of the slurs it is stylish to cast upon it, these days." (Last year about half of the patients discussed were patients of the active staff from Marburg, Brady, and Thayer.)

During the biweekly bedside rounds, the clinical teaching is magnificent, and many doctors, from many parts of the hospital make a point of attending those, too.

A most amusing story which happened during rounds is about a doctor who wanted some information from a patient, male, middle-aged, which the patient didn't want to give. The doctor said, "Damn it man, tell me! I'm trying to *learn* something." The old man, who had a type of arthritis which makes people severely crippled, looked up at him and said slowly, "Mister, you ain't never goin' to learn nuthin' long as you talks thataway."

Another delightful ward story concerns Dr. Winford Smith showing the Queen of the Belgians around the wards, while she and the King were in Baltimore. The King had gone to the Naval Academy in Annapolis, for the afternoon. The Queen had been very interested during World War I in military hospitals in her country. After she and Dr. Smith left, the nurse asked an ancient woman what she thought of the Queen and she replied, "Sh'll do, but dat King, he'd de one!" (OHH, in the first edition of this book, the story was told as relating to Dr. Thayer and Queen Marie of Rumania, but the author was corrected, by letter, by a member of the class of 1910 JHMS who is a famous urologist in San Francisco.)

If you will recall that the Blalock Building has a whole floor devoted to machines to measure, study, and explore the sounds of the heart, and that every person who has heart surgery has to be "medically cleared," as do, also, all kidney transplant patients, before surgery is attempted, you will comprehend some of the present excitement which goes on regarding an Osler patient.

Due, also, to the present diagnostic methods whereby most patients may receive their "tests" prior to becoming a patient in the hospital, the patients who do enter this service are all really sick and require the most skilled attention. A bed, nevertheless, is always found for a medically interesting case, from which the students might learn.

The Osler-Marburg service which takes care of all patients lying throughout the hospital in the internal medicine field has an Osler Chief Resident; a Marburg Chief Resident, 35 interns, and 30 assistant residents, all on a rotating service. They work, too, of course, under the "outside" men having visiting privileges and under the full-time men with similar privileges. A man with visiting privileges may have his patients admitted to the hospital.

As of old the first floor of Osler contains the Assistant Director of Nursing office, the pharmacy, the social service department office, and occupational therapy. The technical term for the latter is Occupational Therapy and Rehabilitation Department. The telephones, the door-locks, the steps to climb and the incline to descend are duplicates of those which the person who has lost a hand or a leg will use in the outside world and which he must re-learn how to use, with what he has left to live with. Here, too, are the whirlpool baths and the exercise pulleys and the therapists who re-teach fingers to regain their former skills. Also on this floor is the room where patients learn to make baskets and to weave hook rugs or to paint. Phipps outpatients, as well as those from the other sections of the hospital, come here.

The pharmacy is covered in "The Unseen Hospital," and the Social Service Department in the chapter on the Dispensary.

On Osler II are the chromosome lab, nurses station, psychosomatic clinic, 31 general medical beds, and the Nursing School classrooms. Again, on Osler III are 31 beds, and the psychosomatic, geriatric, and psychiatry liaison service, both in- and outpatient. (This floor is an excellent example of various disciplines working everywhere throughout the hospital and considering the "whole man.") On the fourth floor are 31 general medical beds, classrooms, instructor's office, and a nurses station.

Also the portrait of Dr. Thomas B. Futcher hangs here.

Dr. Osler brought Dr. Futcher down from Canada and after he had climbed the Hopkins ladder, he became one of the great physicians of Baltimore, and a long-time teacher in the Medical School. His only son, also a Hopkins graduate, is now Associate Professor of Medicine at the University of Pennsylvania and Executive Director of the American Board of Internal Medicine. (OHH:JHMS, 1936)

Osler V is a clinical research floor with 21 beds, private and semi-private rooms. Nowhere in this building, now, are there more than 4 beds in any room, and in most semi-private ones, there are two. All research inpatients of the entire hospital are housed here: renal transplants, heart transplants, metabolic studies, diet studies, obs-gyn and Wilmer research, too, are among these patients. There is a kitchen on this floor and a Special Studies Unit Director, as well as labs and nurses station. All research inpatient food is prepared in this floor kitchen, and all intake and output of each patient is meticulously checked. The patients usually stay about one month and pay nothing. The National Institutes of Health support the floor, for research patients, and it is a pure clinical research floor.

On this floor, too, is the Alan Bernstein Memorial Wing which has just been completed. He was graduated from Hopkins in 1931, died in 1969, climbed the Osler ladder, taught in the Medical School, had a large and devoted private practice in Baltimore, and was particularly famous for his work in infectious mononucleosis; also, as a medical student he was co-author of an excellent paper on a method of measuring oxygen consumption in a single cell.

His death at 63 years of age was a genuine loss to Hopkins medicine and when the money was collected for this wing it came from all sorts of people. "Some gave a dollar; some 50 cents; some substantial contributions. The amazing thing was that people came forward, of their own volition and *asked* to contribute — and many of them were poor patients he had treated right here, in Osler. The whole response was a great outpouring of genuine gratitude." These remarks were made by the Osler Administrator.

The laboratories, conference rooms, library, and examining rooms in his memory will be a great contribution to patient welfare in Osler.

Osler VI, which contains 31 beds, bears the classification of General Medical beds. The Coronary Care Unit is now on Osler VII and is part of the Medical Intensive Care Unit. There are four beds in the Coronary Care Unit and patients pay to lie in these. However, there is a fifth bed, supported by the National Institutes of Health for research on myocardial infarction, and an "M. I." patient admitted to that bed pays nothing; it also is now housed on Osler VII.

Osler VII is now the medical half, 21 beds, of the new Intensive Care Unit, of which much has been said elsewhere. The 21 surgical beds are on Halsted VII. Incidentally, if anything goes wrong with the wiring of these beds, there is a crawl space in the floor below and also in the ceiling above by which the electricians may work on the mechanisms and repair them. In the meantime, while they are doing so, the patient is hooked-up to stand-by instruments.

Osler VIII, which contains 33 beds, has semi-private rooms for private patients and is used by the Department of Medicine. Dr. W. S. Thayer's portrait hangs on this floor and so does the portrait of Dr. Thomas R. Boggs, whom the medical students revered.

A physician and two nurses check a patient in the medical intensive Care Unit.

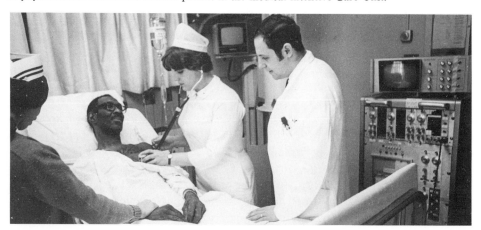

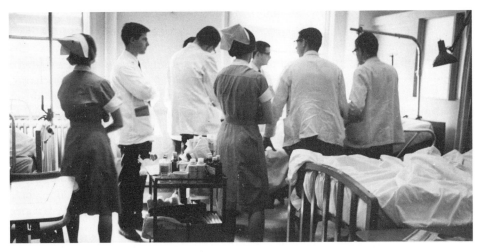
Rounds on an Osler building nursing unit.

The carnation which Dr. Thayer always wore in his buttonhole brings to mind the last Hopkins man to follow that custom. He was the late Dr. Mason Faulconer Lord, certainly one of the most interesting men who ever graduated from the Hopkins Medical School. He was already famous, when he graduated, as an internationally known collector of modern art, and a great authority upon that subject. This hobby had begun during his adolescence when he was obliged to spend the better part of a year in bed because of a heel injury. The physician attending him suggested that he use the time to become an expert in some one thing. Young Mason elected to do so in art and read the literature pertaining to all the reputable modern painters. Both his father and his grandfather were doctors, so it fell naturally into the pattern of his life that he, too, should study medicine.

However, his becoming the leading authority on geriatrics in his generation was again the influence of the physician who had attended him during his boyhood illness. When Mason asked his learned mentor what he would advise him to specialize in, he replied, "Why don't you become an authority on old people? They are the fastest growing segment of the population in this country, and any doctor who is an authority upon them has a fine practice assured him for life."

This Dr. Lord did, and the clinics he began for old people at the Baltimore City Hospitals and later at the Hopkins were soon world renowned. A few months ago, in an impressive ceremony at Baltimore City Hospitals, the old "D" Building was renamed after Dr. Lord. It is in this building that Dr. Lord did his work in geriatrics and which houses elderly patients. For the *Johns Hopkins Magazine,* he wrote a moving, masterly piece called *The Old, The Ill, The Unremembered.* It was always an odd and interesting sight to see this young, very handsome man, always immaculately dressed, with a carnation in his buttonhole, strolling casually to and fro among his ancient and adoring patients. His untimely death was a terrible blow to all of them, as well as to his contemporaries. The operation upon his brain tumor was lengthy and grave and he lived almost a year, afterwards, most of it at the Hopkins.

Frequently, on Saturdays, he managed to attend Grand Rounds, which then were still held in Hurd Hall, and even though he had a Russian turban on his head, he still wore the same jaunty carnation in his buttonhole.

Marburg, where Dr. Lord was a patient, also has its amusing stories; and one of the funniest concerning that service is that of the lady from the South who was supposed to have some rare skin disorder — oriental perhaps — until a Georgia intern followed the big-wigs in, examined her, emerged and said to his superior, "Professor, ain't anything the matter with that lady, 'cept she's just been sittin' too close to the fireplace for years and burned her legs." Her rare disease went up in smoke, as soon as he spoke!

Every day, both residents in Marburg and Osler, make rounds at 8:30 A.M. throughout the entire building; sometimes students join these rounds, especially on patients assigned to them. The early rounds are "work" rounds, not "teaching" rounds. During them the house staff attend to the immediate needs of each patient. For example, should his medicines be changed? Can he get up today? Is his diet appropriate, etc.?

The Osler Building is honeycombed with men doing research; for while there are a thousand men on the medical faculty, there are about three research grants per person. Although the grants are assigned through the Medical School, much of the work regarding them is done in Osler and in Brady.

All interns, throughout the hospital now, are chosen by the Intern Matching Plan, in which all the best hospitals and all the best medical schools in the country now participate. Here is a crude explanation of how it works. In October of his final year, the medical student receives a "Directory of Participating Hospitals" for which he has paid $4.00. This is a case history of each hospital as to its source of control, number of beds, patients admitted, outpatient service, autopsy rate, length of intern program, amount of pay he can expect.

The students chew this over. They can and do apply to as many hospitals as they wish, but all applications must be in and correctly okayed by the applicants

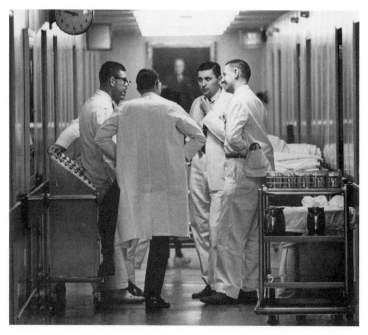

A group of interns and residents consult with a member of the faculty on the unit named for Dr. William S. Thayer, whose portrait hangs in the background. Thayer is on Osler VIII.

by mid-February. The hospitals have also applied for the interns they need and want. The system is designed to match as nearly as possible the mutual choice of both the intern and the hospital for the servicing of the men. The two sets of desires, on February 17, commence their grinding through IBM machines, and by March 17, ALL IS KNOWN and available to the medical schools and hospitals.

It is the fairest system yet devised to give the best man the best chance in the best place of his choice and eliminate favoritism; once he gets on a certain hospital ladder, his ability to stay there or progress reveals itself.

Nowhere else in the hospital do his superiors scrutinize him more closely than in medicine, which, like love, when it is good is filled with satisfaction and there is little to say about it. But when it isn't, the little girl with the curl is a paragon of virtue by comparison.

The tremendous amount of clinical material at Hopkins makes it a particularly choice place to aspire to. In 1971, the medical outpatient clinics clocked up 59,669 visits for the interns and medical students to study. Among these clinics are allergy, arthritis, cardiac, chest, dermatology, diabetes, endocrine, epilepsy, gastroenterology, hematology, medicine, and neurology.

The total of all Outpatient Department clinics for 1971 was 412,126 visits.

A fringe benefit which came out of a Hopkins physician who spent many many hours of his youth in these clinics, and that affected the whole world, came about during World War II. This doctor had a pregnant allergy patient, who got seasick riding the Baltimore street cars. To keep her from sneezing so much and getting upset en route he gave her a new drug called dramamine, which didn't do much for the sneezing, nor her tension, but DID alleviate the nausea. Not a plane flies nor a ship floats now whose passengers are not grateful to that physician, who was smart enough to continue the research on others who were afflicted by car, or seasickness.

One of the first things a man learns in these clinics is to remember: "You see, and you don't know: you know and you don't see; and it's that sense of past-seeing which saves your diagnosis."

The place you get it is in those thousands of hours you spent in the outpatient clinics and on the wards.

Almost across from the entrance to the Osler Building, on the Main Corridor is the Hurd Memorial Hall, which was built with the money Mr. George W. McGaw, of Hopper, McGaw fame (fancy groceries — the store was on the southwest corner of Charles and Mulberry Streets), gave for a memorial to the first Director of the Johns Hopkins Hospital, Dr. Henry M. Hurd. The Hurd family lived on the second floor of the Administration Building and his little daughters were referred to by the resident staff as "the Hurdlets."

In the lobby of Hurd Hall now hang the portraits of Dr. Hurd, of Dr. Walter E. Dandy, and of Dr. Finney; here too, are bronze bas reliefs of Dr. Thayer, Dr. Barker, and Dr. Hurd.

Mr. McGaw also gave the sundial in the front yard of the hospital which is so calibrated as to tell not only the hour, but the time of the sunrise and sunset. The verse upon it was written by Dr. Henry Van Dyke, an eminent author, and reads:

> "One Hour Alone Is In Thy Hands
> The Hour On Which The Shadow Stands."

CHAPTER IX

Cushing Bought It and Brought It

ACCORDING to Dr. Crowe, Walter James Dodd, the assistant pharmacist at the Massachusetts General Hospital, made a tube for the hand-driven static machine which that hospital had puchased, after Roentgen's discovery was announced in Germany, in 1895. The following March, he purchased an imported tube, better than the one he had constructed, and took the first successful X-ray picture at the Massachusetts General.

Dr. Harvey Cushing wished to use the X-rays to take pictures in the out-patient fracture clinic of that hospital, but Dodd wouldn't lend him his tube. So Cushing bought one of his own.

When he came to Baltimore in September, 1896, he brought it with him and made the first roentgenogram at Hopkins upon a woman with a bullet lodged in her spine. Dr. Crowe describes this vividly and remembered it exhaustingly, for he had to assist Dr. Cushing and cranked the static machine for 45 minutes to generate the current while Dr. Cushing exposed the plate!

Until 1897, Dr. Cushing did all the X-ray work at Johns Hopkins.

In 1900, Dr. Frederick Henry Baetjer was a third-year student and may have helped Dr. Cushing in X-ray, and Dr. Cushing may have suggested to Dr. Halsted that young Baetjer had a natural talent for the work. At any event, in 1902, Dr. Halsted asked the then newly graduated M. D. "to do the photographic and X-ray work of the hospital at a salary of $900.00 a year."

From then until he died in 1933, Dr. Baetjer's entire medical life was spent in this field. As has been said elsewhere in this book, the specialty cost him much of

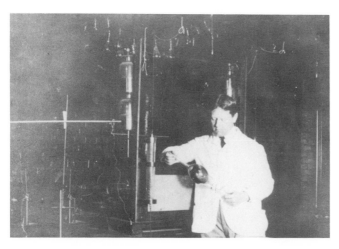

An early photo of Dr. Frederick H. Baetjer (from the Welch Library Collection).

his body, but through his pioneering many thousands have been cured and lived.

His portrait now hangs in the radiology waiting room, opposite the desk of the receptionist.

He was followed in this work by Dr. J. William Pierson, who served until 1946. Dr. Pierson's successor, the 3rd Radiologist-in-Chief, served until 1971, when he was appointed Dean of the Medical School. Hopkins is now searching for the 4th Radiologist-in-Chief. Radiology has grown so much with the advent of nuclear medicine, that it is now called Diagnostic Roentgenology, Radiation Therapy and Nuclear Medicine, having 3 divisions, each of which has a physician-director. His own office is now on the first floor of the School of Hygiene, north.

A man of great vigor, much humor, and an especial favorite of medical students, he still holds forth, frequently, in the Radiology Building which is to the right of the main hospital corridor, beside Hurd Hall. Medical students work here four years; the five-year students coming in in their second year.

This structure consists of 3 floors, 2 of which are below ground. On the first floor are the reception area, and film-viewing facilities. On the basement floor are the administrative offices, the library, and 6 X-ray procedure rooms. In the sub-basement floor are the film vault, photographic section, classroom, and storage.

However, there are other sections or divisions of the department throughout the hospital. Urology sections are on the ground floor of Brady, 2 X-ray rooms, and on the second floor of Blalock, 2 more X-ray rooms. Obstetrics and gynecology sections are on the first floor of the Woman's Clinic where there are 2 X-ray rooms. Pediatric radiology, as you already know, is in the CMSC sub-basement where there are 4 X-ray rooms. The Orthopedic Clinic, on the first floor of Carnegie, has 1 X-ray room. The Emergency Room has 2 X-ray rooms, while the Outpatient Department has 4 X-ray rooms on the third floor of Blalock. The operating rooms on Blalock and Carnegie seventh floors have 2 X-ray rooms. The department has 48 listings in the Centrex phone book.

Cardiovascular radiology on the fifth floor of the Hoffberger has 4 X-ray rooms while the Radiation Therapy, in Halsted basement, has 4 treatment rooms (2 cobalt units) and 1 X-ray room. Nuclear Medicine on Blalock III does over 6,000 tests per year and has 8 Scintiscan units. Radiology Research Laboratory on Blalock VI has 1 X-ray room.

Dr. Frederick H. Baetjer (1876-1933).

The photo-cell image intensifier invented by Dr. Russell A. Morgan, the present Dean of the Medical Faculty, while he was serving as Chairman of Radiology.

In the Radiology Building proper are done routine X-ray examinations on inpatients only and neuro-radiological procedures.

78,071 patients are seen annually in all sections of Diagnostic Roentgenology, and there are 145,259 X-ray examinations. The number of films per examination is 4.3. These are destroyed 5 to 10 years after the last visit of the patient to the hospital for X-ray, unless they contain some abnormality, in which event they are kept indefinitely, as are the X-rays of all autopsy cases. One of the duties of the senior staff radiologist is to attend the weekly Clinical Pathological Conference and discuss the X-ray films covering the autopsy under discussion.

No matter who you are, not where you are lying in the hospital, whether active staff or resident staff, whether private or semi-private, your X-ray charges are all uniform, as are those in the therapy division, also.

Forty to 50 patients per day pass through the Radiation Therapy Division. In the present building, the patient locks the outside door, disrobes, and then draped in the hospital gown, steps through an opposite doorway, without locking possibilities, into the room where his pictures are to be taken. This set-up circumvents the stealing of the patient's clothes while he is disrobed.

The present Dean of The Johns Hopkins University School of Medicine is the inventor of a photo-cell system of fluoroscopic screens which permits you to see through the fluoroscope in the daylight. This is a type of screen intensifier which is used on all new equipment placed throughout the hospital.

Another great time saver on this service is a machine which develops, washes, and drys the X-rays in 90 seconds, thereby making it possible to read and report on the patient while the patient is still on the floor, if so desired.

There is a two-carbon charge slip for billing purposes, but the patient never gets this. In OPD, the patient gets a ticket with charges, in order to pay his bill.

The patient never has his diagnosis. Usually within 24 hours, an inpatient's X-ray diagnosis report is sent in four copies to the following places: the original goes to the patient floor to put in the patient's medical record, a copy goes to the doctor, a copy is sent to keypunch for radiology statistics, and a copy stays with the X-ray film in the X-ray library.

This building is always crowded with students learning to read X-rays,

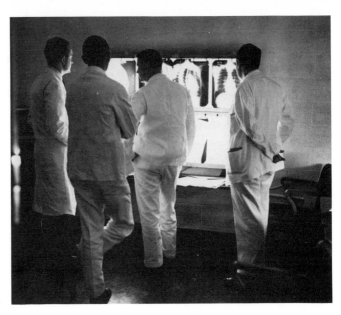
An x-ray conference.

wanting to see what's "cooking," clocking the doses of radium being given in the therapy rooms, studying the X-rays of the patients getting it, watching a series of pictures being shown on the flow-plate screen, or poking their noses into the "hot rooms," as the developing and X-ray rooms in the center of the building are called.

Everybody consults the radiologist, for, in a sense, he does an autopsy upon a living man, via pictures. Surgeons planning operations, physicians searching for colitis or ulcers, neurologists examining a brain or a spinal column, obstetricians looking at unborn babies, pediatricians looking at children, orthopedists watching for fractures, or arthritis, all ask his opinion and are guided by his experienced eye. He has to be able to evaluate anatomy, understand physiology and pathology.

A one year internship and four years of training in radiology are required before a doctor may be called a "radiologist." Also in this department is a School of Radiologic Technology, approved by the A.M.A. This school requires two years of graduate training after high school for one to become a "radiological technologist."

This is one of the fastest growing departments in the hospital and Radiology is always filled with interesting young men. Among the new machines purchased since this book was first written are those which employ the use of motion picture films and cameras in conjunction with screen intensifiers (image intensifiers) to study the dynamics of organs of the human body. Also, now used are closed television systems and videotape recorders in conjunction with the image intensifiers. Used, too, are high-speed filming techniques in cardiovascular procedures (up to 12/sec).

The 300 milligrams of radium which the Hopkins owned — a portion of which belonged to Dr. Hugh H. Young, and some was from the supply which Dr. Howard A. Kelly owned — is gone. The Hopkins sold it and replaced it with 300 milligrams of cesium, which is safer to use.

Before the hospital was equipped to give radium therapy, Dr. Kelly gave free all of the radium treatments upon all the Hopkins Hospital patients who needed them, and could not pay for them, at his private hospital, now demolished, which stood upon Eutaw place.

CHAPTER X

Where the Patients Come in

THE Dispensary of The Johns Hopkins Hospital has always been on Monument Street and from the day the hospital first opened its Dispensary it has always been a "going" concern. In fact the magazine *Resident Physician,* at the time of the 75th anniversary of the hospital stated: "The Dispensary was soon in full swing, with a staff of 11 men. . . . During the first eight months the Dispensary attracted 10,000 people. Six thousand came for treatment in the month of January alone. It became necessary to start charging 10 cents for medicine, which had been given free."

At the time of the hospital's 50th anniversary in 1939, Dr. Chesney states, "By 1/31/14 there had been 1,652,131 dispensary visits." The 25th anniversary of the hospital was in May of 1914. "By 12/31/38, there had been 6,724,006" visits to the Dispensary since May 15, 1889.

In THE SUN MAGAZINE at the time of the 75th anniversary of the hospital it was stated that outpatients now number 350,000 annually. In 1971, there were a total of 412,126 Dispensary visits.

The correct name for the present Dispensary, which opened in 1923, is the Carnegie Building. The money to erect it was given by the Carnegie Corporation. In the outpatient admitting office, there hangs a portrait of the late Andrew Carnegie, who knew what it meant to be a poor boy before he grew to be a rich man. So did Mr. Johns Hopkins, of whom a small portrait hangs in the main Dispensary corridor. Next to Mr. Hopkins is the very large portrait of another man who knew what it meant to be a poor boy, the late Emanuel Chambers. There is a very interesting

A variety of patients gather daily in one of the more than 100 specialty outpatient clinics at Johns Hopkins.

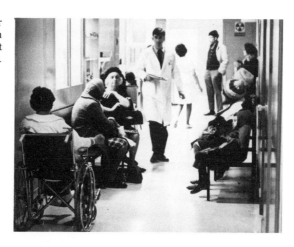

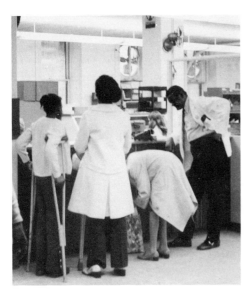

A staff physician chats with patients at the cashier's counter in the outpatient department.

story regarding him, which is told later in this chapter.

Within sight of all three of these portraits, each day, pass the 1,800 out-patients who enter the hospital for diagnosis and treatment, via the Dispensary. Now that there are 5 days and 40 hours in a work week, these people pass through here on a highly efficient system. They sit on benches which are covered with bright vermilion plastic cushions, and on which 30 or 40 people, at a time, may be seated.

These are private, non-private, emergency, both adult and pediatric patients. "Walk-in" non-appointment adult patients are seen by the "screening" or "Triage" doctor in the Emergency Room. "Walk-in" non-appointment pediatric patients are seen by the "screening" doctor in Harriet Lane Home.

Obvious emergency patients are taken directly to the appropriate treatment area, both adult and pediatric cases. Patients seen by a "screening" doctor are referred to one of these five places: emergency area for immediate treatment; Dispensary doctor for intermediate care (not requiring emergency treatment or referral to clinics); appropriate clinic for evaluation and treatment; to family doctor; screened out — medical treatment not required.

The adult screening service operates from 8:00 A.M. to 8:00 P.M.; the pediatric one from 8:00 A.M. to 5:00 P.M. Patients are charged $3.50 for this service. The fee for first appointments to the medical clinics is now $25.00. (Of this the hospital charges $20.00, and $5.00 is for professional services.) Return visits are usually $15.00. (Of this the hospital gets $10.00, and $5.00 is for professional services.)

In both these set-ups a minor charge of $10.00 ($8.00 for the hospital, and $2.00 for professional services) may be added with the approval of the area administrative supervisor.

All the emergency rooms (main, Harriet Lane, and Wilmer) charge $22.00.

In all areas — clinics and emergency rooms — lab and X-ray studies are additional. *Every* basic charge is quoted to the patient when the patient makes appointments.

Patients are asked to bring their "third party support cards," i.e. Blue Cross,

Blue Shield, Medicare, Medicaid, commercial insurance, union, etc., with them when they come to the hospital.

Patients not financially able to meet their medical costs can request a financial interview in the steering clinic, Harriet Lane, CMSC III, Wilmer, or Phipps. Financial interviews for Emergency Room charges are given in the steering clinic — after treatment has already been given.

All new patients are given a plastic plate with the patient's name and history number impressed on it. A financial code is assigned and written on the plate, also. This plate is about 1¾″ by 3½″ and must always be brought by the patient upon return visits to facilitate his progress through the clinic in question.

Patients with incomes which make them eligible for assistance from the State, Medical Assistance patients, formerly called welfare patients, are referred by the admitting officers to the State of Maryland Department of Social Services, which maintains an office on the Main Corridor of J. H. H. adjacent to Hurd Hall.

A "sliding scale" is applied for those patients above state aid, who are unable to pay full hospital fees by the Outpatient Department admitting officers. The availability of other "third party" assistance, the patient's condition with its probable lab and X-ray studies and continued visits are all considered in applying the sliding scale. Also, the family income and the number of members drawing that income is a factor, too.

The state reimburses the hospital the cost for treatment of patients eligible under their program. (State and hospital adjust their mutual books at the end of the fiscal year.)

The Treasurer of the hospital referring to Free Work states, "The hospital renders a great amount of service to persons who are not able to pay fully for their care. Very few patients are treated on a totally free basis, because most can make some contribution toward their care, however small.

"While it is true that public programs such as Medicare and Medicaid have provided coverage for many persons who previously were unable to pay for their care, there still remains a considerable gap between indigent patients and those who can afford to pay fully.

"The Medicaid Program has strict eligibility limits which are rather un-realistic in the light of today's hospital costs, which exceed $135 a day. Thousands of patients come to Johns Hopkins each year, particularly in the Outpatient Department, and are financially unable to pay fully for their treatment and yet are sub-stantially above the level of indigency required for the Medicaid Program.

"Virtually all Blue Cross and insurance plans as well as Medicare and Medicaid have limits on the length of coverage, and the few unfortunate patients who require hospitalization for periods of many months usually become financial burdens to the hospital after all third-party coverage has been exhausted."

This is quoted at length here, because the health of the poor has become such a political football and nobody is supposed to have done or be doing anything about it at the present.

If a patient already has a deficit against him on the hospital books, he is asked to pay all or something on his former debts. However, pay or no pay, he is still seen and cared for. The great mass of the work done in the out-patient clinics is all on pre-arranged appointments; and the patient's case histories are requisitioned 2 or 3 days in advance from the Medical Records Department, also his X-rays, if

Many patients enter The Johns Hopkins Outpatient Department through its steering clinic on Carnegie I.

they are appropriate. Valiant attempts are made to keep the waiting time to the minimum, and it varies according to services. The patient has been advised previously, by mail, of the date and time of his appointment. If he comes from outside the city of Baltimore, he has to be referred to the Outpatient Department by the doctor who has seen him, in his home town.

Patients are expected to pay or present proper third party support cards at the time that service is given. Except for medical reasons, they are not registered by race.

The heaviest clinic days are Tuesday and Wednesday; there are more new patients then and all new patients must be interviewed and financially rated on one of the ten code numbers which are shown on the back of the "chargaplate." They must also be examined and routed as to treatment by the doctor in charge of the steering office.

There is now a "primary care center" in the steering clinic area, where ambulatory walk-in patients are screened by specially trained nurses. Patients are then appropriately referred either to outside agencies, health departments, or to their L.M.D.'s, the Emergency Room, or to be examined by the doctor in the primary care area. This provides treatment to "walk-in" patients with complaints which do not require expensive medical work-ups. It also eliminates the overcrowded conditions in the Emergency Room.

The area controls the referrals to the medical specialty clinics and the correspondence and telephone requests for all clinics.

Spread through the week, there are at least 240 new interviews in the outpatient admitting office; the new central admitting office, on the Main Corridor, is open at night and picks up, via the Emergency Room, for Dispensary admissions then.

To return to cost: however you figure it and whatever is paid, the hospital is obliged to lose; from this great marching mass of mostly indigents which made a total of 412,126 (total) visits to the Dispensary in 1971, the hospital lost almost $2 million in "indigent and bed debt cases."

There are still the worthy poor, and many of them are tragic indeed. Like the man dying of terminal cancer who has expended all of his life-savings and still must have very expensive X-ray treatments, and whom the hospital, after thorough investigation, helps and gladly helps.

Or the patient whose drug bill, even at the about-cost rates at which drugs can be purchased from the hospital Dispensary, runs to about $300 every two months. He is retired, living off a small pension, and has a wife and a mother dependent upon him. Again, the hospital gladly helps.

But when an uncooperative patient who says, "It is none of your business what my finances are," comes through the Dispensary, he is told, "Then it is none of our business what your health is," and refused treatment.

The deserving sick poor are never turned away. Many of the people who interview the new patients remember the cogent remark of that vastly experienced admitting officer, who retired after 31 years, and now works as a volunteer in the clinics, "If you are hungry and sick and poor, you *need* help. *Really* need it."

Humor walks through here, as well as tragedy. A woman in a purple dress with a red coat has to go back to the county whence she came and get her papers approved by the Medical Assistance officer there, and the admitting officer tells her to be sure when she writes sending the approved papers, for an X-ray appointment, that she mentions she is the woman in "the red coat and purple dress" and we'll know who you are. She does and they do, and the appointment postal is dispatched to her.

Patients whom the steering doctor considers medically interesting are always admitted whatever their financial situation. In the medical clinic, a third year medical student works, daily, with a doctor; one student to one doctor, all morning. This student examines patients, goes over his findings with the doctor and together they investigate the student's idea of the trouble.

This system of bringing the 3rd year medical student into the hospital to work owes its origin to Dr. Osler and has always been an integral part of a medical student's training at Hopkins.

There are 45 outpatient clinics a week held in the Carnegie Building, 26 in Blalock Building, exclusive of the clinics in Wilmer, Harriet Lane, and Phipps.

The majority of the doctors who work and teach in these clinics receive no pay, and the service is open to any qualified doctor in the city of Baltimore who cares to apply; so valuable is the look-see into current therapeutics and the ear-to-the-ground into current research that men not Hopkins graduates apply for this training, too.

To teach is always to learn, and many of the most prominent doctors in Baltimore are still learning, and are also still maintaining their privileges to bring their own private patients into the hospital on the private and semi-private services.

As it now costs over $150 a day to keep a patient in the hospital, every effort is made to treat patients, as far as possible, as outpatients.

The early ambulation of patients (that means getting them up), the surgical dressing clinics in which surgical sutures may be removed after the patient has been sent home and returns for dressings, the taking of biopsies in the outpatient clinic, careful diagnosis through the clinics via X-ray and the heart-measuring machines of the patient before he is ever brought into the hospital as an inpatient help to achieve this. In the 1930's a patient stayed in the hospital an average of 30 days; in 1960, he stayed an average of 10.5 days, thanks in part to the highly intelligent use of the outpatient clinics. Now he stays an average of 10.4 days.

One of the heaviest outpatient loads at Hopkins used to be called "Medicine One" and was the clinic for the treatment of syphilis. Thanks to the anti-biotics, the disease dropped in volume, but there is now considerable increase of "fresh" syphilis being found among adolescent and other hospital patients. Every patient admitted to the hospital on any service is automatically given a Wassermann test, and should that prove positive he is written a letter and so advised and treatment recommended.

Many of these people do not return for treatment, as they should; and these cases used to be followed up by the Social Service Department, but that is no longer done. The Health Department makes certain they are adequately treated.

For very many years the salaries of the Social Service Department were one of the responsibilities of the Women's Board, but the department has been taken over by the hospital and the salaries are now paid by the hospital. Nine years ago the department had 6 workers; in 1970 it had 41. The Director of the department points out that "social work goes on from prenatal care through death," and needless to say affects everybody. There are 2 workers in obs-gyn; 13 in pediatrics and psychiatry; 6 in psychiatry 1 in the School of Hygiene; 8 on the medical service; 3 on the surgical service, 1 in the Emergency Room; 1 in neurology; 1 group worker; 1 Director; 1 associate director; and in the units in pediatrics and psychiatry there is 1 associate director each.

Money for the department comes from J.H.H. or grants from the U.S. Government and voluntary health money. The Director is the Assistant Professor of Social Work in the Medical School. Among the "true" poor in America now are rural whites; 'poor-whites' and the proud poor who are not white — many are aged. Federal matching of funds is done in Aid to Dependent Children; aid to the aged; aid to the needy blind; aid to the disabled. Another help is Meals-on-Wheels, which is now expanded to help keep an aged couple together, and to shop and set-up for them for tomorrow.

In the Social Service Department are 30 professional case workers; 11 Social Service assistant clinical social workers; all paid by J.H.H. designations broken down as above; also there 2 grants from the Women's Board: one of $1,000 for patient assistance and one of $500 for the educational fund.

The latter means a 2 weeks refresher course at Smith College, for which J.H.H. paid and which is taken by 2 supervisors and 1 advanced child-care worker. The courses are in crisis work, advanced case work, and advanced case work with the disturbed child.

In 1971 the department, either in their patient-family visits or at the hospital, had 19,100 contacts. These persons include resident staff, Outpatient Department and private patients. Their findings, of course, have to be reflected back to the physicians, nurses, community agencies, etc., etc.

As anybody with a long familiarity with the Dispensary of The Johns Hopkins Hospital can deduce, the load has decreased about 42,000 annually in the number of Dispensary visits in the last 10 years and through the prior engagement system; so has the waiting time per patient, however the present patients grumble. For very many years in the past, you came and sat and waited your turn and then waited, again, while your case history was brought up from the history room, and a doctor managed to familiarize himself with it and THEN saw you. There were no prior engagements; and strangely enough, the patients then were polite and grateful.

One of the mounting problems in America are the geriatrically ill. Generally speaking that means the old people who are going to live a long time, and who are related to younger people who wish they'd die. Modern medicine has increased man's life-span, and modern social service is trying to increase children's love-span for those ailing parents. They, also, have a dead friend who did much to improve their lot in the State of Maryland. His name was Dr. Mason F. Lord.

Old people, naturally, make one think of fractures and one of the largest of the outpatient clinics is the fracture clinic, where the casts are changed, the X-rays taken and studied, while the patient is present, via the 90-second machine described elsewhere. This clinic is held every Wednesday morning.

Because of the excellent work for children done at Kernan and the Children's Hospital School, a considerable part of the large patient load of this clinic is adult, and it provides ample material for study in usage of the patched-up parts.

Looking down upon these patients from the wall of the orthopedic waiting room is a portrait of Dr. George E. Bennett who was a grown man and a Baltimore street-car motorman when he decided to get an education and study medicine. He went on to become one of the most interesting teachers Hopkins ever had and the last word in the baseball world on whether or not a high-priced player was in condition to play. Judge Landis was the czar of baseball, but Dr. Bennett the Absolute Authority on the bones of the players.

No man ever understood the problems of the poor better than he, and even in his portrait, he looks now as if he is going to step down and see if he can help you.

Also on this first floor are the pharmacy, described in "The Unseen Hospital," and the Security Department, also described there. The assistant comptroller of the hospital is here, too, and all the OPD Administration officers, as well as the Assistant Director of OPD nursing, the department head of all the clinics, Lost and Found. The University Health Service and the office of its Director are on Carnegie IV. The duty of that service is to take care of all the health problems of all persons in the Medical Institutions employed by the university.

You must be acutely ill to be admitted to Hopkins. But it is also one of the few large general hospitals in which ALL kinds of illness are treated. A run down of the upper floors of this building will give you some idea of what this means.

Carnegie II houses the gyn clinic; gyn radium clinic; gyn sterility clinic, as well as the Instructor of OPD nursing, med. records room for the Moore Clinic, also on that floor, connective tissue, genetics, hypertension, metabolism, polyarthritis, POPS renal, neurology-adult, cases are seen and studied.

A most touching story about the gyn radium clinic concerns the late Dr. C. Bernard Brack, whose friends referred to him as "Bozo." This is the way a lady in the Admitting Office told it, recently. "He had fought death so long, for so many people, in that clinic on the second floor of the Dispensary, that his patients had come to believe he was invincible. Radium, nuclear isotopes, deep X-ray, *anything* which would help his patients they had! There was even a mysterious fund known throughout the Dispensary as "Dr. Brack's fund," which he used to pay the board of the out-of-town poor, pay for their treatments, to *help people!* To this day nobody knows, for sure, where the fund came from. It no longer exists; it died with him.

"The day Dr. Blalock operated upon "Bozo," as he was affectionately called, the cancer clinics were loaded with patients; then the word came down from the operating room that there was nothing to do. He was riddled with cancer and Dr. Blalock had sewed him up. The doctors in the gyn clinic put their arms upon their

The Consultation Clinic on Blalock III, formerly called the Private Outpatient Service, has a steady stream of patients from all over the globe.

desks and put their heads down in them. The whole place was a shambles, nurses, doctors, orderlies — everybody in total despair. Finally, one old Hopkins nurse, spun round, walked from office to office and said to the doctors, "Get up! Get ready! I'm bringing the patients in. "Bozo *always* said, 'The patients come *first*."

There is no portrait of him there. There should be.

However, there are portraits on that floor of Dr. Frank R. Ford, Associate Professor of Neurology, who died in 1970, and also of Dr. Clark, another Professor of Neurology; also here is the portrait of Dr. Albert Keidel, already described in this book.

On the 3rd floor is the Grant Ward Clinic, previously referred to in the chapter on Blalock, and the obs clinic, a seminar room, and the tumor registry.

The 4th floor houses audiology and speech, ENT clinic, hearing and speech, otolaryngologist-in-charge, otological vestibular lab, the otolaryngology library, private ENT, and also the University Health Service.

Very fittingly, the portrait of Dr. Samuel J. Crowe is on this floor, too. He was the giant of his generation in ear, nose, and throat. The Professor Emeritus of Laryngology and Otology, who recently retired, began a very famous study in neural deafness in 1962, which was financed by the Hartford Foundation, and is the basis for the present knowledge that rock and roll music may leave its hearers permanently deaf, if they are subject to long exposures to the very loud sound.

On the 5th floor are the bacteriology labs of the entire hospital: central, chief, media room, mycology, pediatric, tuberculosis — an immensely busy and important place.

The 6th floor is given over to the blood bank; EEG; general medical clinic; metabolism division; parasitology lab; and the serology lab. Again, a very important place.

On the 7th floor is anesthesia and information GOR as well as the supervisor of GOR; on the eighth is the GOR instructor, workrooms, anesthesia classrooms, anesthetist nurses office, dressing room GOR.

These 2 floors house no clinics and are purely concerned with equipping and manning the 17 operating rooms of J.H.H.

To go back downstairs: another clinic which is run through the Dispensary is what is known as Medical and Surgical Consultation Clinic (OHH, formerly POPS). The persons desiring this service go directly in the elevators of the Blalock Building to the 4th floor, where they are admitted and steered. They pay full fees. They may be seen by an active staff man, either full-time or part-time, of whom they are already a patient. If they have no active staff doctor, they are assigned one, and usually to a doctor whom the director of the clinic believes will be especially competent to handle the problem which the patient presents. All of these visits are by appointment only, after the first steering admission. The doctor seeing them, if he be a part-time physician remits 20% of his fee to the hospital for the use of its facilities; if he be a full-time man, he remits his entire fee to the Medical School. There is a list of professional fees recommended by the hospital, for this type of service, and should a doctor charge more than the listed fee, the hospital has the responsibility to correct the fee. These fees do not include X-rays, lab tests, or special diagnostic procedures. A complete work-up on a patient going through this service now amounts to between $300 and $400.

One of the largest of the outpatient clinics is ENT and this is attributed to the fact that Dr. Samuel J. Crowe and the recently retired professor emeritus revolutionized this specialty and that excellent group of men whom they trained are still practicing here.

If it be necessary to become a patient in the hospital, large numbers of these private outpatients do so under the semi-private Blue Cross insurance coverage, as do, also, non-private patients who are insured.

Medical students still abound throughout the Dispensary. However, there are now medical students assigned to patients of the active staff in Marburg, Brady, Thayer, and Halsted, etc. Medical students work with patients of the active staff and the resident staff. Also medical students may see patients of the active staff in the outpatient clinics, too, but not as frequently as with inpatients. They do not see all patients in the outpatient department: the volume is too great.

Now, however, patients on all services have the added advantage of the scrutiny from their all-inquisitive eyes. At Hopkins, all doctors practicing — emeritus, part-time, full-time, and resident staff are kept on their toes, forever, by that student scrutiny.

One place in the United States where colored people have always had excellent attention, service and care, is The Johns Hopkins Hospital. At least one-third of its bedsick and certainly two-thirds of its outpatient sick have been colored. They have received the same medical treatment, from the same men, the same food, and the same medicines as have the white patients.

In Volume I of his excellent history of Hopkins, Dr. Chesney states, on page 164, regarding the segregation of colored patients: "No ward buildings especially designated for colored patients had been built, and it was necessary at first to admit them to the same wards to which white patients were admitted. The matter seems to have given the Trustees some concern and after an investigation had been made of what was being done in the other hospitals of the city it was decided to set aside for the colored patients the north east small ward, the hall and the dining room of each of the public wards (D,E,F,G and H). This arrangement served for a time but was not wholly satisfactory and eventually (1894) a separate buliding was erected for colored patients only."

Wards existed for all patients, regardless of color, who could not afford private rooms. The Negroes, however, were the only ones of these patients who were segregated. Nevertheless, *all* patients, wherever they were housed, received the same medical attention, care and drugs from the same staff of doctors, nurses and pharmacists. After World War II, when Government money began to be infused into all hospitals, including Hopkins, all segregation and all wards began to disappear.

When this book was first written the author tried in many ways, from many people, to find out if The Johns Hopkins Hospital had ever had a colored benefactor. She was unsuccessful; however, the first physician mentioned in the committee of three doctors who read the manuscript then, and now, wrote the author saying that he had inquired around among his medical colleagues for any information regarding a colored man he recalled having been in Osler, who had left the hospital his life savings.

The late Dr. Henry M. Thomas, whose patient the man had been, gave him all the facts regarding the Emanuel Chambers bequest and he and the author were happy to include them in the first edition of this book. These are the facts: In 1945, a man named Emanuel Chambers, who had been for many years an employee of the Maryland Club, died and left his estate to The Johns Hopkins Hospital. There is a plaque to him in Osler. A rather modest sum of money had been handled for his benefit by a member of the club, the late Mr. Ellicott Worthington, and built into an estate amounting to about $175,000.

According to "Under the Dome," at the time of the presentation by the Emanuel Chambers Foundation of the portrait, in 1965, the estate amounted to $150,230.25 and was for "charitable and education purposes of inhabitants of Baltimore City, regardless of race, color, or creed." The portion which was given to the Hopkins Hospital was $73,500; however, in 25 years, as of 1970, the Hopkins lists the Chambers gift as worth $114,123.

The portrait, as previously stated, hangs in the Dispensary lobby beside a small oil painting by an unknown artist of Mr. Hopkins, who would certainly have appreciated the years of self-denial it took to accumulate the Chambers bequest. He would be proud of having a grateful patient beside him.

Mr. Johns Hopkins (1795-1873).

Mr. Emanuel Chambers (1861-1945) after a portrait by Mary Lewis Carey.

CHAPTER XI

Dr. Billings' First Choice

SO many strange things go into Dr. William H. Welch coming to Hopkins that one holds one's breath when remembering some of them. Had Dr. Billings NOT met him abroad when he and Dr. Hunt went to visit and study the great European hospitals in 1876, had Physicians and Surgeons NOT refused to be interested in pathology and pathologists when their graduate returned from his European study and had Bellevue NOT, finally, given him those three vacant rooms, with only kitchen tables as equipment, on which to pursue his speciality, the Pathology Department certainly would NOT be what it is, today. And one might add, neither would American pathology.

Between June of 1892 and June of 1916, the following men were among the 13 assistant resident pathologists: Lewellys F. Barker, William G. MacCallum, Eugene L. Opie, Charles H. Bunting, George H. Whipple, Ernest W. Goodpasture, Mont R. Reid, and Stanhope Bayne-Jones.

Among the students they taught was a member of the class of 1905 at the Johns Hopkins Medical School, Dr. F. Peyton Rous, who received the Nobel Prize for Medicine in 1966. In 1911, he showed that a chicken sarcoma ("Rous sarcoma") could be induced in healthy chickens by injecting them with a cell-free filtrate prepared from tumors of diseased chickens. He was already associated with the Rockefeller Institute, then, and was 32 years old. He did many other brilliant papers over the years, but only in recent years was his early work recognized for its true significance in cancer research.

Dr. F. Peyton Rous (1879-1970), a graduate of the Medical Class of 1905, received a Nobel Prize in Medicine in 1966 for his work in cancer research. He was the first man to prove that viruses can cause the spread of malignant tumors.

A Max Broedel drawing of Dr. Welch.

Dr. Rous, who was a Baltimorean, was 6 years old when the small two-story Pathology Building was under construction at the a-building Hopkins Hospital, in September, 1885. It was finished a few months later, four years before the hospital opened. Among Dr. Welch's pupils at that time were William T. Councilman, a native of Baltimore County, a graduate of the University of Maryland Medical School, and later Professor of Pathology at Harvard; Simon Flexner, later Director, Rockefeller Institute for Medical Research; Walter Reed and James Carroll of yellow fever fame; George M. Sternberg, later Surgeon General, U. S. Army; A. C. Abbott, later Director, School of Public Health, University of Pennsylvania; Franklin P. Mall, and William S. Halsted, among others. Mall later became Professor of Anatomy at Johns Hopkins and established a School of Anatomy and an Institute for Embryology.

The Department of Pathology has always stood upon the corner where, in 1923, the present building, gift of the General Education Board, was opened. What a satisfaction it must have given Dr. Welch, the first Professor of Pathology, to stand in the library of the present Pathology Building, look across at the School of Hygiene and Public Health, of which he was the first Professor, and on to the Welch Library where in the Department of the History of Medicine, he was also first Professor, and on to the Medical School of which he had been the first Dean.

On the marble wall of the Chief Medical Examiner's Office, in the City of New York, there is a Latin quotation, the translation of which is:

"Let conversation cease. Let laughter
flee. This is the place where
death delights to help the living."

This exemplifies the functions of the pathological staff, which are these: to teach, do research, do autopsies and run the surgical pathological labs; everybody in pathology is striving to learn something, *all the time,* in some manner.

From the moment an autopsy, which requires approximately 4 hours to perform, commences, live men are endeavoring to learn from a dead man, woman, or child, as the case may be; and this learning continues for years and years.

It continues in this way: during the autopsy, the medical students stand by and the doctor performing the autopsy comments upon the organs he removes and examines, with his naked eye and, if he feels it advisable, with a nearby microscope. There are now 4 stainless steel autopsy tables, and 4 autopsies may be in progress in the same old large room, which OHH remember, at the same time. The marble top of the famous, old original autopsy table is now mounted on the wall toward Monument Street.

Before an autopsy is performed the doctor on whose service the patient died, and if he had an "outside" doctor, that doctor, too, is notified of the autopsy hour; and in the majority of the cases they appear to have their errors in diagnosis pointed out to them or their judgment vindicated.

Medicine has always been particularly stern about the presence of the doctor on whose service the patient died; and this, perhaps, is part of the Osler tradition. Before coming to Baltimore, in one year he did 100 autopsies and his hand-written autopsy records in the Philadelphia Hospital *Post-Mortem Record* show his scrupulous exactness.

In all 50 states a dead person's organs are his property and he has the right to donate them. They cannot be bought nor sold, and the body from which they have been removed and upon which an autopsy may be performed, also, is in no way disfigured for an ordinary funeral "viewing." In the case of the eyes, they are replaced by glass eyes and the lids then closed, as they are always closed on all bodies. Kidneys, eyes, lungs, and now bone banks are becoming increasingly important all over the nation. Autopsies are not, however, performed without relative-permission, unless the dying person specifically demands one; but organ-removal is, provided the proper donor papers are signed by the giver, prior to death, or provided that the relatives accede to the dying person's verbal gift, before death.

These donor forms can be supplied upon request, and the Hopkins will be glad to do so. Forms are also included in this book for your use, if you wish to use them. More and more intelligent people are giving their organs, too; for one thing which man is far from creating in a workable form is man, himself. All pathologists know this, all space engineers know this, too. The last 10 years have

The autopsy room's old marble autopsy table is mounted on the wall just to the left of the window in the autopsy room.

118

For many years the late Dr. Louis Hamman (right) and the late Dr. Arnold R. Rich gave a weekly clinical-pathological conference. Dr. Hamman, a superior clinician, reviewed the clinical course of the patient and gave his opinion of the cause of death. Dr. Rich reviewed the findings at autopsy. These conferences, always well attended, were superb learning experiences. The conferences continue today under the present members of the staff of the Department of Medicine and the Department of Pathology.

shown plainly that man remains the same old soul and he operates within the periphery of himself; pathologists know and treasure this and they never do an autopsy that they do not think about it.

It is a sadness to them that the magnificent autopsy rate at Hopkins is declining. Eleven years ago, they did two a day; in the past twelve months, they did 468 . . . not even two a day. However, it is encouraging to know that the number of in-hospital deaths decreased from 1065 in 1959-1960 to 848 in 1970-71. Also the number of patients discharged increased from 28,285 11 years ago to 32,154 in 1970-1971. Eleven years ago, the Medical Examiner did 33 cases, whereas last year he did 46, but his examinations do not count in Hopkins' autopsy percentage.

No doctor can become ostrich-sure of himself when he faces the possibility that the truth will be revealed, regarding his diagnosis, in the presence of the medical students attending the autopsy of his dead patient.

And if you think batting averages in baseball, or touch-down averages in football are well known to these boys, you ought to hear them discuss their superiors' autopsy averages. There isn't a medical student walking around Hopkins now who hasn't picked out the physician, surgeon, and ophthalomologist he wants around when he needs help. Where did he get that knowledge? Primarily in the autopsy room.

One of the most cogent reasons for an autopsy is this: the learning has just begun when it is over. Two weeks elapse while the organs are hardening in formalin before they can be removed from the crocks in which they have been numbered and stored, examined again, dictated about again. Small bits of tissue for later microscopic examination are taken at the time of autopsy. These bits of tissue are first put in a circular bath contraption, made of plastic, about the size of a pint jar; these are set in a circular round disc, attached to a center steel, or aluminum shaft about four inches in diameter, and a center hood-lock top individually covers, under an umbrella cover each of these jar-insets. Within each jar inset are a myriad of stacked, mesh-sided baskets, in alcohol or other chemical solutions. These baskets are plastic and about 2½″ square.

There are two circular discs to hold these baskets upon the center shaft, precisely similar in appearance; and when the machine is loaded with specimens they may be time-set together, or separately, whereby one disc will move up and down, and also circulate the fluid among the myriad tiny baskets for 24 hours, the other disc being simultaneously operating upon a 12-hour cycle; or they may both be set for similar timing.

Millions of hours a year are saved by this invention, as any old-time pathologist who had formerly to turn his specimens by hand, and an alarm clock, can testify. Each tier also includes warm paraffin pint-jars pots, which can be kept at 60 degrees and removed when necessary. This contraption provides beautifully washed specimens; and once removed they are cut with an electric slicer, many times smaller than that provided by the butcher, by comparison as tiny as a child's sewing machine is to a real one. The slides are made on the, approximately, in appearance 2½″ x 1″ glass rectangles, and their dipping in chemicals, still a hand process, follows.

The man who cut the tissue, examined it under the microscope and made all the slides and who had worked in Dr. Bloodgood's laboratory, and at Hopkins ever since is now dead. In his stead a whole team of pathology technicians prepare the slides, which are then put in small manila envelopes about 3″ by 2″ and the doctor who performed the autopsy is notified that the "case" has been cut. Whereupon he takes those slides, re-studies the case and tries to gee up what his eye had seen at the autopsy.

If the two things do not satisfy him, he begins to study the case, restudy it, via the marvelous cross-index system; the original of this system is supposed to have been the invention of Dr. MacCallum. All of this information has been put on a computer and there is now a cross index of slides, diseases and patient histories.

If you die of tuberculosis, but you had four other diseases, too, the slides on your autopsy are cross indexed *under those diseases* also. The pathologist, dissatisfied with his own diagnosis, will resort to the index, take out the slides, go to the library on the fourth floor of the pathological building, take down the books (in which the case histories of all 38,051 — number as of 12/14/71 — autopsies which have been performed at the Hopkins, since it opened are filed) and read, compare, think and, above all, LOOK.

Should he come upon a case in which the slides are blurred, or do not satisfy him, he can go to the room in the basement where the organs of all autopsies are kept — that is enough of the organs for re-cutting — and get the slides on that particular case re-made, again.

When he finally reaches a diagnosis which satisfies him, he then has an interview with a senior pathologist, the Professor, or an associate, presents his point of view and if he is agreed with, the case is closed, and the slides and case history enter into the files and commence their working future.

Should he be disagreed with — and pathologists are notorious for being mental rebels — he must clear his mind and re-start his thinking. And all the time, through all his process, any interested medical student has the right to accompany him.

What the Quaker lady minister said about Mr. Hopkins truly applies in pathology, for there, dead, you are alive. Before that case history enters into its working future approximately six weeks have elapsed.

Also in that library where autopsy descriptions, including some in Dr. Welch's handwriting, are filed is a busted-down old mahogany newel post, standing in a corner looking very like some object from the Easter Islands. It is all that is left of the first pathology building, and the only man in the library, now, who would remember that building is in a portrait: Dr. MacCallum. This portrait hangs over the fireplace and he faces out into the hallway, where he can still, as of old, scrutinize every person who enters. It is very life-like and men who knew him in their youth still expect to be held accountable for the merest thought in the complete backs of their heads. They liked that surveillance, too, for his portrait is flanked by two loving cups; each bear his name and one reads "Second year Class, 1917, College of Physicians and Surgeons," and the other "Second year Class 1909, Johns Hopkins Medical School."

Nearby is a bust of Rudolp Virchow (1821-1902), the great German pathologist, and Dr. MacCallum would be proud to have that nearby, too.

Directly opposite him at the end of the lobby is the portrait of the late Dr. Arnold R. Rich, one of his boys, who succeeded him as Professor of Pathology at Hopkins. He was one of the most brilliant of that long line of brilliant Hopkins pathologists and his textbook *The Pathogenesis of Tuberculosis* is standard student fare at Hopkins.

In between the portraits of these two men are the residency pictures, over the years, of the pathologists who have served the Hopkins. Many old friends, in all their pristine youth, peer out upon you as you study them.

They would be glad to know that the old brown leather chairs are still in the library, and the electric percolator is on the table in the corner, too. Even now, good pathologists do not work by the clock. At all times, medical students are welcome in this library and many a monotone discussion goes on regarding the cases under study.

In a curious way, this whole building acts as a stepping stone between the Medical School and the hospital. Now that the pressure of the ever present patient is no longer upon you, men can come here to contemplate their mistakes, to learn, to pursue, and rectify their thinking. It is an adult place, with a grave and continuing concentration.

Also on the library floor, is the department office, the office of the Pathologist-in-Chief, and of the resident; also of the photography department.

In the office of the Director of the department and Pathologist-in-Chief, on a small table is the duplicate of the long beloved statuette, standing, of Dr. William H. Welch. The original is in the office of the President of the hospital. The one here, however, is the one known to so many pathologists around the world and so treasured by them. Since Dr. Rich retired, there have been two Baxley Professors of Pathology and Directors of the Department of Pathology. The first of these is now Vice-President of Health Affairs NYU Medical School and Director NYU Medical Center; the present one has been in the Hopkins chair for 2 years.

And it is still upon the 2nd floor of this building that one sees where the medical students, in their second year of study, whether they be students who take

Medical students
at their microscopes.

5 (2 years previous college) or 4 (college graduates) years of training keep their microscopes. They now cost $350 second-hand, and $850 new. All second-hand ones, in fact all microscopes, have to be approved by the Microscope Committee of the Medical School. The 1st year in both courses they study anatomy, the 2nd year they get into the hospital and begin using their microscopes in earnest; and in the summer, after that 2nd year, certain chosen students come in for 6 weeks, do autopsies, under supervision, of course, and work up cases.

One of the great weekly events at Hopkins is known as "the CPC" (Clinical Pathological Conference) and all medical students are supposed to attend. They are lively affairs in which the clinician under whom the patient died defends his diagnosis, the resident in radiology brings in X-rays, which are shown, and defends his findings, and then, before proceeding with his own findings, the Professor of Pathology requests the students' diagnosis. All the sheets regarding the case, a copy of which each man has, flutter in expectation and a chosen member of their number straightens the Old Men out. After this, the slides are flashed on the screen, the Professor lectures upon them, reveals the autopsy findings and straightens everybody out. These CPCs are now held in Hurd Hall, but they still occur on Wednesdays and usually to a packed house.

However, the CPC are not held in June, July, or August.

The in-hospital pathology staff consists, since 1969, of 1 Pathologist-in-Chief; 2 residents; 12 anatomical assistant residents; 4 clinical assistant residents; and 6 interns. They, in turn, are watched over by 430 pairs of eagle eyes, otherwise known as students. Some of these are so deeply interested in seeing what actually happened to a man who had a coronary, or a diseased liver, that they come back later in their fourth year or fifth year, as the case may be, according to which way they are going through medical school, for an elective course in pathology.

The whole Department of Pathology, Medical School and hospital, in which some of the above men double, consists of 3 full professors, 10 associate professors, 20 assistant professors, 8 instructors, 1 visiting professor, 1 visiting lecturer, and 1 lecturer in forensic pathology, which means "belonging to the courts or to public discussion or debate." It is one of the most fascinating subjects in medicine and people become as engulfed in it as lawyers do in admiralty law.

122

When there is a forensic angle involved in an autopsy, the tension, the exactitude and the extremely careful choice of words in the dictated descriptions concerning the organs always draws a large, fascinated group of medical students. Criminals have been executed as the result of autopsies on men they had already killed.

In the fact the evidence that "the evil that men do lives after them" is constantly revealed here. "If he'd come in with that cancer a year ago, he'd be alive today." "The patient smoked too much. Look at those lungs." "The surgeon didn't have quite the judgment he needed, did he!" "Learn, be *sure* you learn. Look at it, *carefully.*"

Frequently, they all take turns and go over to the microscope and do just that, as the autopsy proceeds.

Not all their work is in this building, though, for pathologists are noted for getting into the most unusual situations. Some years ago, the resident at Hopkins was asked to perform an autopsy upon an elephant which died at the zoo. He did so, wearing hip boots. Before he was finished, he had all of the elephant's insides laid out around him and it became obvious that he had been wise to come so garbed.

He was operating in a good tradition, though, because there is a wonderful old story about Dr. Welch being interested in studying some hogs, which had died of "cholera." He went down in Anne Arundel County, had them dug up and examined them carefully. The colored man, who dug them up, stood by and remarked disapprovingly, "Certainly was awful to see what some folks would do for money."

There must be something, too, in their very calling, which whets the imagination, for many a middle-aged pathologist in the United States will tell you seriously that he *knows* that Dr. MacCallum, a bachelor, was enamoured of Geraldine Farrar, and that he took a year off and followed her around the world. How he knows this, when his own duties, as a medical student, kept him glued to the microscope, and in residence on Broadway during this Great Period, none can ever explain.

Although the Pathology Building is now air-conditioned, the elevators still labor along, and consequently the stairways are still in constant use. Hopkins is a climbing hospital, and from the first time a medical student pulls up the hill from Reed Hall, until he finally finishes up his training and leaves he is forever climbing.

The stairway between the first and second floors of the Pathology Building is sort of a wind tunnel of medical gossip, in which the obscure young look at the passing Greats, watch their wind-power as they climb, and scrutinize their appearance. Greats who are steadily seen on that stairway, looking at their patient slides, learning something new, chatting with the students peering over the microscopes in the lab, which has always housed those microscopes since 1923, are approved of, listened to, and revered.

Incidentally, each student has a metal locker, with a fine lock upon it, in which to house his microscope because, believe it or not, the thief comes here also.

The animal operating rooms, previously in the Pathology Building have been moved to Blalock XI and XII.

In a general hospital, the surgical pathological labs are particularly valuable and all the small labs previously outside surgical pathology are now combined and located in the surgical pathology area. This lab is on the same floor as the Blalock operating rooms. Eye pathology is now on the 5th floor, but there is still a quick-frozen specimen lab in Wilmer and another in the Woman's Clinic.

The medical couriers still bring specimens over from GOR to the surgical pathological labs, in Blalock, and in 4 minutes, via a frozen section, a diagnosis of the specimen has been telephoned back to the operating room.

Cytopathology and metabolic pathology are on the 6th floor, while the 7th floor houses the autopsy tissue lab, the general pathological technicians, and gyn pathology and gyn residents, the surgical pathological lab reports, and the resident's office. Animal quarters are now on the 8th floor.

At the day's end all the specimens, from all the operating rooms, still come into the surgical labs and in the general surgical lab, a surgical assistant resident, who is required to spend one year of his training in this lab, examines them, dictates upon them, and passes them on to the slide cutting room for fixing and cutting. Tissue is now imbedded, cut, mounted, stained and released for examination by the surgical staff within 24 to 36 hours. It can be done in less time, under special circumstances. These reports go to the operating surgeon concerned; usually, the patient involved is held in the hospital until a slow-cut section can be reported upon.

The Department of Laboratory Medicine now has its own professor, and is on the 5th and 6th floors of the Dispensary, connecting on the end toward Wolfe Street with the Pathology Building. In 1956, because of the need for highly skilled technicians and lack of space, the hospital formed the special diagnostic lab department, with its own administration. In 1963, all these labs were moved to the Dispensary; in 1969, under the present professor, a clinical pathologist, they were re-organized. EKG work, professionally done under the Department of Cardiology is administered by laboratory medicine, and so are EEG and neurometrics, professionally under the Department of Neurosurgery.

In other words, this is the laboratory section of pathology, as opposed to the anatomical section. Anatomical pathology is examination of tissues, after death, and organs, also, BUT in surgical pathology and cytopathology it is also the examination done on a live person.

Clinical, or laboratory pathology means testing in the laboratory of body fluids, including chemical processes, blood, on a live person. (Get your diagnosis and try to keep the person alive.)

Autopsies are now more valuable to have than they ever were, because

The medical student teaching area on Pathology II is used for continuing education of physicians, when students are not using it.

Dr. William H. Welch (1850-1934).

medicine has advanced and is changing so rapidly that further study of these is imperative; only through its consequences upon man can man benefit. The surest way to learn these is by autopsy. For instance, we now know which infections the antibiotics will knock out, which are still left to learn and pinpoint, which have gotten too smart for the antibiotics that formerly conquered them, and which respond to them in no way. A man's killing infection may have been impervious to them, but his case history will show that they conquered his supplementary infections and without his autopsy you could not know this.

There is a "staph" pneumonia which children under three get that no antibiotic will reach; or a man may get well from some infection which can be antibiotically controlled and then die of a fungus which no antibiotic can hit; and always and all the time his secondary infection may cause his slides to throw new light upon an old enemy of mankind.

"Why" has ever been the torchword of pathology and autopsies are the dead man's way, through pathology, to be of use to the living. A person upon whom an autopsy has been performed makes a perfectly presentable corpse to be displayed at a funeral afterwards. It merely delays the removal of the body from the hospital by a matter of a few hours to perform one.

In a teaching hospital, autopsies reveal to the attention of *all* interns, medical students, and men responsible for the patient, their knowledge — or lack of it — in the treatment accorded him.

This is the final helping that any man can bequeath to the hospital and every intelligent, grateful patient should. Practically all doctors do so with their own bodies.

During Dr. Osler's final pneumonia, "when the physician in attendance tried to explain some of the symptoms, he (Dr. Osler) said, 'You lunatic! I've been watching this case for two months, and I'm sorry I shall not do the post-mortem.' "

CHAPTER XII

Pertaining to the Female

THE last of the four men chosen to head the Hopkins staff and the youngest, Dr. Howard A. Kelly, has no memorial at this Hospital; and he should have. If New York can have a statue of Dr. J. Marion Sims, the other great pioneer in American gynecology, at least Hopkins ought to be able to name the new building, which everybody under 50 says must be built *immediately,* for Dr. Kelly. Probably many of the people who insist the structure should be torn down before the year is out, were, themselves, born in the Woman's Clinic, which has been doing business at its present location since 1919. Their great objection seems to be the fact that actual wards existed in it, and patients are still housed in cubicles. (The new building at Guy's, in London, has many open wards.)

To return to Dr. Kelly: he has provided himself with memorials which are daily appreciated by the literati in many a medical library. In the *Medical Index,* up until 1919 he had 485 listings of books and journal articles. When he had been in Baltimore for one year, he married a German lady. They had nine children, and his long-time secretary Audrey W. Davis draws a charming picture of their home life in her book, *Dr. Kelly of Hopkins.* The same volume contains an excellent foreword by his son, Dr. Edmund B. Kelly, who died suddenly in 1964. (OHH:

Dr. Howard A. Kelly (1858-1943) after a portrait by Isabella Hunner Parsons. The painting hangs on Woman's Clinic IV.

JHMS, 1926) He was the only doctor descendant of any of the Great Four. Dr. Howard A. Kelly was the only one of them with now living children and grandchildren.

Because of Dr. Edmund B. Kelly's unique position in the tradition of Hopkins, when the author finished the manuscript of *Miss Susie Slagle's,* she asked him to read it and said if he felt it would damage Hopkins in any way, she would throw it into the fireplace. He read it most carefully, made factual paragraph and line criticism where necessary, (those slips of paper still exist), and gave the book his warm approval. It took him many hours of painstaking, careful work to accomplish this task, and her gratitude will ever be his.

Dr. Howard A. Kelly was 31 when he came to Baltimore; had received his B.S. from the University of Pennsylvania when he was 19; his M.D. when he was 24; and taken two years out of his 31 to recover his health from overwork. He was already interested in botany, reptiles, religion; and his insatiable curiosity was attributed by some to the fact that his mother was a minister's daughter. In the graduating pictures of the early classes of the Medical School, he looks younger and more alive than the boys even. Apparently he was, for in one life, he pioneered operative gynecology, introduced radium in 1913, which he secured directly from Madame Curie, into the treatment of cancer, and his textbook on female urology is a classic. Through his influences, Max Broedel, the great medical artist, came from Germany to Hopkins, and his early operations created at Hopkins are preserved in the beautiful illustrations, in color, which Broedel made. In later years Broedel's school of medical artists, at Hopkins, became world renowned.

Under Dr. Kelly, Dr. Thomas S. Cullen started the "GYN" pathology laboratory, which was the mother laboratory of most of the gynecological laboratories in this country. Until 1960, it was always required that the resident in

Dr. C. Bernard Brack (1907-1963).

gynecology spend one entire year of his training in the GYN pathological lab at Hopkins.

When Dr. Kelly retired as Gynecologist in Chief in 1919, Dr. Cullen was appointed Visiting Gynecologist in charge, and eventually succeeded Dr. Kelly.

In 1890, Dr. Cullen, a young Canadian, came to attend the first post-graduate course in gynecology which Dr. Kelly gave, and stayed on to assist in the "GYN" operating room, built in 1891.

In 1905, Dr. Cullen wrote an article, which the *Ladies Home Journal* published, publicizing the symptoms of uterine cancer. It was a revolutionary step to mention the word, let alone print it, and Dr. Cullen showed great courage to do so.

This form of cancer has ever been subject to particular investigation among Hopkins gynecologists. When the radium clinic was started in the Woman's Clinic, in 1940, American women began to receive irradiation therapy for carcinoma of the cervix.

Dr. C. Bernard Brack, who was the original pioneer in this work, died of cancer which many medical men thought had been brought on by radium exposure. It was a rare type of cancer. His courage sustained him to the end and his friends last saw him at a luncheon for 800 people which was arranged by the Board of Directors of the Baltimore Symphony, of which he was president. He lived for many months in Marburg and discussed his case daily with Dr. Blalock, who had operated on him, and with the radiologists who were treating him. The hospital took care of him with grief — and pride. He was 55 years old when he died. And the reader already knows him by the same name that his many hospital friends did, "Bozo."

Some of the men who did that early work are still in practice. To date they have seen and treated more women for this type of cancer (of the cervix) than any men in America, and their cure rate in the early cases is almost 100%.

Based on brilliant studies done in Harriet Lane, regarding the diagnosis and treatment of endocrine disorders in childhood and adolescence, there have been worked out, in the Woman's Clinic, a gynecologically feasible procedure for the correction of hermaphrodites. The operation was done a number of times in the early sixties at Hopkins, but it has now become much more infrequent. Probably this is because other gynecologists elsewhere have learned to do the operation and so admission of such patients here is not necessary.

There is an amusing gynecological story regarding a resident, about to operate on a woman who weighed 400 pounds, who had an ectopic pregnancy and was bleeding, internally. The surgeon turned to the assisting interns and said, "Remember, when last seen I was entering the peritoneum of this elephant. Better tie a string to me, boys."

Thanks to the example Dr. Kelly set, these Hopkins gynecologists have been a group of textbook producers. One of the leading textbooks on operative gynecology now in use is the work of the Professor Emeritus; the textbook on gynecological pathology, which is also a very popular undergraduate textbook, was done by a former staff member, the late Dr. Emil Novak.

Now that there is so much talk of tearing down the Woman's Clinic, or placing the gyn-obs patients elsewhere in a new building, an historical paragraph about the women and the work done there seems in order. The building which was remodelled to form the east wing (A) of the present Woman's Clinic, according to

Dr. Chesney, was completed in 1894 for the exclusive use of colored patients.*

As one Hopkins nurse who has spent her entire life in the Hopkins Hospital said last fall, "I know nearly every man, woman, and child in East Baltimore. I've bathed them as babies in the Woman's Clinic, and nursed them and bathed them again, as women and men in Halsted and Osler. And I loved with all my heart to hear them sing. Every afternoon, when the porches were still on those three buildings, before they were glassed in, and the patients were rolled out onto them, the singing would spring up and go from floor to floor, building to building, until the entire back yard of the hospital was athrob with spirituals. 'Steal away — steal away to Jesus — steal away home!' I can hear them now! It was wonderful, wonderful when they'd go into 'Onward Christian Soldiers,' or 'What a Friend We Have in Jesus.' All the patients from Marburg, Wilmer, and Harriet Lane on the upper corridors lying in the sunshine would listen, too. It was hard times, then, the depression was on and we were all so poor; but everybody was so polite and the patients were so grateful. I loved being at Hopkins. Just LOVED it. Everybody did!"

Three medical schools in the country had their gynecological and their obstetrical training separated. They were Harvard, Syracuse, and Hopkins. When the Professor Emeritus, the first full Professor in gynecology, who was also the first resident in gynecology in the Woman's Clinic, retired, and the Professor Emeritus of obstetrics retired — both July 1, 1960 — the two professorships were combined under a single man. A recent portrait-photograph of him, Dr. Allan C. Barnes, is hung in the clinic.

He has gone elsewhere and the position is now filled by a newly-appointed Gynecologist-Obstetrician-in-Chief, a brilliant young man, 40 years old.

The hospitals and medical schools enumerated in *Hopkins Is the Neighborhood Hospital of the World* frequently ask for, as exchange professors upon their faculties, a famous husband and wife gynecological-obstetrical team, both of whom are Hopkins graduates and Woman's Clinic trained. Another Woman's Clinic trained man, the Professor of Gynecology-Obstetrics, who is also the Associate Professor of Pathology, has been declared by post-doctoral students from other countries as "the finest teacher I have ever had"; and he, too, is in demand as an exchange professor.

Dr. Howard A. Kelly separated the two services when he made Dr. J. Whitridge Williams head of the outpatient obstetrical service in 1894, and of the inpatient in 1896. Prior to that Dr. Kelly had been Obstetrician-in-Chief. The full professors who have gone out from the system of separation and the textbooks which have been produced under it are of world renown. The incoming Professor of the joint services has a noble heritage in the Woman's Clinic of brilliant accomplishment.

Dr. J. Whitridge Williams, who was from 1899 until 1931 Obstetrician-in-Chief of the hospital, found time during those years to write his definitive book, which has been revised by his successor. He found time, also, to serve as Dean of the Johns Hopkins Medical School from 1911 to 1923 and was greatly beloved by the boys.

---

* The Johns Hopkins Hospital and the Johns Hopkins University School of Medicine. Alan M. Chesney, M.D., Volume I (The Johns Hopkins Press, (1943).

As so much of an obstetrician's time is perforce spent in waiting, and his office was also adjacent to the Medical School, Dr. Williams was usually available to his boys at all hours and became their confidant, as well as their adviser. He knew a lot about getting into life, but he knew even more about how to get through it. One of his residents, who is now President Planned Parenthood World Population (OHH JHMS 1923), wrote a most charming biographical sketch of him after his death. Among other things he states: "He was by all odds the most popular teacher in the Medical School. He gave a justly celebrated course in anecdotal midwifery. His supply of stories was inexhaustible and he told them in a rare Rabelaisian vein completely unmindful that a half-a-dozen women medical students were present. I have frequently heard that Gertrude Stein, the famous authoress, left medical school because of this. It is reported that she went to Dr. Williams and complained that he was so unnecessarily outspoken in his classes that she had decided to remain away. Dr. Williams said that since they were a part of the curriculum and since he was free to teach them as he wished, he was forced to require her presence or ask her to withdraw from the school. This she did, which some may consider a boon to modern literature."

Apropos of this, during the eclipse of the sun on a summer afternoon, in the early 1930's, a woman in labor was walking up and down the gallery of the Woman's Clinic when a social worker approached her holding a piece of X-ray film and asked, "Don't you want to take this and look at it? It won't happen again for 50 years."

"Fifty years, huh? I sure does want to look at hit. Dis yeah thing I'se doin' happens reg'lar every year."

Outside of the eye operating rooms in Wilmer, those in the Woman's Clinic — 3 delivery and 5 operating rooms — are the only ones, except General Operating Rooms in the hospital. A total of 3,793 gynecological operations (3,550 eleven years ago) and 3,302 (607 eleven years ago) obstetrical operations were performed in 1971. An explanation concerning the increase in the obstetrical figure

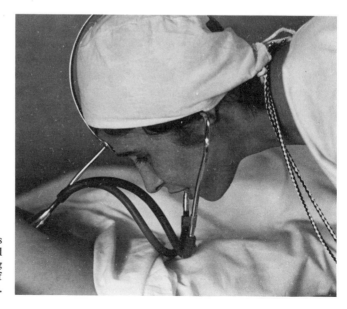

A nurse listens for a fetal heartbeat during a prenatal check of an expectant mother.

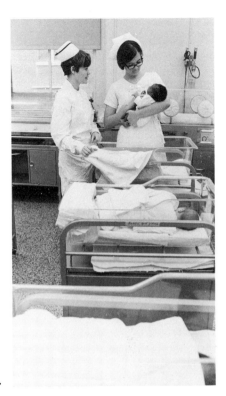

Nurses comfort a new born boy in the nursery.

is given later in this chapter.

To refer again to Dr. Williams. Once during prohibition, the Woman's Clinic developed an odd, but familiar, odor which turned out to be a barrel of hops owned by the interns, who were making their own beer and sterilizing their bottles in the Woman's Clinic sterilizers.

Dr. Williams had been Dean of the Medical School so long that nothing which a mere intern might do could frighten him. "Bull," as the medical students affectionately called him, mildly reprimanded the interns for using the sterilizer, but insisted that the barrel of mash move out. Due to a friendship between some housemen in the Woman's Clinic and some assistants in pathology, the barrel took up new quarters. And, in due time Dr. Williams was presented with several bottles of Hopkins beer, which he referred to most proudly as "My Boys' Brew."

Although an obstetrical hospital is always the happiest portion of a large general hospital — or used to be — not all of life in the Woman's Clinic was or is beer and skittles.

In 1971 there were 7,211 days of care to newborns of inpatient mothers, remaining in the Woman's Clinic, while the days of care of new borns in CMSC (the preemies) was 558.

In 1971, 1,670 babies were delivered in the Woman's Clinic. In 1970, the delivery rate was 2,156; in 1969, the figure was 2,286, while in 1968, it was 2,649. There is a steady decline in the birthrate, as you probably know from reading the press. Eleven years ago, the average number of babies delivered in a year here was 3,300 to 3,400.

From 1896 the number of delivered in the Hopkins Hospital to 1971 is

131

125,618. From 1958 through 1971, 35,558 babies were delivered.

The oldest person delivered in the Hopkins Hospital would now be 76 years old.

Of those 1,670 deliveries a year, 27% are private and semi-private patients, while 73% are semi-private patients were taken care of by the resident staff. Now, there is no flat rate for pre-natal, delivery and post-natal care for resident staff patients.

As doubtless you are aware of from the press, Maryland now has an abortion law and these are done at Hopkins according to the rules and regulations prescribed by the state law. The hospital does have a policy of aborting Marylanders first, so there are a minimal number of out-of-state abortions performed at Hopkins Hospital. How many have been performed in the last 10 years here is unknown; however, in 1971 about 1,600 were performed. The fee, if done in the Outpatient Department, is $100. Others are charged normal room, delivery room, operating room, and doctor rates.

Sterility operations are also performed both on the outpatient and inpatient level. There is a very active program on contraceptive devices — and the pill — held in the Dispensary. Also, any woman coming to these clinics with more than one illegitimate child is counselled by psychiatrists, social workers, and/or gynecologists and obstetricians.

The medical students come into the obstetrical service to work during their 3rd year, if they are going through in 4 years, and 4th year if they are going through in 5 years. They still function as "junior interns" handling ward (resident staff, OHH) patients under supervision. In the 3rd year, students have 2 hours of obs-gyn twice a week for 9 weeks. In the 4th year, they get 4½ weeks straight.

Midwifery is now a project of the School of Hygiene and graduate nurses taking the course receive a MPH, and are eligible for certification by the American College of Nurse Midwives. They get their clinical experience in the Woman's Clinic. Hopkins has been training nurse-midwives since 1956; and up until August of 1971 had turned out about 73 of these skilled women who now work throughout the United States, Europe and Africa.

Many of these nurse-midwives go into the mission field and do magnificent work for the remainder of their lives.

Each of the 66 bassinets in the Woman's Clinic has its own "work station," where all of the baby's feeding, bathing, measuring, and medication equipment is kept SEPARATELY for that baby ALONE. This is of paramount importance in the control of the deadly "staph" infection which still stalks American hospitals, and cannot be stressed too constantly in combating the infection.

Much current research is going on in the Woman's Clinic, as usual. A study has been carried out to determine mechanisms by which various materials are transferred from the mother to the infant across the placenta; this has increased the knowledge regarding the passage of water and sugar to the fetus.

There is also a clarification of the changes in metabolism during pregnancy and a current study is being made to view hormonal control of the environment within the uterus during pregnancy.

Studies have been begun to measure the psycho-social factors which precede and follow the search for and the performance of abortion. Newer surgical methods and more effective systems of service are being investigated and implemented.

In 1964, the year of the 75th anniversary of Hopkins Hospital, an assistant professor of Gynecology-Obstetrics, International Health, Population Dynamics, at Hopkins, developed an ingeniously simple method for women to receive a cytologic (cell study) examination by taking a sample of body cells at home with a pipette, and mailing it to Johns Hopkins for analysis. He stated that 2% of the women in the United States are affected by cervical cancer needlessly, which is "more curable than appendicitis." The method has caught on like wild-fire and in the long history of the Hopkins Hospital, his work will certainly deserve high praise. Thousands of women have had their lives saved thanks to his effort.

By 1967, the Hopkins was studying 50,000 cervical smears a year obtained by this method.

There has recently been revived and refined at Hopkins a method of determining prenatal sex which has proved 95% accurate and will enable therapeutic abortions to be done with sexual accuracy on those hereditary deficiencies; among these are Tay-Sachs, and sickle cell anemia.

One of the things for which Dr. Williams was so famous was manipulating a fetus through a rachitic pelvis, a malformation frequently seen among colored people, which due to better nutrition has largely disappeared from obstetrical practice. Another thing which has disappeared is the service which used to be known as Externe Obstetrics in which a pupil nurse and a medical student, in the 4th year, went out and delivered babies in the patients' homes. Now, thanks to the great advances in public appreciation of the vastly better care such patients receive in the hospital, this clientele has ceased to be.

Recently a woman was in the Main Corridor looking for the "eternity ward;" and an intern she queried pointed toward the clergy office and quipped, "There it is!" Then he scrutinized her and said, "Where you want to go is the Woman's Clinic and you'd better get there, fast." Then he directed her to the door at the end of the corridor.

The building in which these two specialties — obstetrics and gynecology — have been practiced since its completion in 1923 was given by a patient of Dr. Barker's who knew Dr. Williams, Mrs. Lucy Wortham James of New York; and a drawing of her hangs opposite the elevators on the first floor of the clinic.

The Woman's Clinic has a total of 139 beds, and they stack up now as follows. Eleven private rooms for gyn-obs are on B4, while 35 resident staff semi-private beds are on A2 and 3; resident staff semi-private ones are on A3; 16 semi-private are on A3; 4 semi-private on B4 (obs); 25 resident or outside staff ones are on B2 and are semi-private; 28 resident or outside staff are on B3, obs semi-private; 17 active staff semi-private are on A4, for gyn, only. All of this totals to 11 private, 62 semi-private, 66 resident staff, and the 66 bassinets are (24 on 2nd floor, 25 on 3rd floor, 17 on 4th floor.

All of the babies occupying these are under the care of those CMSC pediatricians who, as previously described, know the VERY shortest distance between there and the Woman's Clinic. The nurseries they enter are broken down into small units; and every man has to be in sterile cap, gown, and mask before he enters.

Perhaps the next door relationship between Pathology and the Woman's Clinic has had something to do with it, but research is forever going on among these obstetricians and gynecologists, and they are frequently explaining their "finds" at CPC.

133

The delivery rooms in this building are on the 5th floor and the GYN operating rooms are on the 6th floor.

Outside the nursery on the 4th floor is a veritable portrait gallery of the Greats in these two services. Dr. J. Whitridge Williams and Dr. Howard A. Kelly are there; and Dr. Kelly has his rose, as usual, in his buttonhole. He always said to anybody who complimented it, "See how fresh this rose is; this is how I keep it so." Then he would show the glass vial filled with water under his lapel and continue, "Water to that rose is like prayer is to a Christian. Be sure you use it to keep your soul alive."

Dr. Thomas S. Cullen's portrait is here too, as are the other famous gyne-cologists: Dr. Edward H. Richardson, Dr. R. W. TeLinde, and Dr. Guy Hunner. Again, you are abreast of the long history of the Hopkins Hospital when you look at these portraits for many of them were painted by Dr. Hunner's daughter, Isabella Hunner Parsons. More of her portraits hang throughout the hospital than those of any other artist except Thomas Corner, also a Baltimorean. Both Mrs. Parsons and her husband, Dr. John W. Parsons have died since this book was first published and

The portrait of Dr. Houston S. Everett recently added to the 4th floor collection is done by his daughter, Martha Everett Peterson.

OHH will be most interested to learn that an endowment fund in their memory was established in the Hopkins Medical School, in 1969, by their daughter, "to provide financial assistance to needy and worthy students in the School of Medicine."

There must be something about gynecologists which breeds "artist daugh-ters" for a recent addition to this medical portrait gallery is a splendid portrait of the Associate Professor Emeritus of Gynecology and Obstetrics, painted by his youngest daughter. He has spent his entire medical life working in and for The Johns Hopkins Hospital. He is Dr. Houston S. Everett, and mentioned here by name because all of these portraits hang in the corridor on the 4th floor of the Woman's Clinic between buildings A and B, which leads to the delivery rooms. A Hopkins sightseer is not welcome here. As soon as one steps from the elevator, one sees a large sign which says: SILENCE. And quiet must and does prevail.

Even the streets surrounding The Hopkins Hospital are hallowed ground, and the following story is included in this chapter so that you may forever after remember where you are, when you walk upon them.

The southeast corner of Monument and Broadway, at 4:00 A.M. was not always a place no medical student would dare to venture. On the wall of the expectant-fathers' waiting room, on the 4th floor of the Woman's Clinic hangs the portrait of the late Dr. John M. Bergland. On his 76th birthday, March 5, 1955, he told a reporter from THE SUN this experience.

On a hot August morning, in 1904, he won a lifelong victory over fear when he decided "women were hard to kill". He had delivered babies under experienced supervision, previously, but that summer day, as a Hopkins intern he was on his own in an obscure little house 3 blocks from the Hospital. In the early morning hours, a frantic father came to the hospital beseeching aid for his unmarried, 16 year old daughter who had produced a child, but needed immediate aid. With a senior medical student and a nurse, the intern went to the house where the young mother was hemorrhaging. They were not able, through pressure to bring about the expulsion of the placenta. The patient's pulse faltered. No telephone, no ambulance were available. They scribbled a note to the assistant resident, but he could not correct the situation, either. So the girl, weighing 150 pounds, and now unconscious had to be taken to the hospital. How? Medical equipment and the baby had to go, as well as the dead weight patient. The baby and equipment were carried ahead by the others.

The intern and the medical student carried the mother. At Broadway and Monument Street, their own strength failed.

"We squatted on our heels, holding the girl across our thighs, to try to rest a little. By this time the bed clothing had fallen away from the body of the nude patient. Hemorrhage continued.

"An unidentified workman with a lunch pail contributed the added muscles. Dawn long since had come and the remarkable tableau was clearly visible.

"Inside the hospital, the placenta, which had created the problem took care of itself. The girl and her baby lived.

"A great obstetrician had come of age."

In a final paragraph THE SUN concludes: "Generations of Marylanders of wealth and position have been born with the help of his wisdom, but Dr. Bergland measures also in his career thousands of others in slum homes, which he reached either by trolley or on foot. From North Avenue to the waterfront he followed the stork, but not once since that August in 1904 has Dr. Bergland been afraid."

It is axiomatic that a woman forgets her labor pains, but no woman forgets when she leaves the hospital with her babies within her arms. Someone gave a fund for her to do this under shelter, and hence the portecochere. For many years this triumphal exit was made under a huge umbrella, which many a Baltimore grandmother recalls.

One of the nicest honors ever to come to any man trained in the Woman's Clinic is that there is now a loan fund for students in the School of Medicine, given by a grateful patient, and named for a gynecologist (OHH: JHMS, 1915) still practicing at Hopkins, whose son (OHH: JHMS, 1947) and namesake is also practicing there.

Medical Students Will Wear You Out

Medical students will wear you out
        Near about!
Medical students will drive you crazy
        They're so lazy.
Medical students will frighten you to pieces
        And scare your nieces.
Medical students will cut you up
        If you ain't looking, while you're cooking.
Medical students will give you pills
        Which cause chills.
Medical students will turn and stare,
        They don't care.
Medical students will remember like 'elle-fants'
        If you give 'em the chance.
Medical students are filled with gore
        And they slam the door.
Medical students keep bottles under their beds
        And hands that are dead.
Medical students dissect a fly
        Just to look into his eye.
Medical students are full of the Devil
        And pass it out on the absolute level.
They'll worry you, pester you, drive you to drink
        And then put a skeleton under your sink.
Medical students are hard to endure
        If you are pious and proper and peaceful and pure.

Where the Students Come in

THE Women's Liberation movement missed a golden opportunity when they failed to give praise where praise is due. The most amazing building still standing at Hopkins — and still in use — is on the corner of Monument and Wolfe Streets, right next to the Welch Library and it is named "The Women's Fund Building." Every medical student has to pass it every day, one way or another, and here is its history.

When the hospital was finished there wasn't any money to build the Medical School; and a committee of ladies, mostly daughters of the Trustees, set about raising money, nationally. Miss M. Carey Thomas, who established the Bryn Mawr School for Girls in Baltimore and became president of Bryn Mawr College, backed them up as did Dr. Mary Putnam Jacobi in New York, and Mrs., S. Weir Mitchell in Philadelphia, among others. They got stuck at $109,000 and Miss Mary E. Garrett, whose father had been president of the B. & O. Railroad, offered to give $100,000 more, provided women would be admitted to the Medical School on the same terms as men. Financially, this history becomes too involved to cover in detail. Suffice to say, Miss Garrett gave $354,764.50 in all toward the project and demanded, too, that all medical students must be college graduates and have had two years of German and French.

Dr. Osler is said to have told Dr. Welch that he was very glad he wasn't trying to qualify, for he doubted if he could have passed the entrance requirements to the Hopkins Medical School. Nevertheless, the Women's Fund Building was erected and the first class of students, 15 in number, entered in 1893. ("Eight city medical schools, white and colored, turning out graduates now existed in Baltimore.") *

Through some method of finagling, though, in the last 11 years the ladies' stern edict has been eroded away. There are now 3 types of medical students at Hopkins. Those admitted on 4 year programs, "must have the B. A. degree or its equivalent *prior* to matriculation." Those admitted on the 5 year program have had "at least 2 years in attendance at an accredited institution. Students must complete the requirements for the B. A. degree during the first 2 years of the program; this degree will be awarded by the Faculty of Arts and Sciences at the end of Year II."

They still take students in the 3rd and 4th years from other schools, but only after severe scrutiny. Also, men who already have an M.D. degree may enter Hopkins as postdoctoral students. One may also now get an M.D.–Ph.D from Hopkins, but it is too complicated a course of study to describe here.

When pinned down by the ladies at the Hamilton Street Club, where he was

---

* When The Hopkins Came to Baltimore, A. K. Bond, M.D. The Pegasus Press, Baltimore, 1927.

The Women's Fund
Memorial Building houses
the Anatomy department.

lecturing, the Dean who resigned in September, 1971, admitted a couple of years ago that there were certain students in the Hopkins Medical School on "special admissions."

Also, the old figure of 75 students within a class has gone with the wind, too. In 1961, the class was increased to 90 students, and in 1965 to 95, and in 1970-1971 to 115.

As of 1971, house, food, books, tuition, medical care, telephone bills for a medical student cost about $7,200 per year for everything; tuition had increased to $2,750. Here is how these figures break down: Books, $200; Rent, $924; Utilities, $300; Food, $1,140; Miscellaneous, $1,000 (clothes, etc.); Phone, $150; Entertainment, $350; Microscope rent, $68.91 a year. Also included is one Round-trip home, and Tuition.

If you are thinking of leaving an endowment to put a medical student through Hopkins, brace yourself. It will take at least $70,000, because you'll need 9% money, as the University nicks the Medical School 3% for handling such funds.

This year (1972) Hopkins received about 1,800 applications for a class of 115 students. (1,500 more applications than last year.)

Many of the professors will tell you that this present crop of students is much more interested in being of service to humanity and much less interested in being financially successful than were their recent predecessors. They are all tremendously fired up over the two Health Care Programs Hopkins is so deeply involved in. The one in Columbia, Maryland, serves a population of 10,000 people, at present. Columbia now has 13,000 inhabitants and is expected to grow to 110,000 by 1982. The fee per family, regardless of the number of members, is $61.49 monthly, and that covers hospitalization as well as health care. A hospital is being built there and the whole Columbia project is staffed by Hopkins men and backed financially by the Connecticut General Life Insurance Company. It is anticipated that it will be self-supporting within two years.

Medical students in advanced years work there, too; and one advantage it has is that it brings them in contact with the middle-class patient from whom a doctor generally derives his income.

A similar set-up, as regards the clinic facilities, has been started in East Baltimore several blocks away from Hopkins; and this was financed by Federal, State, and City agencies. Here, too, the members pay a modest stipend.

The center will ultimately serve 25,000 residents of East Baltimore, and the medical students are highly enthusiastic about the project. When one points out to them that in the first 6 months the Hopkins Hospital was open, 10,000 patients were seen in the Dispensary, by a staff of 11 men, they cannot believe what you say. In January, 1890, 6,000 of those patients were seen. To older OHH these present do-gooders have a very provoking way of seeming to be the first people to work at the Hopkins Hospital who ever helped or knew, the poor.

Regarding these two clinics, the *Carnegie Quarterly,* summer, 1970, says, "Furthermore, they will stimulate a rethinking of the traditional approach to medical education, at Hopkins at least. And when Hopkins rethinks, so do most of the medical schools in the country."

The fact that all the specialists are under one roof, the patients know precisely what they have to pay, and that they see the same doctor repeatedly are tremendous advantages. And it is to be hoped that waiting times may be cut down through prior engagement systems.

Another "new" for Hopkins happened in these 11 years, too, and it happened twice. In 1966, Dr. F. Peyton Rous, won the Nobel Prize in Medicine. He was a graduate in the class of 1905 and spent his entire professional life at the Rockefeller Institute. On March 9, 1970, JAMA said of him: "The Nobel Laureate who first demonstrated the viral etiology of some animal cancers is himself dead of cancer at the age of 90."

Dr. H. Keffer Hartline, a graduate of the class of 1927, received a Nobel Prize in Medicine in 1967 for his work in the primary chemical and physiological processes in the eye. He succeeded in demonstrating the reaction pattern of individual vision to variations in kinds and amounts of light.

In 1967, the Nobel Prize for Medicine was awarded to Dr. H. Keffer Hartline, who graduated from Hopkins in the class of 1927 and is now at the Rockefeller Institute. The *Johns Hopkins Journal* says of him: "Former biophysics department chairman . . . a specialist in how visual cells send messages to the brain, Dr. Hartline shares the award with two other scientists for work on the 'primary chemical and physiological processes of the eye.' "

Also in this epoch, the hospital became 75 years old (1964), the Medical School became 75 years (1968), and 4 of the Stalwarts of Hopkins died: Miss Lawler, Dr. Winford Smith, Dr. Blalock, and the great historian of the Medical School and the hospital, Dr. Alan M. Chesney.

When the first edition of this book was being written, 12 years ago, the author went over to see Dr. Chesney in the office in which he was writing his monumental, definitive, magnificent history: *The Johns Hopkins Hospital and The Johns*

Hopkins University School of Medicine, which should be required reading for every medical student.

Like so many things at Hopkins, what one saw and heard was obviously true, and quite unbelievable, simultaneously.

The office was a small obscure room in the Hunterian Building, behind the Women's Fund Building, and was reached via a freight elevator. The whole floor reeked of animal odors and sounds. The latter, Dr. Chesney could not hear and the former, he ignored. In the small office was a single north window, a flat-topped desk, his desk chair, two metal filing cabinets, innumerable books stacked against the wall and mounds of papers on the desk. He even had to go elsewhere and borrow a plain classroom chair for his guest to sit upon. On his desk was also a long, yellow, ruled, rectangular pad of paper; and it was upon this in long hand that he penned his accurate, brilliant history.

In speaking of the author's project he insisted, "You be sure you describe those 3 meetings with which this chapter of the book you are thumbing through begins. They laid down in those meetings the whole structure and future of a great medical school, and thanks to those meetings, we've got one." Attending those 3 meetings were: President Gilman, Dr. Billings, Professor Remsen, and Professor Martin.

To return to his own writing, Dr. Chesney had a faithful typist who, several times a week, took his accumulated pages and typed them. His writing was very clear, his mind extremely lucid, and there were few corrections.

Because of his great knowledge and intense interest in acquiring more knowledge there was a strange, forever youthful, quality about this sandy-haired, gentle, blue-eyed, almost totally deaf man, who listened acutely with all of his perceptive faculties (and a hearing aid he loathed).

He said that when he first embarked upon his history, he was in the office of the then Director of the hospital, Dr. Winford Smith, and with the Director's permission began rummaging in an old. recently found, safe.

A typical late summer afternoon Baltimore thunderstorm was brewing. He still rummaged and found nothing of particular significance. The storm struck; he felt the alteration in the temperature, but paid scant heed, for by then he had found a hidden compartment and unearthed therefrom the minutes of the meetings of the first 3 years of the Board of Trustees of the brand new hospital! The first secretary had carefully recorded everything and the man for whom he had so valiantly labored was painstakingly reading all he had written.

When Dr. Chesney looked up because of the fading light, the storm was over, west Baltimore was ablaze with a glorious sunset, and the Hopkins Hospital and Medical School had found their historian.

He was deaf — but so was Beethoven and their endless, alone, and very great works will long endure.

Here are the paragraphs to which Dr. Chesney referred:

Before Dr. Welch had even been invited to come to Baltimore, on January 2, 9, and 16, 1884, President Gilman, Dr. Billings, Professor Remsen, and Professor Martin had three meetings in which they outlined precisely what they wished the Medical School to be and to do. In the first meeting they decided they would have only students, who had a "general liberal education." They would provide instruction in all branches of medical and surgical art, encourage research, and obtain the proper teachers and laboratories therefor. They agreed, also, that they would take men having an M.D. who wished to do advanced study.

In the second meeting they set down precisely what a candidate had to know to get in. He had to know enough mathematics, Latin, and English to qualify for "Course III" at the university; enough French and German to translate ordinary prose at sight; enough physics, chemistry, general biology and physiology and histology to be acceptable in "Course III." For the other courses usually given in "Course III" to provide a liberal education, he could substitute Greek or more mathematics or more Latin; or a more thorough study of logic, ethics, and psychology than "Course III" required.

They also decreed that "the Faculty should have the power to test in every case the fitness of a candidate by examination in such subjects as they believed desirable, quite apart from any testimonials, diplomas, or certificates presented by the candidate."

In the third meeting, they studied the catalogues of the leading German, French, English, and American medical schools, decided they came up to required standard, but also decided that no medical school worthy of a university could be operated without hospital wards. They did think, however, that it might be feasible to start courses before the hospital was opened in experimental and comparative pathology, experimental therapeutics, and pathological histology and chemistry. Therefore they decided to have medical fellowships in the laboratories for men not permitted to practice, whose income would be board and lodging in the hospital, if they wished to devote themselves to clinical study; or an annual stipend for men who desired, in the laboratories and wards, to qualify themselves as teachers or experts in pathology, medical jurisprudence, hygiene.

They knew what they wanted. They made it plain in September, 1884, when Dr. Welch came to Baltimore to implement their desires.

It is interesting to note that when those three momentous meetings regarding the Medical School were held, President Gilman was 54 years old; Dr. Billings, 46; and Dr. Newell Martin, 36. Dr. Martin was supposed to be the first Professor of Physiology in the Medical School, but when he came to Baltimore in 1876, at the age of 28, he was made Professor of Biology and soon organized a biological lab, which became a great center of physiological research. In that captivating little book *When The Hopkins Came to Baltimore,* Dr. Bond, who was one of the Baltimore students working in that lab, describes Dr. Martin as a man who had "a fascination for his students. He had a poor delivery; but the most intelligent blue eyes I have ever seen, and when he was stirred up over some scientific recital they fairly danced with excitement." Many brilliant young men were attracted to work under him; the local ones had names some of which still echo in the Hopkins' corridors: Woods, Trimble, Thomas.

The present Professor of Physiology says, "Dr. Martin was a very great Physiologist. He was the first man to work with an isolated heart preparation, and he trained half a dozen of the first Professors of Physiology, including our first, Dr. Howell."

He had been born in Ireland, educated at the University College in London, and later became a fellow at Trinity College, Cambridge, from whence he came to Hopkins. As already stated he was to have been the first Professor of Physiology at JHMS; but, alas, tuberculosis sapped his strength. He resigned and returned to

England, where he died at the age of 45. While in Baltimore, he married a daughter of General Ewell, of Confederate fame.

Hopkins owes much to this brilliant, stimulating young man.

Of all the portions of the Johns Hopkins Medical Institutions, none has required the services of as many heads as the Medical School. Dr. Welch held this position from 1893 to 1898; Dr. Osler from 1898 to 1899; Dr. William H. Howell from 1899 to 1911; Dr. J. Whitridge Williams from 1911 to 1923; Dr. Lewis H. Weed from 1923 to 1929; Dr. Alan M. Chesney from 1929 to 1953 and Dr. Philip Bard from 1953 to 1957; Dr. Thomas B. Turner from 1957 to 1968; Dr. David E. Rogers, 1968 to 1971 and the present Dean, who took over in mid-September, 1971. He is the former Professor of Radiological Science and Chairman of that department in the School of Hygiene and Public Health and Professor of Radiology and Director of that department in the School of Medicine, and Radiologist-in-Chief of The Johns Hopkins Hospital. Also, he is a long time Great Favorite of medical students. His radiological reports at CPC conferences were vastly respected and much enjoyed by those ever-critical students.

In the early 1960's, Dr. Chesney embarked upon the third volume of his history of the Hospital and the Medical School, and was fortunate enough to finish it before he died in the fall of 1964. Dr. Turner is now carrying on Dr. Chesney's great work and has also written a fine book *Accounting of a Stewardship,* being a record of the Medical School during the years he was Dean. The fourth and eighth of these Deans were graduated from the University of Maryland Medical School.

There is no doubt that medical students will keep you on your toes, but they will also provide you with an everlasting capacity to work, if you survive them, as witness Dr. Chesney and Dr. Turner. To June, 1971, 5,544 students "endured" these 9 deans, and were graduated; more than 4,000 of these graduates are believed to be alive. Another 405 students started but failed to complete the medical course.

From the day a boy enters Medical School, he is always considered as belonging to the Hopkins Hospital community. In fact, the first time the Dean ever addresses himself to the entering class is either in Hurd Hall, off the Main Corridor, on in the "new" auditorium, directly across from the canteen shop. After that meeting, a Hopkins medical student has the right to go about the hospital at will.

The following paragraphs are included for the interest of all OHH and complied from the catalogues of the School of Medicine for 1960-61 and 1970-71. The figures for 1960-61 are put in parenthesis. There were (322) students of which (24) were in year I and (20) were women. At present there are 427 students of which 21 are in year I, and there are 45 women. The faculty numbered (760) of which (1) full-time Professor was a woman, while on the faculty in all there were (74) women. Now the faculty numbers 941, and there is no full-time woman professor, but there are 117 women on the faculty. In 1960-61 fellows were defined as "Fellowships constitute a category of Graduate Training in Medicine" and there were (491) of these, of which (26) were women. Now they are not defined in the catalogue and there are 1,267 fellows of which 96 are "Predoctoral students"; of that 1,267 fellows, 91 are women.

In 1960-61 tuition was ($1,200) per academic year and covered all normal charges except living expenses and student health fee. Accelerating students paid ($300) for required work in the summer session, and no tuition in Year V. Now the tuition is $2,750, covers what it did before and no mention is made concerning

Year V fees.

In 1960-61 the hospital had approximately (1,000) beds; now it has approximately 1,200; then it took care of (1,200) outpatients daily; now there are 1,700. In 1960-61, by departmental count in the Medical School catalogue, there were (120) full-time professors; now there are 248. Then there were (280) part-time professors; now there are 505. Also then, there were 180 clinic physicians and none are listed now. Then, there (220) interns and residents and now there are 365.

People have always WORKED hard at the Hopkins Hospital and certainly those 3 members of the first graduating class who were still alive 10 years ago wouldn't have batted an eye at that dispensary figure. They were veterans of the days when their teachers had among them those 11 men who cared for 6,000 dispensary patients in 1 month. Doubtless they regaled the 18 medical students comprising that first class, 3 of whom were women, with what a rough road lay ahead of them, once they got in the dispensary. Competing with the women in the classes has always been rough, too, for invariably they come from the *best* colleges. Of those first 3, Smith, Vassar and Wellesley each had a representative. The Vassar girl graduated from Hopkins Medical School; the others did not. The graduate's name was Mary S. Packard.

Oddly enough, those 3 members mentioned in this book 10 years ago, as then alive were all graduates of The Johns Hopkins University. They were the beloved and esteemed Dr. Louis P. Hamburger, who died in August, 1960; Dr. James F. Mitchell, who became a famous surgeon in Washington and died in May, 1961, and Dr. Eugene L. Opie, who went on to the Rockefeller Institute and became one of the leading pathologists of the world. Dr. Opie was a pioneer in the study of diabetes and his textbook, published in 1902, *Diseases of the Pancreas,* became a standard text in medical schools for decades. He died in March, 1971.

However famous Dr. Mitchell and Dr. Opie became in the outside world, though, they altered forever the lives of medical students at Hopkins. Dr. Osler was

The W. Barry Wood Building of the School of Medicine provides space for basic science departments and the Dean's Office. Dr. Wood, a graduate of the class of 1936, died in 1971. He served as Vice-President for Medical Affairs and later as Chairman of the Department of Microbiology.

Reed Hall, named for the late School of Hygiene Dean and University President Lowell J. Reed. It is a residence hall for single students, interns and residents.

opposed to taking transfer students and when Opie, who had had one year at the College of Physicians and Surgeons, in Baltimore, where his father was the Dean, applied to enter Hopkins, in 1894, Dr. Osler voted against permitting him to enter. At the next meeting of the Advisory Board, Dr. Osler was not present. The matter was re-opened after a brilliant young Canadian William George MacCallum was decided to be admitted on such a basis; Opie's backers (President Gilman and Dr. Remsen) described him again as having an "Excellent record as a student." When the matter came to a vote he was allowed to enter the second year class with a "condition in physiological chemistry."

Dr. Chesney remarks wryly, that it was most fortunate for Hopkins and the world that Dr. Osler was not present at that meeting!

Dr. Mitchell, when a medical student, was drafted by Dr. Finney, after Dr. Halsted refused to accept a nurse assigned to him without prior consultation, as head nurse of the General Operating Room, to act in that capacity in the operating room.

Mitchell, the medical student, acted as head nurse with such excellence that the nurses had difficulty making final peace and re-capturing their duties.

Thereby was started a precedent which still continues, for one of the Crimmins boys to whom the plaque in the Main Corridor of the hospital refers, and who was killed in World War II, was a scrub-up orderly in the General Operating Room before he went into the service; and recently there was a Homewood student, among the hospital volunteers, performing that same function, and intending to go into medicine, eventually.

The name of Dr. Hamburger brings to mind the reverence which Jewish doctors have ever commanded in this medical school and hospital. Dr. Simon Flexner trained here; Abraham Flexner used his influence to bolster and to get money for this medical school; Dr. Charles R. Austrian was a long time member of the Medical Board and Chairman of the Private Ward Medical Committee. He was a great clinician and a noble friend. He said, to a complaining patient, during the last spring of his life, "Pain is a yardstick. When you are in pain, you are alive. When I'm out of pain, I'll be dead." Dr. Joseph L. Lilienthal and Dr. I. William Nachlas have left work and reputations which other men might envy. Another among these, Dr. Jonas S. Friedenwald, when he was dying, never had time to die, so busy was he trying to complete his monumental research upon glaucoma. And the Alan Bernstein Memorial Wing has just been added in Osler, and will be a great adjunct in the teaching of medicine there.

Since the hospital opened its doors, Hopkins has been fortunate in its great Jewish physicians, brilliant pathologists, fine pediatricians and psychiatrists, excellent obstetricians and gynecologists and brilliant ophthalmologists. The Star of David as well as the Star of Bethlehem has shone over His hospital and medical school. These Jewish doctors have been superb teachers, too.

Of the 41 scholarship funds listed as available at the Johns Hopkins Medical School, 10 of them were given by or in memory of Jews. Of these 41 funds, 3 are to be used specifically for women medical students, 1 of these being the fund from the Johns Hopkins Women's Medical Alumnae Association, called the Florence Rena Sabin Scholarship Fund. She was a member of the Class of 1900 JHMS, and is the first citizen of Colorado honored by a statue in the rotunda of the Capitol in Washington. The statue shows her seated in a laboratory chair, dressed in a laboratory coat. She taught in the Hopkins Medical School from 1902 to 1924, was a member of the Rockefeller Institute 1925 to 1938, and head of the Colorado Public Health 1944 to 1953. She was the first woman ever appointed to the staff of the Rockefeller Institute and the first woman to be made a life member of the National Academy of Science. Regarding the scholarships, the income is available for "deserving women medical students of academic distinction and promise, preferably a student entering in Year II."

There is also an endowed scholarship for qualified Chinese students, or if there are not qualified applicants, then it is to be used for students of other foreign nationalities, or the third preference is for American students. It was left by the late Dr. David J. Carver.

A fund established in 1958, principally through the efforts of Dr. Lawrence S. Kubie is specifically for Negro students at JHMS who need financial help; or for promising Negro applicants who seem deficient these funds may be applied to post-graduate, premedical training, if the Committee on Admission so recommends. After such training, the student's application will be reconsidered.

Also, medical students in Years II, III, IV, V are eligible to apply for scholarships under the Health Professions Scholarship Program.

There are 10 loan funds, too, and of these 2 are by grateful patients in memory of still living doctors. Of these 10, one is the Health Professions Assistance Act Loan Program, by which medical students in Years II-V are eligible to apply for long-term loans under the Health Professions Assistance Act of 1963. Year I students are eligible to apply for loans under the National Defense Student Loan Program.

It all sounds like a lot of money is available, but it doesn't seem to be when you are trying to qualify for a loan or a scholarship. If a man wants to get a long-time good out of his money, for the most benefit to the most people, he should leave it for a medical student scholarship.

No student enters this school who has not been subject to careful screening. Of the 8 member Admissions Committee each member devotes the equivalent of four 40-hour weeks to the task of screening applicants. If possible, a student comes for a personal interview to the Medical School; if impossible, he is interviewed by one of the Hopkins men in the locality where he lives and the interview is carefully reported to the Dean.

In 1971 the applications total 2,787 for Year II program; 275 for advanced standing; 218 for Year I program. The tabulation by geographical area of the entrants were: Alabama 4, Arizona 2, Arkansas 1, California 17, Colorado 2, Connecticut 11, District of Columbia 3, Delaware 1, Florida 17, Georgia 6, Hawaii 3, Idaho 1, Illinois 29, Indiana 10, Iowa 3, Kansas 6, Kentucky 4, Louisiana 3, Maine 2, Maryland 47, Massachusetts 26, Michigan 13, Minnesota 4, Mississippi 3, Missouri 5, Nebraska 2, New Hampshire 1, New Jersey 33, New Mexico 1, New York 79, North Carolina 5, Ohio 26, Oklahoma 4, Pennsylvania 30, Rhode Island 2, South Carolina 4, South Dakota 1, Tennessee 7, Texas 11, Utah 2, Virginia 8, Washington 4, West Virginia 5, Wisconsin 8, Canada 2, England 1, Iran 1, Mexico 1, The West Indies 3.

Since the majority of students go through in the 4 year course, no extensive effort is made here to cover the courses offered in the 5-year course. In the 4-year course, you get to the cadavers, as you always did (benefit OHH) but now 4 students work on a single one, one of whom is the reader, a second the dissector, the third the describer, and the fourth member is the writer. (This terminology was supplied by a medical student and needs no explanation.) The Anatomy Department is still in the Women's Fund Building, only now they get away with calling it the Anatomy Building. Histology is here, too; but the student's microscopes, as already stated, are still on the second floor of the Pathology Building, except for the ones necessary for teaching purposes, here.

Another change is that these students get over into the hospital, in their first year, in an introduction course to psychiatry and the behavioral sciences, and also one in medicine. Their courses are so arranged that they have 2 free afternoons a week and at least half of Saturday is free. In their second year, although they continue in the basics, they have many elective courses and one whole quarter is free to use as they desire.

In their third year and fourth years they are back among all the old faithfuls: medicine, neurology, radiology, surgery, pediatrics, gyn-obs, and psychiatry. They serve a medicine clerkship,, surgery clerkship, pediatric clerkship, one in gyn-obs and one in psychiatry.

A clerkship means not only is the student working constantly in the hospital with the patients. He would have graded responsibilities at the level of his competence at that time in his training.

He may be full of knowledge when he graduates, but he is not full of ignorance on how to learn more, and the faculty feels that he faces his future training with more maturity than formerly.

To take care of this great influx in student-increase, at all levels, the Hunterian Building was renovated in 1962. The Basic Science Building was opened in 1959; the Biophysics Building in 1961; the swimming pool was built behind Reed Hall in 1961; the Children's Medical and Surgical Center, Hoffberger Research Wing, and the Wilmer Research Building were all built in 1962-1963; the addition was put on Reed Hall in 1966; the Kennedy Institute was built in 1967; and the Traylor Postdoctoral Building and the Turner Auditorium Complex were built in 1968.

Regarding the Traylor Building, according to the Development Officer for the JHMS (Fund raiser, OHH), "Mr. Traylor just came along, and said he was grateful to and admired the Hopkins and would like to give them a million dollars for something they *really* needed. What was it?" When they caught their breath, they replied, "A research building. *Entirely,* for research." Again, according to the

Students attend a session
in a Turner Building seminar room.

fund raiser, "He said, 'All right' and made out a check. He never bothered anybody anymore and when the building was completed, he came for the opening. That portrait which hangs in the lobby is of his father, Mr. Samuel W. Traylor, Sr., who was a Texan. He later settled in Allentown, Pennsylvania, where he became a financier, manufacturer of heavy equipment and mining developer, with international interests."

Then the Development Officer for JHMS looked off into the distance and said to himself, almost, "I often dream how nice it would be if I could meet another man like him!"

The Traylor is a beautiful, completely modern building devoted entirely to pure research "as it applies to patient care." Here are a tremendous number of those "fellows" already spoken of elsewhere. The Postdoctoral Research Center of the Department of Medicine has the 8th and 9th floors, the physiology on the 8th and the biochemistry on the 9th. Neurology has the 7th floor and the neurology labs are on the 6th floor, the Pavlovian labs on the 7th. The laboratory of bio-medical engineering has the 5th floor; while the 3rd and 4th is given over to the Division of Otolaryngology, where Mr. Traylor's interest apparently originated. Also here are the electronics development, electron-microscopy, and the temporal bone bank, too. And computer speech is also here. The Endocrinology and Metabolic Disease Division is on the 3rd floor, too; while the 2nd is given over to gyn-obs laboratories. The 1st floor contains the lobby (ground floor, really) and the laboratory of animal medicine, and the veterinary medicine — the whole Department of Animal Medicine has been moved over here — with the exception of some experimental animals on top of Blalock and Wilmer. They have full operating facilities here and many experiments, the results of which will eventually move upstairs and after further testing into treatment of patients, are being conducted here.

A large segment of the postdoctoral fellows, listed previously in this chapter, work in this building and are in constant contact with their opposite number who work in the different departments of the hospital and affiliates.

In thousands of different places which the patient never sees, hundreds and hundreds of men are busy inventing, or refining or improving, methods, drugs, chemicals, types of treatment, for his betterment.

As to where some of these machines are, it should have been mentioned that in the Basic Science Building basement, is a vast quantity of machinery in rooms and laboratories, which is too heavy to be put higher and in constant use for a multitude of jobs to cut down cost and improve patient care. For instance, there is an electron magnet connected with various sorting machines, which will run tests on how penicillin works with different blood situations, or cells with oxygen or cells without oxygen may be measured or studied. All of these results go into a master sorter, connected with a computer which stores in its memory the results. Blood work which used to take hours and hours to be done in laboratories and which may have to be done quickly to save life can be accomplished here in seconds.

Another machine there, which was invented at Hopkins, uses the polarization of light in studying tissues run through different color syndromes.

The cost of this type of experimental machinery runs into the hundreds of thousands of dollars and many of these ideas being explored are fringe benefits from moon-shot medicine. Much of the work is financed by the NIH grants.

To return to the Postdoctoral Complex, which is what the Traylor-Turner

147

Auditorium is known as: one may go down the stairway from Rutland Street, past a playing fountain on the left, with the Turner Auditorium concourse beyond, (and the Traylor on the right) and enter the Johns Hopkins Medical Book Center. Very pleasant people run it, and people affiliated with the hospital or Medical School may purchase medical textbooks, all medical books published by Hopkins doctors (and they are expensive too; one recently revised Hopkins' doctor's textbook in 3 volumes costs $105; another Hopkins' doctor had an updated 3-volume surgery text which sells for $150). The shop also sells current paperbacks and some second-hand books on medical subjects. Tennis shoes, sweat shirts, etc., colored photographs of famous Hopkins paintings are sold here, too.

People connected with the Medical Institutions get a 10% discount on their purchases. Ambulatory patients don't frequent this shop, but learned patients, who are interested in medicine and are in street clothes, are welcome.

There is a U corridor behind the shop through which one can achieve three things: they are Kennedy Institute (described shortly, among the affiliates), the Turner Auditorium, and the elevators in CMSC.

The Turner Building contains much of the future of the hospital, the past, and the present. Here are housed the Archives Office, where the Dean Emeritus, for whom the building is named, is continuing Dr. Chesney's great history of *The Johns Hopkins Hospital and The Johns Hopkins University School of Medicine,* which Dr. Chesney carried from 1867 through 1914. He, too, writes with clarity, humor, and exactitude; and it is Hopkin's great good fortune that after his already vast labors, he is still willing to work so exhaustingly, for the Hospital and the Medical School.

The grand design of the Turner Auditorium has to be seen to be appreciated, but it is described in much detail, later, in "The Unseen Hospital" chapter. As to the actual auditorium itself: 757 people may be seated here, TV monitoring does away with loud-speaker doctor calling, there are no center aisles, therefore the space in front of the seats allow ample leg room, for a man may walk in front of you and not inconvenience you. The stage has curtain walls so that the draperies may be opened to make it large enough to house a symphony orchestra, or small enough so one man

Dr. Thomas B. Turner.

Dr. R. Carmichael Tilghman.

can stand on it and not seem lost. The acoustics are perfect.

Directly below the Turner Auditorium is another auditorium seating 153 and equally well equipped. It is called the Tilghman Room. Also there are two seminar rooms, on each side of the Tilghman Room called Seminar Rooms A and B. They have sliding walls and may be divided, again, if necessary for a multiplicity of meetings; they are piped to relay speeches, originating elsewhere for overflow crowds. There is yet another seminar room known as the Miles Room. And a final room known as Seminar Room C. Thus there are 4 seminar rooms in addition to the 2 auditoria. The 4 seminar rooms and the Tilghman Room, together, seat 350. Consequently, it is possible for 1,107 people to be seated in the building at one time.

Through the entire building the furniture is most modern and the seats are surprisingly comfortable.

The Tilghman Room is named for the Editor of the *Johns Hopkins Medical Journal* and his wife. Dr. R. Carmichael Tilghman is also Director Emeritus of Johns Hopkins University Health Services, and author of *"L.O.D.-YES,"* that much treasured, privately printed short history of the Army's 18th General Hospital in the Pacific, during World War II. He is frequently referred to as "Mister Alumni," as he knows practically every graduate of The Medical School by first name, and has been Assistant Dean and was on the Admissions Committee.

The Miles' Room represents a Hopkins First, and he is one to whom every graduate of the Johns Hopkins Medical School would rise in honor. He graduated in 1940 and when the room in his honor was dedicated on March 1, 1969, a classmate of his made some remarks in his memory. They are so beautifully written that direct quotes from them occur repeatedly in this chapter.

"On August 7th, 1942, during the battle of the Solomon Islands, Samuel Stockton Miles, Lieutenant Junior Grade, USNR, went ashore on the island of Tulagi with the First Raider Battalion of the Marine Corps. Three men in Company D were dead, and numerous others wounded. Lieutenant Miles attempted to cross a zone swept by hostile fire in order to administer first aid to the wounded and isolated men. He never reached his objective and was killed by the enemy . . . a Silver Star medal was awarded posthumously on September 4, 1943. As far as can be ascertained, Sam Miles was the first and only Johns Hopkins physician who died as a direct result of enemy action during World War II.

"Shortly after the war, several of Sam's classmates, scattered about the country, spontaneously expressed a desire to create a memorial in his honor. The fund later became part of the Hopkins Annual Roll Call . . . additional gifts . . . from time to time . . . representing continuing remembrance of Sam . . . with development of this new building complex, and assistance and guidance of Dr. Turner, Dr. Asper, and others, tangible recognition of Samuel Stockton Miles is being dedicated today."

His family were distinguished in Baltimore and his father, headmaster of Gilman School, had been a hero in World War I, severely wounded, decorated for gallantry.

"Father and son shared many qualities — dignity, honor, humor, and imagination. Sam was a earnest, diligent student . . . consuming interest in all things. Entered Medical School intending to be a research biologist . . . while at Hopkins wrote a scholarly paper on the innervation of the shoulder girdle of the nine-banded armadillo — surely a unique effort even in this great institution . . . armadillo, tenderly wrapped, in the family ice box, next to the Sunday roast, while the study was in progress.

"The lives of all of us enriched by having Sam as a friend . . . kept us on an even keel by somehow adding element of fun to . . . serious matter of attending medical school. Dr. Firor, in a noon surgical clinic, presented a patient with history of obscure peritonitis, and then with diabolical calm asked, "Miles, what laboratory test do you think is indicated?" Sam without hesitation replied, "Frei test." Dr. Firor . . . visibly shaken and somewhat crestfallen. "You've just correctly diagnosed one of the few proven cases of lymphogranuloma peritonitis in the history of the hospital." After clinic, Sam accepted congratulations . . . with his usual candor suggested that he might have been dozing, and came up with the first test that occurred to him . . . we never knew for sure."

Later in this chapter this completely charming paper continues.

During each year in the Turner Auditorium complex also are held a series of brief postdoctoral courses. In June and December, gynecology and obstetrics hold such courses, while in May, medicine always offers a series of lectures and conferences on internal medicine; and the Wilmer residents meet in April each year. During February-March medical genetics takes a week and so it goes. Many doctors, from all over the country avail themselves of these courses, and any one desiring details can get them from the Assistant Dean, Office of Continuing Education, JHMS.

They are housed in the Turner Building as are also the Archivist, and the Computer Center.

As with so many wonderful things at Hopkins the piece of research which may well ultimately prove to be the most valuable one ever undertaken here existed for "thirteen years over the drugstore." This is the description which the very famous Professor Emeritus of Medicine, who directs the Study of Precursors of Hypertension and Coronary Disease wrote to her boys around the world in 1966, just before the unit was moved to the renovated Hunterian Building. It is now the Biophysics Building.

In 1946, some of the very first money which was ever put into medical research for use in voluntary medical schools was granted to Hopkins by the National Heart Institute to study the genetic, physiological and metabolic, and psychological data which could be gleaned from a thorough periodic examination upon every medical student entering JHMS.

Describing the project she says, "Planned in May, applied for in June, and granted in September, 1946, we opened shop early in 1947 in a single room in the School of Hygiene, plus borrowed space in the Physiology Lab. The classes of 1948 and 1951 were the first ones studied — '48 toward the end of its medical school course, while '51 was registered on admission in the fall of 1947."

HEW renewed the grant without question, until recently and some people now alive may live to see the brilliant results which will surely accrue from the work of this most learned circulatory expert, upon these highly intelligent very competent subjects. Every graduate is reminded of follow-up examinations and required to send in the record therefrom. And the work still goes on with every entering class of the Medical School. However, how long it can continue without further supportive funds is problemical. No man could leave his money to a better cause.

One of the most interesting affiliates Hopkins has is directly on the tunnel route from the Postdoctoral Complex to the hospital. It is the John F. Kennedy Institute for Habilitation of the Mentally and Physically Handicapped Child, finished in 1967, and was the first building to be built with Government money after President Kennedy got the bill through Congress to help the handicapped. It is a beautiful structure with every modern device, and has a capacity of 40 inpatients, 100 outpatients a day; there are 250 on the administrative, service staff and medical staff and the latter hold appointments in JHMS faculty.

Also affiliated with JHMS is Sinai Hospital of Baltimore with 490 beds and 93 bassinets. It, too, is brand new and beautifully equipped.

A third affiliate, the Good Samaritan Hospital, was built with the money left by the Baltimore department store owner Mr. Thomas O'Neill. It was 284 beds and everyone of its medical staff have appointments at Hopkins also. It takes patients over 14 years old with long-term chronic illnesses, and has been a great boon to Hopkins in caring for long-term arthritics and stroke patients.

Baltimore City Hospitals is a long time affiliate and has 1,059 beds.

Spring Grove State Hospital and Fort Howard and Loch Raven Veterans' Hospitals enjoy the same standing.

By going through, from the corridor, via Kennedy, one may achieve footing, again, on the old familiar ground of Broadway. The great mass of medical students and postdoctoral fellows still live either on or near that old familiar street.

Thanks to an anonymous donor, twice anonymous and twice the same donor, the center parkway, first from Orleans to Monument and now from Monument to Eager has been relandscaped, replanted and beautified. It is a pleasant, pretty oasis which cost in all $100,000. While some students still live in houses up Broadway, the majority live in Reed Hall, the Compound, and 550 Broadway, known as the Broadway Management Corporation.

The Lowell J. Reed Hall is right down McElderly Street, opposite the front gate of the hospital on the right. There are 2 buildings, in a T-type construction. House staff, predoctoral and postdoctoral, other fellows and trainees, and paramedical students may all live in them. Double rooms are $49 to $54 and single rooms are $59 in the west wing. In the newer wing, which faces the hospital and has suites, the rents are $75 to $81. Some parking spaces exist and cost $12 per month. Compared to the old medical boarding houses, it is swank, grim, lonely living; and the food in the cafeteria would give the old boarding house keepers nightmares. It may be fine calorically, but it isn't visually, nor gastronomically.

"The Compound" and 550 Broadway, which provide nearby housing for married interns and residents.

The Compound is still its same old self, only the rents have gone up. A single bedroom is now $158 to $164 per month; 2 bedrooms are $180 to $192; while a 3 bedroom apartment is $216 to $222.

Incidentally, the most beautiful children you ever laid your eyes on are still playing there, too.

550 Broadway is still partially doctors and hospital offices on the lower floors, with the apartments above. (It is 11 stories tall). There a 1 bedroom apartment is $158-164, while a 2 bedroom is $180-192 and a 3 bedroom is $216-222. Now that interns and residents get a real salary, not all of them live hereabouts, but many of the swank ones live in 550, although the Compound still has its faithful friends. There is a high chain link fence around the Compound now, but the gates through the ends are opened all day long and the only secure place for little children to play is still in the inner compound behind the apartments.

Children and play go together and each spring there comes a day when the whole hospital is abustle with this truth. The Turtle Derby, started in 1930 and held on the tennis court adjacent to Harriet Lane, is about to commence. Only it is no longer held there, but at the tennis courts, adjacent to the swimming pool behind Reed Hall, where no patients ever see it unless they are well enough to walk down and climb back.

Tradition has it that a group of witty interns, led by the late Dr. Edmund B. Kelly, decided to guy the Preakness and instigated this annual event. Each department of the hospital and Medical School enters at least one turtle and they bear names which would require considerable fumigation to be printed outside the program sold at the Derby. Money from the Derby is primarily used for buying equipment for the Compound playground and for the house staff cooperative nursery, which is conducted in Harriet Lane. It also goes to some community projects and occasionally is used to aid in the financing of various house staff social functions, one of which is the Derby Dinner and takes place now afterwards in Turner, with candles on the tables, a bottle of wine on each table, a dance floor and red tablecloths. This year they provided cash prizes to a number of Hopkins Hospital employees who had given outstanding service to patients.

But to finish with the Derby first. Bets run high, turtles are studied in the "stables," usually a pasteboard box, doping is suspected, balloons fly on long strings, and future residents and interns waddle around in their diapers, while their mothers discuss the horrible amount of work their fathers are required to do by the "old men." Nurses flit by, a program of medical skits is given, and then the race is run. Lemonade, popsicles, and thousands of bottles of soda pop have gone down the gullet before the sun sets; and money, which never cares what company it keeps, has gone from one pocket, to pay lost bets, into another. Thousands of feet of film are ready to be developed and treasured in an intern's "declining years," too.

The Pithotomy Club, which for so many years was directly across from the hospital, is now situated up Broadway one block on the same side as the hospital.

The Pithotomy Club Show goes on though, every spring as usual, and the boys perform their verbal dissections of their superiors with just as much ribald gusto as previously. This annual event is avidly anticipated by both the august victim and the perpetrators and many a famous doctor has had the opportunity to see himself as the students see him. Among the Pithotomy Show's most steadfast attenders were the late Ogden Nash, and Gerald W. Johnson; the late Mr. Mencken never missed one either. They are completely stag affairs and the scuttlebutt among the ancients is that if your name is mentioned, but misspelled or substituted for so that it is still recognizable, they like you; but if it is reproduced upon the highly lewd program precisely as *you* spell it, your stock is minus zero. No doctor who can navigate and no male medical student, if he can squeeze in, would miss this performance for money — if they are invited. One of its most amazing features is the fact that the doctors who are sitting there, taking it, will be giving the examinations to these same tormentors.

For many years, after the show, a beer slide was held, whereby beer was sloshed on the floor of the old hallway of the row house across from the hospital and world famous doctors vied with medical students to see who could slide furtherest and still stay on his feet.

Also, when the club was opposite the hospital, after the veterans came back from World War II married, and wife and offspring accompanied but too poor to afford baby sitters, there developed a regular custom of baby-sitting, done by the boys who were studying in the club living room. One student burped the babies; one changed diapers; one fixed formulas.

In those wonderful notes about Sam Miles this occurs:

"One Saturday night some students were tossing a football around on the ground floor of the old Pithotomy Club building at 510 North Broadway. Sam, all eagerness, was itching to get his hands on the ball, which kept eluding him. He finally saw his chance, grabbed and threw. The ball knocked a piece off the chandelier and drove the rest of it up against the ceiling, where it shattered. Glass fell for at least 10 seconds. Clearly, thus began the eventual demolition of the entire 500 block of North Broadway.

"Sam was short, stocky, and curly headed. It was inevitable that he was nominated to assume the role of the cherub who traditionally sits astride the barrel at the conclusion of the annual Pithotomy Club show. And it was also inevitable that his enthusiastic performance caused the barrel to creak ominously and finally collapse. Sam emerged from the wreckage cheerful, dignified, and unhurt, being helped to his feet by a concerned Dr. Alan M. Chesney who was occupying one of the front row seats."

Two of the gayest medical school stories hinge entirely on the names of the participants. The first concerns two now very renowned pathologists, one who recently died at Hopkins, the other still alive in Virginia. The day they entered medical school, they sauntered up and down Broadway, trying to find a place to board. Every time a lady said, "What are your names, boys?" they'd reply, "Cash and Rich." Her retort would be, "Get right straight out of here! I've had enough trouble with medical students and their jokes as is."

In this vandalizing age, the other story sounds untrue, but it isn't. Broadway once had urns of geraniums, beds of canna lilies, and a green grass strip, which was plainly marked, "Keep off," the entire length of the center strip, to North Avenue. Two medical students taking a walk, failed to heed those reoccurring signs. They were arrested and firmly dressed down by the policeman, too, for the names they gave, which were Weed and Goodpasture.

It seems a far cry from Broadway to the Pennsylvania Academy of Fine Arts, the Chicago Art Institute, the Whitney Museum of American Art, and many others at which was shown, in the travelling Andrew Wyeth Exhibit, a tempera portrait which attracted millions of admirers. It was — and is — entitled Children's Doctor 1949, and the catalogue states, "to the horror of her conservative Baltimore mother, she chose a career in medicine and was one of the first women to graduate from Johns Hopkins Medical School. She took care of the Wyeth boys and many other children. . . ."

She is a very excellent pediatrician, in Wilmington, Delaware, and a member of the Class of 1916 JHMS: a quiet, modest, beloved doctor.

The two junior reviewers of this book were both graduates of the Medical School during the period when Dr. Chesney was Dean. Among the charming tales they relate, are these:

"For many years, the fiscal affairs of The Johns Hopkins University School of Medicine were conducted from a roller-top desk in the Physiological Chemistry building, now demolished. The desk was the fortress of Mr. Harry C. Burgans, who ran the school on a pay-as-you-go policy. If a student was one hour, one day late, in

The famed Yardley cartoon, "Medical Students at Play."

Postgraduate Class, 1897. Drs. Cushing, Kelly, Osler and Thayer.

Buildings on the School of Medicine grounds. Women's Fund Memorial Building — Physiology Building.

Dr. John Whitridge Williams (1866-1931). Dean of The Johns Hopkins University School of Medicine from 1911-1923.

meeting his bills, Mr. Burgans called him to the chair beside that desk and so informed him. Excuses were no good. Either you paid up, or 'out you went.'

"This room of decision was on the second floor and Mr. Burgans was aided and abetted by two little birdlike old maids — the Misses Bush — and they knew more about Hopkins medical students than any other two females alive. All the Administration Records of the school, such as applications, prospective students, grades, recommendations, and minutes of the Advisory Board were kept by them.

"When Dr. Chesney became Dean and moved in with his roller-top desk, they kept him straight, too. In time, he came to understand, as Mr. Burgan had so long ago found out, that although he could roll the top of his desk up and down at will, he could not alter the Misses Bush's minds, once they had set their interior computers on a course. And in each succeeding class, the mightiest medical student, also, stood in awe of them."

With less external equipment than probably any other group in any other major American medical school, those four people arranged, controlled and aided the destiny of first rate medical education in this country.

All are dead, now. Nobody knows where the roller-top desks are, now. And it takes 1 Dean, 1 Associate Dean, 5 Assistant Deans, and an administrative staff of 6 to run the Medical School, which now has 115 in a class, against 75, then.

Another colorful personality of those days was "the late William Mansfield Clark, distinguished Professor of Physiological Chemistry and inventor of the term pH used to describe acid-base balance or hydrogen ion concentration. He was a forceful lecturer. In telling about a substance in urine known as 'indican,' he always told the students they could remember it as 'in-the-can.' "

Great stories have always abounded around the Medical School and although this story should go in the pathological or the Welch Library chapter, since it came from the same source, it is included here.

"On the third floor of the Welch Library was a small lecture room, with a rectangular platform at the end of which were 3 short steps, with 1 side rail. The room was reserved for Dr. Welch to use when lecturing to medical students, and the rail was so placed that when he came down from the platform, he could hold on to it, and thereby insure himself a safe descent. As he was so rotund that it was impossible for him to see his feet, a thoughtful carpenter had built the rail."

The opening of the Welch Library was a great intellectual event and during the various celebrations, Dr. Welch gave a lecture in a much larger room, probably the Great Hall, which was covered by a reporter from THE SUN. "The lecture was attended by very learned men, and Dr. Welch outdid himself in brilliance and erudite references, many of which were highly technical. Afterwards when he was receiving compliments upon it, the reporter shyly came up and said, 'Dr. Welch, would you be so kind as to let me glance over your notes? I want to be sure I am understanding you accurately and spelling your references correctly. Your lecture was so brilliant, it deserves careful reporting.'

" 'Certainly,' Dr. Welch said, 'I'll be glad to lend you my notes.' He handed the young man the sheaf of papers, which he had turned while he was delivering the lecture and which were now rolled in his hand. The young man went over into a quiet corner, sat down on a chair and unrolled the precious treasure, reverentially.

"Every sheet, on both sides, was completely clean, unwritten upon. Dr. Welch had spoken — without notes!"

CHAPTER XIV

Hopkins Is the Neighborhood Hospital of the World

IN the last 10 years the world-wide work of the Johns Hopkins Medical Institutions — namely The Johns Hopkins Hospital, the Johns Hopkins Medical School and the Johns Hopkins School of Hygiene and Public Health — has increased at least a hundred-fold. The dream which Dr. William H. Welch had when he went out and persuaded the General Education Fund, headed by the late Dr. Wallace Buttrick, whose daughter is a graduate of Hopkins Medical School, to put up the money for the School of Hygiene has far exceeded Dr. Welch's fondest dreams.

The nidus of this tremendous expansion came about in a very curious way. In a fascinating paper entitled "The Exchange Programme Between the Medical Institutions of Mr. Thomas Guy of London and Mr. Johns Hopkins of Baltimore," the present Vice-President of The Johns Hopkins Hospital, in charge of Medical Affairs, wrote an account, published in the *Guy's Hospital Gazette*. At that time he was Professor of Medicine and Associate Dean of The Johns Hopkins University School of Medicine; he quotes as follows, from the late Mr. Lees Read, then Clerk to the Governors of Guy's:

> "I think it was in 1945 that I attended a luncheon of the Clothworkers' Company as a guest of the late Mr. John E. Humphery, then Treasurer of the Hospital, and after lunch there was a report from an officer who, I believe, was titled 'Chairman of the Committee of Almoners' of the City Company'. He reported on their income and various proposals for using it. Included in these was a suggestion that a considerable sum of money per annum should be set aside for an exchange scheme between an English and an American University under which students should visit the respective countries and study methods of producing and finishing cloths.

> "I happened to have been born and brought up on the borders between Lancashire and Yorkshire, i.e. between the two big cotton and wool manufacturing areas of this country, and I commented to Mr. Humphery that most of the worthwhile knowledge connected with the processes involved in the manufacturing of cloth were trade secrets of the firms carrying out manufacture, and I thought it highly unlikely that the exchange would really do a great deal of good.

> "The Clothworkers' Company is wealthy and Mr. Humphery then said to me: 'If we can't establish scholarships to study the manufacture of cloth, can you suggest an alternative?' I suggested medicine, pointing out that there were really no trade secrets, except possibly methods of manufacturing drugs, and

further, I suggested that an exchange of teachers rather than students would bring greater benefit to the participating institutions.

"Some little time afterwards I was informed, officially, that the Clothworkers' Company would be prepared to finance such a scheme, and this was the beginning of the exchange scheme between the Johns Hopkins Hospital and Guy's Hospital. Mr. Humphery died about, or possibly just before, the time that the first exchange took place and in the Clothworkers' Company records the exchange scheme is always referred to as the 'John E. Humphery Exchange Scheme.'"

This article, published in *Guy's Hospital Gazette* on March 20, 1965, continues, "Since 1947, 35 members of the Guy's faculty have visited Johns Hopkins, and 26 from Johns Hopkins have visited Guy's."

In 1971 there had been in this exchange 49 from Guy's and 35 from Hopkins.

THE CENTURY DICTIONARY of the ENGLISH LANGUAGE states:

Cloth-workers' Company, one of the twelve great livery companies of London.
B. Jonson, in *Epicoene,* 111, 2, says of them:
He got this cold with sitting up late, and singing catches with cloth-workers.
And *English Gilds* (E.E.T.S.) p. clxxi states:
No cloth-worker was allowed to bring his wares for sale in these halls, unless he has served a seven years' apprenticeship.

When one scans the history of cloth in this dictionary, the ancientness of it comes home in the different type-names: Albert cloth, American cloth, Board of Green cloth, Camel's-hair, Cloth of Arras, Cloth of Bruges, Cloth of Gold, of silver, of state, of Tars, Empress, enamelled, painted, wire paper.

As you can see, the Clothworkers' Company is an ancient, honorable hardworking guild of men, who take their charity seriously, and thanks to the presence of Mr. Lees Read at their luncheon in 1945 a world-wide exchange of medical knowledge has eventuated.

When one considers that President Truman proclaimed the cessation of hostilities in World War II on December 31, 1946, and the Clothworkers' offer

The Entrance Court,
Guy's Hospital.
Photograph copied from
Mr. Guy's Hospital.

was made shortly after that luncheon in 1945, it was indeed a most generous and noble gesture for them to foot the bills for the Guy's men to come to Hopkins. Between 1940 and the date they made that offer, members of that guild had participated in, died in, or worked through the retreat from Dunkirk, the destruction of Coventry and Birmingham, and much of London, as well as the loss of the British possessions in the Far East.

The Dean of Guy's Hospital Medical School (Dr. E. R. Boland) wrote to the Dean of Hopkins Medical School (the late Dr. Alan M. Chesney) in the summer of 1946 making the proposal. Dr. Chesney consulted with the Hopkins faculty, and the President of the university, Dr. Isaiah Bowman; and on October 12, 1946, Dr. Chesney wrote accepting the offer.

Many famous men have gone both ways in the intervening years, on this exchange; the first from Hopkins being the late Dr. Blalock; the second, the present Professor of Medicine and Physician-in-Chief; and among the Guy's men was Sir Heneage Ogilvie, the renowned editor, for so many years, of *The Practitioner,* which is the oldest medical journal in the English language in *continuous* publication. (The *Lancet* is older, but it suspended for a few years.)

Since World War II, there has been a late flowering in the Hopkins Medical School and in the hospital concerning post-doctoral medicine. What is curious about it is that The Johns Hopkins University set up, manned, and became internationally famous for the first graduate school in America. Among its brilliant graduates were Woodrow Wilson and Walter Hines Page. Thanks, after all of these years, to the Clothworkers' of London, the Medical School has taken a fresh interest in post-doctoral men, too.

As of now, there are at Hopkins Medical School and Hospital 236 postgraduates, and their points of origin are given in the table at the end of this chapter.

This exchange system has also extended, however, to undergraduate medical students, of which Hopkins last year had 15 from abroad; and 21 from Hopkins went abroad.

So successful was the Guy's Exchange Program, that in 1959 Dr. Milton S. Eisenhower, then President of The Johns Hopkins University, created a standing committee on post-doctoral education; and thanks to a study initiated by the Dean of the Medical Faculty, it was decided to expand the places whence these doctors came, and to do so with the emerging nations particularly.

After a very careful and lengthy consideration and investigation, three medical schools and adjacent hospitals were chosen to provide these men: they were the University of Ibadan in Nigeria, the American University of Beirut in Lebanon, and the Peruvian University of Medical and Biological Sciences (Cayetano Heredia) in Lima. Because of the travel difficulties of arriving at these remote spots, the tenure period was altered from one month's duration to three months.

Thanks to the Commonwealth Fund, which was established in 1918 by the late Mrs. Stephen V. Harkness as a memorial to her husband who was an official of the Standard Oil Company, the two-way money for this medical educational exchange was provided. This fund, whose chief purpose has always been medical education and medical research was set up with such sanity, it has been of enormous benefit to mankind. The Board of Trustees is self-perpetuating; and they may use their annual funds entirely as they see fit, provided the projects are those of medical education and research.

The new Rimac Hospital (300 beds), the teaching hospital of Cayetano Heredia Medical School in Lima, Peru. The University's basic science building is in the background. This photograph was taken in July 1971 by Dr. Richard T. Johnson, professor of neurology at Johns Hopkins, during his exchange professorship with this affiliated school.

Since 1960, one of the brightest stars in their medical crown has been this program which they have made possible at the above named university medical schools and hospitals.

As already stated the first selected was the University of Ibadan, and the first fellow from there arrived at Hopkins in 1963; the first from AUB also arrived in 1963, while the first from Peru arrived in 1966.

The first exchange professor from Hopkins to Nigeria was Associate Professor of Pediatrics; the first Hopkins professor to Beirut was then Associate Dean of Post-Doctoral Study, now Vice-President of the hospital. He subsequently has returned twice to Beirut to work on the exchange program. He also has visited most of the principal medical schools in the Middle East. The first Hopkins professor to Peru was the Professor of Medicine, who is Director of the Department of Medicine at Hopkins.

Regarding his visit to the Department of Medicine, Universidad Peruana "Cayetano Heredia", for three months in 1965, the Professor of Medicine, Director of the Department of Medicine of The Johns Hopkins University and The Johns Hopkins Hospital says:

"Cayetano Heredia was formed only five years ago. At this time a law was passed in Peru which in essence gave effective control of the university governing body to the students. The majority of the members of the medical faculty at this juncture resigned and formed the new medical school with which we now have the Exchange Program.

"As a result, they have a very excellent and well-trained basic science and clinical faculty which is freed of many of the hampering traditions which exist in many South American schools and their efforts are fully directed toward true university goals unimpeded by political activities, student strikes and other restrictive influences.

"They have set up an excellent admissions system which is based on intellectual qualifications and not subject to outside influences for the admission of students. Thus they have a very keen, well-qualified student body who are there to devote themselves to getting the best possible education free of the distractions of political activity. . . .

"I found that a knowledge of Spanish was very important. Many of the

The new hospital and out-patient buildings of the American University of Beirut. These buildings opened in 1970 replacing the outmoded facilities which have been demolished.

faculty members and students are not fluent in English. All ward rounds were conducted in Spanish and during my stay I gave twenty-five full hour lectures in Spanish. Making this effort to learn their language, I believe, has an important role in getting the Exchange off to a productive start. . . ."

This is a remarkable statement indeed! That a doctor would make the effort to become proficient enough in a language which he had just learned so that he could deliver those lectures in that language evoked great appreciation and gratitude from the faculty at Cayetano Heredia.

Regarding the background of the American University at Beirut, a Commonwealth Fellow from Lebanon remarks:

"It has now been one hundred years since The Reverend Doctor Daniel Bliss, an outstanding man, founded in Beirut the Syrian Protestant College, the now very famous American University of Beirut, which is incorporated under the laws of the State of New York. . . .

"This college is for all conditions and classes of men. . . . A man white, black or yellow, Christian, Jew, Mohammedan or heathen may enter and enjoy all of the advantages of this institution for three, four, or eight years and go out believing in one God, in many gods, or in no God, but it will be impossible for anyone to continue with us long without knowing what we believe to be the truth and our reasons for our belief. Today the American University of Beirut has approximately 3,000 students. One thousand are Lebanese and two thousand come from all the Middle East and Arab countries — from Casablanca to the Persian Gulf, from Turkey, Africa, Pakistan, Afghanistan, Persia, and some from Europe. The American University of Beirut is the only American school so far from the United States to have grown and to have achieved such a success.

"The American University appears as the outpost of American culture placed in Beirut at the junction of three continents: Europe, Africa, and Asia. Already a new research medical center has been established and 32 million dollars have been invested toward this achievement. Twenty million more dollars are necessary to continue and achieve the goals of this program. . . ."

Ibadan was chosen because it was a well-established university in Central Africa and thanks to its former history with British Colonialism there was no language barrier to be overcome.

Two of the early fellows from there did not return to Ibadan, when their time was up in Baltimore, because they were Ibos; however, they did return to a different part of Nigeria and met the stipulation laid down in their fellowship papers of promising to return to the country of their origin and aid in the teaching and treatment of their peoples. Their Baltimore friends kept in touch with them, one way and another, and know that they did fine work where they found themselves.

Also, all the exchange professors, both ways, after they returned home wrote their counterparts long letters of suggestions and gratitude and they, too, keep in constant touch.

In such a letter, one of the Hopkins professors who had been to Ibadan wrote:

"Another teaching exercise used extensively in the States (U.S.) is probably the best attended and most effective method of all. I'm sure you're familiar with the open forum conference that we call "grand rounds." These are held each week . . . for all of the staff and for any members of the profession in or outside of the institution who may wish to attend. These consist of case presentations by the chief resident, with the professor (or his substitute) acting as a combination master of ceremonies, referee, and father confessor. Any questions or criticisms from the professional staff and visitors are invited, and indeed, encouraged. The cases are selected in retrospect, usually on the basis of an unsuccessful outcome but occasionally on the basis of a notable triumph. This open discussion of cases is very instructive for all. It affords an opportunity to learn from the mistakes of others as well as the chance to exchange ideas. The fact that at future 'grand rounds' the chief resident or any member of his team may have to account publicly for an omission or an oversight in a patient's management tends to improve the on-going quality of medical care considerably. In addition, having to defend one's decisions before such a large and august body usually motivates an avid interest in the current literature. I think this type of conference would be a very useful adjunct in training your own registrars."

Three medical students have been among the exchanges from Hopkins to Lima, support for one of them being obtained through the Maryland Heart Association. One medical student has been to Ibadan, under the Commonwealth grants and numerous medical students have been to Guy's under the Guy-Hopkins Exchange plan.

Also, one house officer worked for two months at the American University Hospital in Beirut.

Fellows from the affiliated schools are estimated to total 10 annually. Most fellows remain in residence for 2 years, some come for one only and some for 3 years. An average stipend for senior fellows is $9,500 each, depending upon the number of dependent children. Additional expenses for travel of these fellows to special course of instruction and meetings and for tuition for special courses while they are here is estimated at $5,000 annually. Commonwealth Fellows pay standard rentals for apartments at Reed Hall or 550 Broadway, and for their own living expenses out of their Commonwealth stipend.

Each professor who accepts a Commonwealth Fellow for training agrees in advance to give his own personal direction to the fellow and, in addition, to provide adequate laboratory and office space. Moreover, each professor is requested to support the research activities of the fellow. It is conservatively estimated that $50,000 in research funds has been expended by the 18 Commonwealth Fellows whom Hopkins has had in residence since the beginning of the program.

The same guidelines are employed in the selection of other foreign trainees as are used in the selection of Commonwealth Fellows. The average stipend of them is $7,500 annually. Approximately $1,717,500 for scholarships from numerous sources goes into the Foreign Exchange Program, and about $450,000 is used to support their training in research.

Men are encouraged to research in problems related to their national disease difficulties, thus the Africans are particularly interested in Burkitt's tumors — a type of cancerous tumor to which they seem peculiarly liable. On the other hand, the men from the Middle East have discovered many things of value there. One such is that the polio virus will not grow in Mediterranean Sea water; however, once the water is boiled it looses much of its lethal properties. The young man making these discoveries has received over 500 requests for reprints of his paper thereon. The study was begun at the suggestion of the President of AUB who noted the high incidence of polio in Lebanon, and asked for an opinion on the safety of Mediterranean Sea bathing during polio epidemics; the study indicates that such bathing is probably quite safe.

As the Dean of the Post-Doctoral Program put it:

"People included in the program are medical students, residents, junior faculty, and senior faculty. The purpose is to prepare young people for permanent academic posts. What it really amounts to is an international scrutiny of brains.

"When you go abroad in one of these assignments one of the greatest stimulants is working with the intelligent, excited young; you get appraised of local problems and see others helped in programs of international or internal research."

One such program now underway is the study of goiter in Lebanon. Goiter is prevalent among those living in the hills and endemic among those in the mountains, such as around the Cedars of Lebanon; yet it is rarely found among people residing in the coastal area. Why? Two possible explanations are being investigated. The first is that those in the mountains have goiter due to iodine deficiency, as rain water which they drink and the foods which they eat contain miniscule amounts of iodine. Also the sea-salt they use has but little iodine, as it evaporates during the sun-drying of sea water. The coastal inhabitants, however, who bathe in sea water and eat seafood, get an adequate intake. The second cause of goiter may be an hereditary defect in the synthesis of thyroid hormone. In nearly one-third of all marriages in Lebanon the marital partners are first cousins, and accordingly the likelihood of such hereditary defects is increased.

Not only the microscopes of the world are available to such problems through a program like that being carried out at Hopkins, but the brains, everywhere, are pondering upon them, too; and this brings about an international comprehension and desire to help which is beginning to show results in world-wide medical good-will. To obtain such accord without give-aways, but through self-help is the goal of Clothworkers and of the Commonwealth Fund.

As regards the exchange fellows, two from Beirut have now been made Chairman of the Department of Pediatrics and Associate Professor of Microbiology, respectively, upon their return.

Another Commonwealth Fellow in Anatomy from Lebanon, has received accolades which are most uncommon — in fact, almost unheard of in medical estimates by their seniors of young doctors, anywhere. They say of him, "has not been surpassed by any other Lebanese Fellows, nor indeed by any of our U. S. Fellows in the Department of Anatomy. There are those in our Department of Anatomy who consider him to have the talents of a genius. Perhaps these strong statements can be supported by the fact that he is publishing several papers of unusual merit of his studies with us. . . . Already he has been assured by the faculty and by the administrative officers of AUB of appointment to the Chairmanship of the Department of Anatomy upon his return to Beirut in July, 1968."

At the time the above quotation was written to the Commonwealth Fund, the Professors of Surgery (Johns Hopkins) and of Pediatrics (Johns Hopkins) also were in Beirut on exchange. The new Director of Surgery at AUB was being assisted by his former associate, as was also the former Commonwealth Fellow, by his former chief, in the organization of the Department of Pediatrics.

These things work both ways, though, for the Professor of Neurology at Beirut had just been on a three-month exchange at Hopkins where "His teaching rounds were superb. When he gave a brilliant CPC the students burst spontaneously into applause at the conclusion."

All during the construction of the new hospital at AUB the President of The Johns Hopkins Hospital has been an advisor on its present expansion program, and a former Administrative Assistant at the Hopkins Hospital has become Associate Director of the American University Hospital in Beirut. Incidentally, one of the things the former Hopkins Administrative Assistant has done is to install a computerized billing system, WHICH WORKS, "for in Lebanon patients who are discharged from the hospital disregard any bill for late charges. On the other hand, if their bill is complete upon discharge, even though not fully paid, they accept their responsibility for making monthly payments until the account is settled . . . thus the bill is prepared for the patient in three minutes, showing an itemized accounting of all charges including room and professional fees."

If Hopkins can achieve the same, many thousands of people annually would have their blood pressure immensely improved.

The more one learns of these foreign affiliates and our contacts with them, the more one realizes that it is like turning an old-timey, perfectly made kaleidoscope in which the rays dart in all directions to and fro, in designs most carefully planned

Dr. Abdel Salem Majali, right, president of the University of Jordan, in the Middle East, consults with Dr. Samuel P. Asper at Johns Hopkins about a new medical school the University of Jordan is forming. Dr. Asper is the Hospital's Vice President for Medical Affairs and architect of many of Hopkins international programs.

and executed. From the Middle East, from Central Africa, from Peru, Hopkins receives as well as contributes.

The men who go abroad from Hopkins may have their horizons broadened, but they do not have their work load lessened. In October, 1967, the Associate Dean for Post-doctoral Study at Hopkins, "spent ten days at AUB to strengthen the exchange, as no Hopkins professor had been in residence there for a number of months due chiefly to the Arab-Israeli conflict." He also visited the President of the University of Jordan in Amman to discuss with him and with General Majali, the Director of Medical Services of the Royal Jordanian Army, their plans for a medical school. . . . "Excellence is their by-word, and the medical school will open in September, 1968, with fifteen carefully selected medical students. The course will be six years . . . the teaching hospital will open in September 1972, in time to receive the students for their two clinical years.

"A new medical school has been started at Aleppo, under the guidance of AUB; one is being considered for construction at Amman. Also, King Faisal of Saudi Arabia intends to build a modern hospital and possibly a medical school, probably at Riyadh. Planners for this school are obtaining advice.

"At the request of the U. S. Department of State we recently received Dr. Said Abdul Kader Baha, Professor of Medicine and Dean of the Medical School in Jalalabad, Afghanistan.

"The University of Shiraz has also sought assistance. This medical school is well known to us, its former director of its major clinical unit was a graduate of the Johns Hopkins School of Hygiene and Public Health, while the former Professor of Pediatrics is a graduate of Johns Hopkins University School of Medicine. The Associate Dean for Post-doctoral Study JHMS has twice visited the school."

Later, in the same report it is stated, "We note an increasing interest in international medicine and particularly in our affiliated schools by younger members of our faculty, house officers, and medical students. Excellence is as much the key word in the selection of foreign post-doctoral students as it is with the U. S. students."

The young doctor before referred to as a genius has become an expert in the use of the electron microscope, his field of special study being in electromicroscopy of muscles and nerves. While there is (at the writing of the report) no electron microscope at AUB, upon his return one is to be purchased. Under consideration is an RCA model costing about $30,000 and a Japanese model costing about $45,000. It will be the first electron microscope in the Middle East and is greatly anticipated by all research medical men from those countries.

(It is a pleasure to state that in June, 1971, the instrument was in operation and several studies involving its use are already published.)

Not only the fellows, but the exchange professors, too, work hard. The Professor of Neurology from AUB writes of his stay at Hopkins, "Through your advice I was a consultant to the medical students and the resident staff on neurological patients. We had grand rounds, neurological conferences and clinical-pathological discussions. . . . I was privileged to attend many congresses and conferences, the American College of Physicians in Boston, American Society for Clinical Investigation and The Association of American Physicians meeting in Atlantic City. I gathered plenty of ideas and concepts on basic medicine. . . . I learned much about research that had been done in the last twenty-five years. . . .

I have become more aware of the new, fast traumata of life (alcohol, smoking, fast driving, drug dependency). One can call them the 'new pleasure epidemics causing disease.' They are more difficult to eradicate than the plagues of the past.

"As for The Johns Hopkins Hospital, I have enjoyed every hour of my stay and end this three-month sojourn by joining the author of the Proverbs and replace the word Johns Hopkins for wisdom:

> "Wisdom has builded her house, she has hewn out her seven pillars. She has mingled her wine; she hath also furnished her table; she cried upon the highest places of the City. For him that wanteth understanding, come, eat of my bread and drink of the wine which I have mingled. Live; and go in the way of understanding. For by wisdom thy days shall be multiplied, and the years of life shall be increased."

Between 1963 and 1966, 3 professors were exchanged from Hopkins to Beirut; 1 Professor of Medicine; 1 Associate Professor of Pathology; 1 Associate Professor of Pharmacology, Experimental Therapeutics, and Medicine. The professor just quoted above was exchanged from Beirut.

To Ibadan went 1 Professor of Medicine and Director of Biomedical Engineering; 1 Professor of Medicine; 1 Associate Professor of Gynecology and Obstetrics; 1 Associate Professor of Pathology; 1 Associate Professor of Pediatrics, while from Ibadan came 3 visiting professors.

To Lima went the Professor of Medicine and Director of the Department; and 1 Associate Professor of Mechanics; and from Lima came 3 professors on exchange.

From Ibadan came 6 Commonwealth Fellows: 1 in Pediatrics, 2 in surgery, 1 in urology, 1 in physiology, 1 in ob-gyn. From Beirut came 1 in pediatrics, 1 in microbiology, and 1 in surgery. From Lima there were 1 in genetics, 1 in surgery, 1 in medicine, and 1 in physiology chemistry.

The first of those Commonwealth Fellows from AUB who was at Hopkins from September 1, 1964, to June 30, 1966, gave an excellent description of how his time at Hopkins was spent. He writes: "The months of September, October, and November, 1964, were spent in the clinic working up children with various endocrine problems in the Children's Medical and Surgical Center at The Johns Hopkins Hospital. The patient material during these three months covered most aspects of pediatric endocrinology.

"From December, 1964, on, I have been in the laboratory . . . introduced to various methodologies and use of instruments. . . . I completed a project on the extraction of human growth hormone from the urine and I set up the radioimmunoassay for human growth hormone in plasma. In the future, I hope to work on steroids, in particular secretion rates of cortisol, aldosterone and related compounds.

"Spring, 1965, attended course of radiostope instrumentation . . . plan to attend this fall the course of biological chemistry offered to students of year I medicine.

"Benefits accrued from my stay are many . . . difficult to enumerate individually all the experiences, skills, and laboratory 'know how' one acquired in such training. On my return to AUB hope to establish various methods of endocrine investigation not available there which will be useful tools for both clinical and research endocrinology. I plan a research project on the endocrinology of malnutrition, a subject that has not been explored extensively."

The report to the Commonwealth Fund regarding the racial problem comments: "This has been so small as to be hardly worthy of comment. To our knowledge, there have been no difficulties within our institution . . . confident they would have been called to our attention had they occurred. There have been only minor problems outside our community and clearly this has dealt more with the acceptance of the Nigerians by some of our colored population who are reluctant to "associate with foreigners." Likewise, the Nigerians have on some occasions shown indifference toward our local colored people. This stems from a more distinct class consciousness in Nigeria than in the United States. Steadily through education and association even these minor problems are being corrected."

While the AUB Fellow quoted several paragraphs above was writing of his stay at Hopkins, the Exchange Professor of Medicine from Hopkins to AUB who was there from November 15, 1963, to February 20, 1964, was describing his duties, too. This is some of what he said:

"Each morning I made rounds with the medical students and house staff of the American University of Beirut Hospital from 8:30 a.m. until 11:00 a.m. On these rounds we saw patients on the wards and occasionally in the Out-patient Department. The clinical material at the American University Hospital is superb. The hospital receives patients . . . not only from Beirut and other parts of Lebanon, but also from other countries of the Middle East, especially Syria, Jordan, Saudi Arabia, and Yemen . . . an air ambulance service in the Middle East is well developed . . . immigration authorities are cooperative in facilitating the transfer and exit of patients from other countries.

"At 11:00 a.m. . . . time for Arabic coffee . . . here I came to meet each member of the faculty, to learn his interests and even his problems. From 11:30 a.m. to noon, I saw selected patients with endocrine disorders, which is the field of my special interest . . . or took care of correspondence with the assistance of a secretary in the Department of Medicine, graciously provided by the University.

"Daily, at noon, I attended a conference and, in fact led one of these each week throughout my stay. In my own clinic I reviewed, in a series of ten seminars the entire field of endocrinology. Other conferences included medical staff rounds, CPC's and special lectures by members of the faculty.

"Lunch generally takes 1:00 p.m. to 2:30 p.m. and includes a "siesta" . . . followed by a period of intense work, which lasts until 7:00 p.m. . . . My late afternoons were taken up in several ways. I made it a point to visit in every major research laboratory of the hospital and medical school, and to observe, at first hand, the work that was going on. On other occasions, I spent these hours talking with medical students and house officers, either singly or in small groups.

"Most evenings, my family and I were invited to the homes of one of the members of the faculty . . . these invitations frequently included interesting trips into the country side on weekends, which gave us a most helpful insight and understanding of the people of Lebanon."

A present Professor of Medicine, who is Director of the Biochemical Department at Hopkins was in Ibadan from July 30 to October 12, 1963, and he has some very interesting comments, too: "After a two-week period of familiarization with the Department of Medicine and some of the clinical problems they encounter,

I took over one of the clinical units as the consultant. The regular consultant returned to Britain for his annual leave. . . .

"Throughout the remainder of our stay, I ran one of the medical inpatient wards, one of the out-patient clinics, taught medical students and house officers. . . . A senior house officer on my unit was awarded a U.S.P.H.S. International Post-Doctoral Research Fellowship, and spent a year in my laboratory here (Johns Hopkins). He has now been selected to have his specialty training in neurology at Johns Hopkins. Upon completion of his training, he plans to return to Ibadan, which, at present, has no neurologist. This might be regarded as an added benefit of the exchange program.

"The benefits of the exchange program to me were great . . . my horizons of the problems in medicine broadened. . . . I gained real respect for preventive medicine . . . learned much about the management of tropical diseases from students, consultants, but most of all from my house officers . . . also learned that nontropical diseases are different in the tropics."

All of the exchange professors say that they regret their stay was for 3 months only, and repeatedly suggest that the tenure be extended to 6 months; as one cannot get much research commenced in 3 months, and it takes that long to get the feel of the school and comprehend the problems of the country involved.

The Commonwealth Fund, upon presentation of the reports which have been used as the foundation of this chapter, was renewed in 1968 for five years; and it was agreed during the second five years to an increase of exchange professors from the affiliated schools to six annually.

It should be mentioned, too, that one of the greatest aids in instituting this exchange was the present Dean Emeritus of the Johns Hopkins Medical School. Prior to assuming the Deanship, he had spent many years at the School of Hygiene and Public Health at Hopkins, and was — and is — very conscious of world-wide medical needs and problems.

As of June 1, 1968, Hopkins had sent 5 exchange professors to Ibadan, 5 to Beirut, 4 to Lima. From overseas from these 3 affiliates had come 4 exchange professors from Ibadan, 3 from Beirut, and 4 from Lima.

Through 1967, foreign post-doctoral fellows, including Commonwealth Fellows, at the Johns Hopkins Medical School numbered 1 from Nigeria, 11 from the Middle East, 14 from Peru, and from other foreign countries 200 or 236 in all.

Internationl students gather, some in native dress, at an International Club Welcome Reception.

The chart attached to this chapter shows their distribution by departments.

One of the great helps and pleasures, at Hopkins, which the Women's Board sponsors, is the International Club. It has many hundreds of members and maintains an office in the Administration Annex. They go on sight-seeing tours, outings, picnics, have dinners, give balls and have a multi-lingual good time. All foreign students, or fellows, or post-doctoral students at Hopkins are eligible to become members; the annual dues are $2.00 per member.

Not a single day passes, now, that men from all over the world are not working or studying under the banner of The Johns Hopkins Hospital and Medical School, and as a consequence there has grown up an international, bi-lingual confraternity of medical men which actually circles the globe.

It is strange and wonderful, too, to remember that all of this began because the Clothworkers decided, through Guy's Hospital and Medical School to send medical men to Hopkins. Hopkins was successful, encouraged by the Guy's experiment, in obtaining the money from a fund created in memory of a dead capitalist named Harkness to extend this great learning circle and cycle to Asia, Africa, and South America.

Whenever one becomes disconsolate about the current world, he would do well to remember that EVERYWHERE there exists in it a group of men who talk the international language of medicine and whose primary motivation is to aid, cure, and comprehend sick people. Whatever their national origin, their personal ambitions, one needs but to see a group of these men together to realize that man, regardless of his station or his location is now gifted with the laser beams of exchanged knowledge and opportunity.

While in all the countries affected, learned older medical men are constantly scrutinizing and evaluating younger medical men to see if they are of the calibre to participate in this mental-medical world, on which the sun never sets.

As the sea-shell carries the sound of the sea, knowledge echoes and re-echoes and rides with the post-doctoral candidates and exchange professors on the air-ways of the world, to and fro, wherever they go, en route from that Neighborhood Hospital Of The World: Johns Hopkins.

ENROLLMENT OF FOREIGN POSTDOCTORAL FELLOWS
THE JOHNS HOPKINS UNIVERSITY SCHOOL OF MEDICINE
SEPTEMBER 1, 1971
DISTRIBUTION BY DEPARTMENT

Gynecology and Obstetrics	13
Medicine	61
Neurology	5
Ophthalmology	10
Pathology	10
Pediatrics	20
Psychiatry	12
Radiology	13
Surgery:	
General, Plastic and Pediatric	13
Anesthesiology	13
Dental Surgery	0
Laryngology and Otology	5
Neurological Surgery	6
Orthopedic Surgery	3
Urology	3
Anatomy	2
Biomedical Engineering	2
Biophysics	0
Lab Animal Medicine	1
Microbiology	0
Pharmacology	10
Physiological Chemistry	9
Physiology	4
TOTAL	215

DISTRIBUTION BY COUNTRY

Argentina	5	Guatemala	1	Nigeria	1
Australia	7	Hong Kong	2	Norway	3
Bolivia	1	India	15	Pakistan	1
Brazil	2	Indonesia	2	Panama	5
Burma	2	Iran	17	Peru	15
Cameroon	2	Ireland	6	Philippines	5
Canada	15	Israel	1	Poland	2
Ceylon	2	Italy	5	South Africa	2
Chile	1	Japan	13	Spain	4
China (in exile)	12	Jamaica	1	Switzerland	1
Colombia	1	Jordan	1	Thailand	3
Costa Rica	1	Korea	5	Trinidad	1
Czechoslovakia	1	Lebanon	8	Turkey	5
Egypt	1	Mexico	5	U. Kingdom	15
Germany	9	Netherlands	2	Uruguay	1
Greece	2	New Zealand	1	Venezuela	1
				Yugoslavia	1

CHAPTER XV

A Storehouse of Knowledge

ONE of Dr. Osler's greatest assets was the catholicity of his literary tastes; and he early employed his persuasive influence to the end that the younger men, at Hopkins, should *know* and realize that books were bulwarks, beacons, and man's best mental friend. He was aided and abetted in this attitude by Dr. Billings, who was among the early lecturers at the Hospital Historical Club. That live men stand on dead men's shoulders and are indebted for their knowledge to their predecessors, was one of the cardinal precepts which they hammered into the heads of their, as yet, wet-behind-the-ears medical cubs.

A charming picture shows the library of the hospital in the Administration Building, with books to the ceiling and a second gallery of them with a walk-around, at the height of the high mantelpiece mirror. Comfortable leather chairs are set near the book shelves, and around a center table are ranged those still-used, and still-uncomfortable, curved-back, spindly legged, banquet-type chairs. Proudly shown over this table is a circular white opaque-glass globe, suspended from what is obviously a chandelier and obviously electrified. It is breath-taking to contemplate how much erudition has been added to the book shelves of the world by the men who sat in that library increasing their mental horizons. Had a tape-recorder been available then, what conversations one might be privileged to listen to now!

Over the years, it became increasingly plain that all the libraries tucked here and there throughout the hospital, ought to be gathered into one single building; too many collections which might have come to Hopkins perhaps, if adequately housed, went elsewhere. Dr. Cushing gave many books to Yale; Dr. Osler left his library to his alma mater, McGill; while the ever generous Dr. Kelly, in memory of his friend, Louis C. Krieger, of Baltimore, gave a priceless library on fungi, embracing 12,000 titles, to the University of Michigan.

Bibliophiles, in New York and elsewhere, including the Doctors Flexner, who neither slumbered nor slept where any project for the betterment of Hopkins was concerned, gossiped around the nation; and the Welch Library, to house all the medical libraries and the Institute of the History of Medicine, resulted.

It was dedicated in October, 1929, the gift of the General Education Board, which also provided a fund with which Dr. Welch was to "shop" for books, and he did so in Europe, from May to September of 1928. Among the kindest of the early donors was Dr. Kelly, and since its opening, this library has become a respository of the valuable collections of Hopkins' doctors.

One of Dr. and Mrs. Barker's wedding presents was a perfect first folio edition of the "Fabrica of Vesalius," given to them by Dr. Osler, and which they gave to the Welch Library in 1940. The late Dr. J. Earle Moore gave the library over 300 volumes, and a number of valuable books belonging to the late Dr. Walter

The Welch Library, right, forms the south side of the School of Medicine's basic science quadrangle.

E. Dandy have also been presented.

Between 1960 and 1970 many notable books have been received; two wonderful bequests were, in 1960, 459 volumes on the History of Syphilis, from Dr. Louise Pearce, who graduated from JHMS in 1912, and was a member of the Rockefeller Institute for Medical Research; and in 1969, 1,487 volumes, from the libraries of Doctors Ernst Bodenheimer and Jonas Friedenwald, on Medicine and Ophthalmology. Dr. Bodenheimer was trained in Vienna, where his father was a very famous ophthalmologist. He came to this country in the early 1930s as a protégé of the Doctors Friedenwald and always practiced with them. Dr. Jonas Friedenwald was a 1920 graduate of JHMS and one of its most famous and renowned heroes. "One hundred years from now," the late Dr. Alfred E. Cohn, of the Rockefeller Institute said, "the man who will shine as the Wilmer Star is Jonas Friedenwald."

Both he and Dr. Bodenheimer had the intensity, the knowledge, and the comprehension to be excellent ophthalmologists. Their patients revered and treasured them. They were splendid examples of that long line of German-Jewish doctors which for so long contributed so greatly to American medicine.

In 1961 Mrs. L. F. Barker gave 377 more volumes on general medicine from Dr. Barker's collection, and Dr. William Rienhoff, Jr., gave 185 volumes from his father's medical library, also on general medicine. In 1964, 8 volumes of medicine in the early 18th Century were given by Mrs. R. L. Castendyk. They were from the library of Elisha Perkins, (1741-1799) who invented metallic tractors which were supposed to cure disease by magnetism.

In 1968, the Welch Library purchased from the library of R. De Saussure 621 volumes on psychiatry. Dr. De Saussure was a prominent Geneva psychiatrist.

Also, in the last 10 years, among the rare books purchased 9 were paid for by the Jacobs Fund, which was left to the library by the late Dr. Henry Barton Jacobs, whose wife was the widow of Mr. Robert Garrett for whom the Robert Garrett Fund

172

Turnstiles have been added to the library's entrance, and books are checked here too, as well as at the lending desks upstairs.

was named. Of all the Maryland families, certainly the Garrett-Jacobs family is the largest continuing contributor to the Hopkins. Of those rare books 4 bear the publication dates of 1556, 1565, 1588 and 1593; 3 are 1617, 1646, and 1697; while 2 are 1756 and 1824, respectively. All are on rare medical subjects. The library is most fortunate in having an assistant director and curator who reads rare books catalogues with the same astuteness and concentration true gardeners reserve for seed catalogues, but with this difference: the garden of knowledge knows no seasons and so she must be on her toes, forever.

At the present writing, the library contains 220,000 volumes, and regularly receives 2,200 periodical titles, including 30 received by the Institute of History of Medicine. A recent annual figure shows that the reading room served 80,000 readers and 120,000 volumes were taken out.

Through an IBM cross-indexing, all the periodical titles in the 40 departmental libraries throughout the hospital are currently available in the Welch Library. Monthly the library puts out a list of recently received books, and so, also, does the Institute of the History of Medicine. On inter-library loan (between Welch and the world), the library borrowed 5,000 volumes and loaned 15,000 last year.

A recent sampling of just how modern this library is can be gleaned from the Acquisitions List, #9, November, 1970, which lists 123 new 1969/1970 titles on all the various divisions of medicine and ailments of man; for the Institute of the History of Medicine it has 22 new acquisitions, for the Nightingale Room, 1, and 9 new journals, as well as 26 journals "received bound," the last one being *Yearbook of Nuclear Medicine, 1970!*

As you have already gleaned, peppered in and out throughout the hospital are the different departmental libraries, many with their own librarians; for Hopkins is not only a teaching hospital, it is also a learning hospital, at all levels, everywhere.

The greatest of these libraries, in fact the greatest of its kind, is the Friedenwald Library in the Woods Building at Wilmer.

Also peppered throughout JHMI are many lecture halls, which are covered in this little book elsewhere.

The offices of the Dean of the Medical School and the Assistant Deans, formerly in the Welch Library, have moved to the Basic Science Building. It seems a pity, in a way, that they have because it was pretty sobering to a boy, sweating it out, waiting for an interview, to look at the displays hereabouts.

Recently, he would have had an opportunity to see an extensive display of books celebrating the 150 Anniversary of Florence Nightingale's birth, taken from the Kelly Collection, now housed in the Nightingale Room at the Welch Library. In a nearby case were many books devoted to the controversial rubber glove dispute, while one of the large standing cases housed a beautiful display of ancient apothecary jars. Among the items in the wall cases were a set of surgical tools, owned by the famous Doctors Gross of Philadelphia (Mrs. Osler was the widow of the son). In that same case was, also, one of the statuettes of Dr. Welch riding a hill pony in China, where he went with Dr. Buttrick and his daughter (OHH:JHMS, 1923) in 1915.

On a wall, nearby, there used to hang the two long, lovingly fashioned, and utterly beautiful Chinese embroideries on a red silk background with appliqued lotus-flowered centers, and black embroidered figures on the right hand side of one and the left of the other. Beyond this, each bore an intricate embroidered border.

The first one's lotus flower characters read: "His long life is as fruitful as that of Wen Lu Kuo" (scholar, statesman Sung Dynasty). The legend in black along the right border reads: "To Dr. Welch upon his Eightieth Birthday."

The second one's lotus characters depict: "His achievements, of universal reach, resemble those of Ku Fen-Yang" (soldier, statesman of Tang Dynasty). The legend in black upon the left border read: "With Congratulations from the members of the Peiping Medical College."

These — alas — have become the victims of silk's greatest enemy: gravity. After an unsuccessful attempt to restore them, they have been taken down and put away. They are described here in such detail, because it is well to remember that in April, 1930, when that 80th birthday celebration for Dr. Welch occurred, Peiping Medical College still existed, and Hopkins people were staffing it. Now that the Communists have taken mainland China, the China Medical Board uses its funds for medical education elsewhere.

Speaking of the early days of the Welch Library, Dr. Welch himself chose Dr. Fielding H. Garrison, a former librarian of the Surgeon General's Library and the biographer of Dr. Billings, to be the first librarian of the Welch Library. Dr. Garrison was the author of an excellent *History of Medicine* and was one of the most learned men who has ever been at Hopkins. He was very much in the Billings' tradition.

On the floor below the one just sketched is the room known to OHH as the general reading room, but before covering its present function, it is wise to cover the Nightingale Room, which can be approached by walking through this reading room to the wire-cage elevator in the stacks; but it requires intricate directions to achieve the room through the stacks above. It can also be reached with mountain-goat legs via the stack stairways, but it is always kept locked so prior arrangements must be made to enter. The room is small with locked cases to the ceiling and not only contains books about Miss Nightingale and nursing history, but also women's work in general. Here are a few spot titles: *Woman's Work in the Civil War, Types of Canadian Women, Journals at Kartoum* (Gordon), *Life of Lord Lawrence* (First Baron Lawrence of the Punjab), *History of Epidemics in Britain 1666-1893,* and a whole shelf of suffrage books. Also 4 volumes of The History of the Knights Hospitallers, Edinburgh 1757. (Unfortunately 1 volume is missing).

There are 500 volumes in the collection here. Two rare volumes which are

Welch remodeled Great Hall holds a portrait of Dr. Philip Bard and the recently restored Sargent portrait of The Four Doctors.

now on display in the Nurses Library in the Main Residence were published in 1857 listing the Voluntary Contributions in Britain, during that year, to support nurses in the Crimean War and a History of the Crimean War.

It seems a shame that the history of anything which has been so valuable to the world as nursing, and nurses, has to be under lock and key in a rare book library, but discretion is the better part of possession these days.

To return to the general reading room, it has been altered into a general periodical room. Chairs and tables are still there and the portraits still look down upon you, but the catalogue has been moved to the hallway connecting this room with what was the Great Hall.

For all OHH who ever attended a graduation reception there or received an honor in the room, things are irrevocably altered. The catalogue stands are screwed to the floor, tables and chairs are about, and the hall is now referred to as the Reference Library. Even the Great Four and Miss Garrett's portrait, all by John Singer Sargent, have been "restored."

Here is what was said about them in the first edition of this book:
"Here, also, is the Great Hall, wherein hangs the portrait by John Singer Sargent, which Miss Garrett commissioned him to paint, of The Great Four. Dr. Osler is seated nearest the globe of the world, in full academic robes, with Dr. Kelly on his left hand, ready to explore all it contains, while Dr. Welch is seated around the corner of the table, his eye ready to judge and evaluate.
"The only figure standing in the portrait is Dr. Halsted, and looking closely one sees in the background, Death, on a white horse, stalking these men. An interesting anecdote of this painting is to the effect that Dr. Halsted would not give Mr. Sargent the co-operation he desired and, in retaliation, Sargent used different pigments upon him and, therefore, he is "fading out"; there is no doubt that he seems to be becoming less present than the other three.

175

Miss Mary E. Garrett (1854-1915)* After a portrait by John Singer Sargent.

*Miss Garrett demanded Equal Rights for the admission of Women in The Johns Hopkins Medical School before she gave the money to insure its completion. She also stipulated that each entering medical student hold a baccalaureate degree. This portrait hangs over the fireplace in the Welch Great Hall, now a reference library.

"No visitor to Hopkins who relishes art, or reveres history, should fail to see this most moving and magnificent painting."

Well, if you never saw it before, maybe it will suit you now. The patina is gone, the four ginger jars on the back wall seem to be lighted from behind, the white horse stands out most plainly, and one is told "please note that if seen closely, the white horse is not death, but has a rider and an escort such as French or English Renaissance would paint — a fair damsel and her champion."

Gone are Dr. Kelly and Dr. Halsted's blue eyes, gone are "The Horsemen of Medicine" and gone is all reference to the Apocalypse! The portrait now turns out to be in three pieces, the seams of which are plainly discerned. Some now say, it arrived in Baltimore in that condition and was "put together here."

The portrait which Mr. Sargent did, prior to The Four Doctors, of Miss Garrett, hangs over the mantlepiece. It looks very Dutch and one would never imagine that this lady called down Dr. Gilman for mis-listing The Women's Fund Building as the Anatomical Laboratory in the University Directory and made him change it, too. By her act in providing the money to open the Medical School, on the proviso that women be admitted on the same basis as men she altered, forever, the status of women in medicine throughout America. (If Miss Garrett could see the present Centrex telephone guide for the Medical Institutions, she'd come down out of her portrait and say a few things!)

Thanks to the "restorer" both of these portraits by John Singer Sargent glisten sufficiently to make excellent color photographs. The portraits in the old reading room do not appear to have received similar attention and they are listed at the end of this chapter for the reader's benefit.

A third painting has just been hung in the Great Hall, the excellent portrait of the Professor Emeritus of Physiology and Dean Emeritus of the Medical Faculty. The presentation, acceptance and acknowledgement were moving experiences and fortunately were published in *The Johns Hopkins Medical Journal*.

Also, in the Welch Library is the Henry Barton Jacobs Memorial Room, given and endowed by the late Dr. Jacobs to house his medical rarities. He was a profound student of medicine and spent his life collecting. As a young man he did notable work in tuberculosis and much of his library relates to that subject.

The Maurice H. Givens Rare Book Room.

Another gift, a recent, magnificent one, was left by Dr. Maurice Givens, who died of a heart attack on April 19, 1970. He attended Hopkins Medical School for a short time in 1909. Some years later, he received his Ph.D. in chemistry from Yale; in the interim he had worked with Dr. Hunter, the chemist, at Cornell and also with Dr. Goldberger on pellagra in the South.

His gift to the Welch Library is in 2 parts, one of which has already been used to create the Givens Rare Book Room; the residue of his wonderful gift becomes the property of the library after the death of his widow.

He could not have given his bequest at a more opportune time, because the Welch, as well as other learned libraries, has been plagued with rare books developing "wings," and this permits them to assemble all such books in the beautiful Givens room under the watchful eye of a constant librarian. Admittance here is only on request and for specific purposes.

Another doctor who never forgot his Hopkins relationship was Colonel Henry Beeuwkes (OHH:JHMS, 1906). Last year from the estate of his widow, the library received $30,000, the income of which is to be used to purchase books for the historical collection.

Colonel Beeuwkes graduated in 1906, Dr. Givens was at the Medical School in 1909. Who was the teacher who made these two medical students so aware that knowledge descends through books?

Stairway niche, between first and second floors, holds a bronze bust of Dr. Welch.

At top of stairs is portrait of Dr. Wade Hampton Frost, Prof. of Epidemiology (1921-38).

On right wall of right wing of stair, portrait of Dr. Welch.

In the old reading room:

Dr. Lewis Hill Weed, Prof. of Anatomy and Dean of Medical School

Dr. Daniel Coit Gilman, first President of JHU

Dr. Franklin Payne Mall, Prof. of Anatomy

Dr. Lewellys Franklin Barker, Prof. of Medicine

Dr. Florence Rene Sabin, Prof. of Histology

Dr. John Whitridge Williams, Prof. Obstetrics and Dean of Medical School

Dr. Henry M. Thomas, Associate Professor of Medicine

Dr. John Jacob Abel, Prof. of Pharmacology

Dr. William Henry Howell, Prof. of Physiology and Dean of Medical School, Director of School of Hygiene and Public Health

Dr. Theodore Caldwell Janeway, Physician-in-Chief

Dr. Elmer Verner McCollum, Prof. of Biochemistry

In The Great Hall:

The Four Doctors (London, 1905) by John Singer Sargent

Miss Mary E. Garrett (London, 1904) by John Singer Sargent

Dr. Philip Bard by Herbert Elmtree Abrams

Post-Graduate Health: School of Hygiene

AFTER World War I, there was a world-wide zeal toward improving the health and habits of people everywhere, and a prime mover in this endeavor was Dr. Welch. In 1916, he had inveigled an appropriation from the Rockefeller Foundation of $267,000 for a "school or institute of hygiene and public health" at Hopkins. The grant was given on the proviso that he devote all his energies to the project; this he did and in 1922, the Rockefeller Foundation granted him $6 million more; and the School of Hygiene and Public Health opened its doors, at its present location, in 1926. Since 1919, 3,485 degrees have been given by the School with students receiving either a Master of Public Health, Doctor of Public Health, Master of Science, Doctor of Science, or Doctor of Philosophy degree. Starting in 1970, a new degree program, Master of Health Sciences, was offered. It will provide general training in the field of public health and also specialized training in a field of the student's choice.

Professor Donald Fleming in his wonderful book on Dr. Welch remarks, "The school has been the model, too, for similar institutions in London, Toronto, Copenhagen, Sao Paulo, Zagreb, Prague, Tokyo, Ankara, and Sofia." It has brought to the Hopkins people from everywhere, and a roster of its graduates reads like an Almanach de Gotha of international medical scholars, which indeed it is. One of the best schools of public health, patterned on the Hopkins one, is at the University of Pittsburgh.

The School of Hygiene and Public Health at Hopkins now has an enrollment

The School of Hygiene and Public Health with its recently added wings. The South Wing (foreground) is named the Ernest L. Stebbins Building, in honor of the former Dean.

of 480 (in the first edition of this book the enrollment was 120). All of these students are either M.D.'s to start with, or have a B.S. degree and are working toward one or more of the degrees above listed. Many who come to get a M.P.H. go home to do their field work and come back later to get a D.P.H. The student enrollment at present breaks down to 343, full-time; 69, part-time; 115 foreign students; 325 men; 155 women; and 65 nonresident students in the field, and 3 on leave of absence.

To house this tremendous growth, the School of Hygiene has sprouted wings. Where the sheep used to graze toward Welch Library, a research wing 8 stories high new exists. In the basement until recently were the computers for all of JHMI — Johns Hopkins Medical Institutions. They have been moved to the Turner Building and are hooked up with the computers at Homewood and the APL — Applied Physics Lab in Howard County; these result in "one of the most sophisticated computer systems in the world."

The first 4 floors of the North Wing of the School of Hygiene building are devoted to radiological Science and the chairman of the department has his office here. The upper 4 floors of the wing are devoted to research, some of which is referred to later. Among them are: nutrition studies, industrial hygiene, and chronic disease.

In the old main section are still the Offices of the Dean and three Assistant Deans, Admissions, Curriculum, and Student Affairs. The Emeritus Dean of Student Affairs, also formerly Secretary of The Johns Hopkins Hospital, has a maginficent knowledge of the past and the present of the institution.

The present Dean holds both a master's degree in public health and a doctorate in public health administration earned at the School of Hygiene, and he has a wide knowledge of the world, through U.S. Public Health Service work, as well as of the ins and outs of Hopkins.

The Dean Emeritus, who retired in 1967, is still very active in world health circles and a learned counsellor to the world. In the many years he was Dean, much

Dr. Ernest L. Stebbins,
Dean Emeritus.

180

The School's new cafeteria, on the 9th floor, overlooks the harbor and the Hospital's Dome.

happened around the world and a great deal of it healthwise was directed and guided by the School of Hygiene. It is fitting and just that the beautiful new south wing of the building be named the Ernest L. Stebbins Building. Dedicated in 1968, it is devoted almost entirely to teaching, there being 56 individual offices for study area and office space for graduate students, as well as a large room on the ground floor with 32 study carrels. Also, there are 130 offices for faculty and supporting staff, as well as 20 lecture, meeting, and seminar rooms.

On the 9th floor, atop the building, is a cafeteria seating 180 people and providing not only a beautiful view of Baltimore harbor, but also excellent food.

The east wing, which is attached to the center rear of the original building, contains an auditorium to seat 275 people, as well as many research departments; as was the South wing, it was financed by a $3 million grant from the U.S. Public Health Service and an additional $1.5 million from private sources.

This may seem a lot of money, until you think of things like this. From 1956 to 1966, "the United States Surgeon General, Deputy Surgeon General, several Assistant Surgeons General and four of the seven Directors of the National Institutes of Health were all graduates of the School of Hygiene and Public Health"; at present 650 of the alumni, across the world, are living and working in public health related fields.

Among the international activities of the School of Hygiene and Public Health are health-planning studies in Chile, Peru, India, Nigeria; population dynamics field studies in India, Chile, Nigeria, Pakistan, Indonesia; health manpower studies in Taiwan, Turkey, Peru, and Nigeria; analysis of rural health centers in India, Turkey, Taiwan; child health-care in Nigeria; health in developing countries in Ethiopia, Peru, Chad, Afganistan; rural health internships in India; community health at Lagos Medical College in Nigeria; leprosy in Bengal province, India; International Center for medical research training in Calcutta, India; public health, Pakistan; faculty exchange, Philippines, India, Nigeria.

Of 3,485 degrees awarded since 1919, M.P.H. numbered 2,005; M.H.S., 1; Sc. M. Hyg. 111; Dr. P. H. 308; Sc. D. 90; Ph.D. 42; Sc. D. Hyg. 358; Sc. M. 59. C.P.H. (none since 1939) 493; B S. Hyg. (none since 1929) 18.

For many years one of the finest teaching adjuncts of the school was the Eastern Health District, started in 1932, and comprised of 24.2 square miles to the

Sister M. Rosaria Kranz, OSB, M.H.A., M.P.H., who is a candidate for Dr. P.H. in the School of Hygiene and Public Health. Her chief interest is in comprehensive health planning.

north and northeast of the School of Hygiene. It was a special unit of the Baltimore City Health Department and a training center for these Hopkins hygiene people, where much was learned about practising public health methods and helping underprivileged populations. The students ran service clinics, teaching clinics, and worked in close cooperation with the Social Service workers. Many strange sights came their way. One of these was the poor family to whom they had given a seat to put on their uncovered toilet. They returned to find the toilet still uncovered, and the seat being used as a frame in which to house a brand new photograph of the entire family.

In the first edition of this book, a study regarding premature birth weight was discussed. It was concluded 4 years ago and one of the conclusions the study indicated was that "the smaller the baby, the less favorably the baby compares in many measurements. For example, the possibilities of its effects on the child's physical and psychological aspects, as well as the child's I. Q."

There are studies now in progress to determine the effects of a pregnant mother's diet has on her offspring, and what are the minimal food requirements needed to recover malnourished children. Incidentally, the School of Hygiene has banned cigarette vending machines from their building, as has also the Medical School.

The most important period of a man's life, according to an old Chinese proverb, is spent in his mother's womb. Remembering this truism a Chinese professor in biochemistry at the School of Hygiene set out to apply and evaluate it. Due to his brilliant work, many obstetricians now advocate that pregnant women gain, not lose weight.

Much of the many years of study, work and observation done in the Eastern Health District will be of invaluable aid to the East Baltimore Clinic Project, which the Hopkins is now involved in. Learned, kindly, thoughtful men have devoted their lives to endeavoring to improve the conditions in East Baltimore, whether the persons benefited thereby appreciate it or not.

182

One of the most interesting examples of this concerns the origination of the school as described in Dr. Huntington Williams lecture "Osler and Welch Founders of Modern American Public Health" read before the History of Medicine section of the Richmond Academy of Medicine, in February of 1953. In that paper he credits Dr. Osler's great concern for tuberculosis and typhoid having a profound influence on Dr. Welch, and their mutual determination to better the lot of the poor.

In the strange way that the mortar of now is laid in the bricks of then, there is an odd situation at the School of Hygiene concerning early Hopkins; Dr. Crowe, in his *Halsted of Johns Hopkins* describes a brain operation done by Dr. Cushing upon General Leonard Wood, at Hopkins, in February of 1910. The operation is described in detail, and it was long, and tedious, but General Wood recovered completely and became Chief-of-Staff of the Army, and Governor of the Philippines.

Well, in 1959, the Leonard Wood Memorial Leprosy Research Laboratory was moved to Hopkins from Harvard Medical School, and the doctor in charge of it, who had been affiliated with the laboratory for 22 years, came to Hopkins. He is still at Hopkins, and is now a Professor of Pathobiology. At this writing, Hopkins' researchers are in India taking skin samples to find out more about leprosy, for it has been established that the bacteria associated with leprosy is in people who have no outward signs of the disease. Are they carriers of the disease, spreading leprosy? The work in India is combined with work at the Wood Laboratory where they are attempting to grow the leprosy bacteria in test tubes. This has never been done, but it must be, if a vaccine for leprosy can be developed. In the world 11 million people suffer from leprosy.

Another disease which is rarely seen in the United States, though about 50,000 residents of New York City — mostly Puerto Ricans — have it, is schistosomiasis. However 200 million people in Egypt, Africa, Puerto Rico, Brazil, other parts of Central and South America, China, Japan and the Philippines suffer from it. "It is an infectious disease, caused by a parasitic worm, and transmitted by certain freshwater snails living in the streams, and rivers of many underdeveloped countries. It affects various parts of the host, including the liver, the lungs and the central nervous system. Next to malaria, it is man's most serious parasitic infection."

In 1965 at the School of Hygiene, the World Schistosomiasis Research Center became the first laboratory equipped for a multi-disciplinary study of the disease. The Wellcome Trust of London (Burroughs-Wellcome drug people) put up $53,000 toward the study, and the World Health Organization is financially assisting it, too. Another team, headed by a professor of pathobiology, pharmacology, and experimental therapeutics, are studying the physiology of the parasite. What is essential to its survival? And can they design drugs to eliminate it? Part of their research is to anesthetize hamsters, put them in dishes of parasite-infested water, then test various drugs on the infected hamsters.

Population studies, birth control studies, health manpower work studies, pollution, of all types, are only a few of the many fascinating facets of life at the School of Hygiene.

Some of its most delightful aspects are it has a polite doorman; a guest book which every visitor signs; clean halls; quiet; and everywhere the sense of knowledge, imagination, and a true concern for all mankind whatever his whereabouts or his politics.

These are adult people, concerned with adult problems, in an adult way.

CHAPTER XVII

To Mend the Mind

FEW people realize that the Director of The Johns Hopkins Hospital from 1889, when it opened its doors, until 1911, was a psychiatrist. In those days he was called Superintendent of the hospital and his name was Dr. Henry M. Hurd.

When the invitation was issued to him to come to Baltimore, Dr. Hurd was Superintendent of the Asylum for the Insane at Pontiac, Michigan. He was 46 years old when he came to Baltimore and had graduated in medicine from the University of Michigan in 1866. He, too, had seen troublous times in America and understood the distress of conflict and war weary men.

From the opening of the Medical School, Dr. Hurd not only ran the hospital but he also lectured in psychiatry to the medical students. In 1905, he asked to be relieved as Professor of Psychiatry; and 3 younger men took over the duties which he had performed in that field and kept them until Dr. Adolph Meyer came to Hopkins in 1914. Therefore, for the first 24 years, there was no psychiatric building at Hopkins.

The man who had more to do with the building of the Phipps Clinic than anybody else was a writer named Clifford Beers. In 1908, he published a book called *A Mind That Found Itself*. Dr. Welch read it, liked it, and in a casual conversation with Mr. Henry Phipps, a wealthy Pittsburgher, he praised the book at length. Shortly afterwards, Mr. Phipps wrote Dr. Welch that he would like to endow a

Dr. Henry M. Hurd
(1843-1927),
Superintendent of
The Johns Hopkins Hospital
from 1889 to 1911.

184

psychiatric clinic at Johns Hopkins. This he did, and Dr. Adolph Meyer, who had helped Mr. Beers with his writing, became the first Director of the Phipps Clinic, which opened in 1913. Dr. Meyer also became the first full Professor of Psychiatry.

It is impossible to describe how modern, beautiful, and commodious the Phipps Clinic was considered in 1914, at the time of the 25th anniversary of the hospital.

Again, as with the building of the hospital itself, money had been provided by the donor for Hopkins to send 2 doctors abroad to Holland and to Belgium, this time, to study the types of psychiatric hospitals existing there. The plans for the Phipps Clinic had been most carefully worked over and criticized and everybody was thoroughly satisfied with the resulting building.

When the building opened in 1913, it must have been the proudest day of Dr. Henry M. Hurd's life. He had retired as Superintendent of the hospital in 1911, at the age of 68, therefore when Phipps opened, he was 70 years old. It was a psychiatrist's dream of a perfect hospital.

Twelve years ago, the then Director of the Department of Psychiatry and Psychiatrist-in-Chief, was credited with having introduced group therapy to Hopkins, and had many interesting things to say about Phipps and the following paragraphs reflect some of his ideas.

Phipps is primarily a place where people learn to live; some learn it is all right to know what you want and to try to get it. A considerable number learn that they should not be resentful of life because it didn't bring them their desires. They come to understand that many people get sick because they have ignorant or false notions: they comprehend the necessity of telling the truth.

When one understands that many of the Osler patients and Marburg patients are sick for psychosomatic reasons (the concordance of these figures is nationally proven), one grasps the importance of psychiatry and the place of Phipps in the Hopkins scheme. Colorado General Hospital was first to chart the fact that one-third of the people are ill from clearly organic disease, one-third from wholly emotional reasons, and one-third from partly emotional and partly organic sources — hence their dependence upon psychiatry in their treatment and recovery.

Another duty of Phipps is to advance knowledge and then to diffuse knowledge: part of this consists in testing knowledge and ideas; part of testing means you use it in treating the patient.

The Phipps garden in winter.

The group theory which this Psychiatrist-in-Chief (who is still living) brought to Hopkins means a group of 6 or 8 patients, a doctor, and an observer meet together and the patients discuss their problems among themselves and combat the doctor in his advice to them about those problems. The observer says nothing and listens. By this method the patient will learn to advance his thoughts, defend — or if the error of them be made plain to him — reject them, and express himself anew — and differently. Milieu or group therapy is adjusting to the social system as it exists.

There is a portrait of the Psychiatrist-in-Chief who inaugurated this form of treatment in the Phipps Common Room, on the first floor. The same artist who did the portrait of Dr. Austrian, in Osler, also did the portrait of Dr. John C. Whitehorn. He was succeeded at Phipps by Dr. Seymour Kety, now at Harvard, who, in turn was succeeded, in 1963, by the present Psychiatrist-in-Chief and Director of the Department. He was a young man when he came and will always appear so. Medical students get on with him. He was trained in England and under his guidance Phipps is now organized on the British Firm System, of which more anon.

Group therapy is still used, but now in combination with individual therapy. Individuals who would benefit from the additional group experience go into groups.

By dramatizing among a patient group a patient's essential difficulty, that patient may *recognize* it is his difficulty, and learn to face it in an acceptable manner. For example, a child who hates its mother will either become anxious to strike the person impersonating the mother — or when the group discusses the shortcomings of the mother-character, the child will gain a new concept of the mother. If this occurs, the child will then see the situation in an acceptable manner.

As already seen repeatedly in references to the "whole man" throughout this book, psychiatrists work, literally, throughout the entire hospital now. Many of them are in daily consultation in CMSC, both on the adolescent and younger-children floors, as well as elsewhere, in other buildings.

One important piece of research to come out of Phipps concerned the screening of the different types of doctors who are successful with different types of patients. Twenty-four doctors were screened; treated by one group of those, 75% of a given number of schizophrenics improved, whereas 25% of a given number failed to improve. When these doctors were tested to see why this was so, it was

A group of Phipps patients gather on the lawns for a spring afternoon recreation session.

found that these same 24 doctors when treating patients who were neurotic or depressed charted in the neurotics an improvement rate of 80% and with the depressed a rate of 75%. In an endeavor to find out why, the 24 doctors were tested by a testing system comprised of numerous questions intended to reveal their strong vocational interests. Two series of tests, regarding the recovery, under their care, of schizophrenics showed that doctors who fell into the lawyer-type vocational category tested ten on the first group of recoveries, and eight on the second; four of the doctors were neutral, whereas the doctors with the poor recovery percentage, whose vocational category was of the printer, high school mathematics teacher, or policeman type, had a recovery rate of minus ten and minus eight.

In other words, a doctor who was not rigidly set within a prescribed range of conformist pattern, but had the mental flexibility of a lawyer, was vastly more successful at persuading these withdrawn people, who had pulled the curtain down between themselves and the world, to take their mental fingers from in front of their eyes, turn their faces out from the walls and look at the world, than were the doctors who were, themselves, inclined toward rigidity.

This is a very important treatment-tool when one considers that the majority of psychiatric patients come from too rigid backgrounds.

As of the spring of 1970 there were reputed to be 6 million mentally disturbed adolescents in this country between the ages of 16 and 24, less than 1 million of whom are receiving any kind of psychiatric help. On the basis of these statistics one begins to comprehend why psychiatry and behavioral sciences has one of the largest faculties of any department in the Medical School, numbering 210 members. Although the group above cited has increased about 32% in the last 10 years, the increase in mentally disturbed youngsters has been as high as 150%.

The interest in these subjects has become so great that any time you see two or three psychiatrists gathered together, you will probably see at least two or three or more medical students with them.

Studies on all sorts of subjects are in progress. In the Center for Training and Research in Community Psychiatry, there is a study on a grant from NIMH in the study and prevention of suicide; the program aims to prepare individuals of various disciplines for positions of leadership in treating, teaching, administration, and research in the area of suicide prevention, emergency mental health care in suicide prevention centers, emergency mental health services, and community health programs.

Another subject under scrutiny is Curricular Options Study. Which students should accelerate through medical school in 3 years? Which need 4 years or 5 years?

In the Children's Psychiatric Service, there is a study being conducted in group psychotherapy with dialysis patients, who have to follow a complex dietary program on which their lives depend. (Misery needs company, and if it knows it has company, it can sometimes stand the misery better.)

The medical student now takes Psychiatry in Year II, Year III, and a 9-week course in the last quarter of any of the following years: III, IV, or V. During this course, the students serve as clerks on the Phipps wards. Each student has one or more patients from which he takes the initial case history and follows the patient's course, under supervision from a preceptor. In addition, the medical students evaluate and treat patients in the Phipps outpatient and adolescent services,

Children's Psychiatric Service; they also observe outpatient group therapy and see psychiatric emergencies. They learn, too, the use of psychotropic drugs, methods of supportive therapy and attend clinics at Spring Grove State Hospital and Patuxent, and they attend seminars on topics of psychiatric interest, including major psychiatric syndromes.

Learning to counsel and then withdraw is a very important part of the Phipps man's training. As a result of the Harriet Lane Psychiatric Outpatient Service, the pediatricians learned much pediatrics, in the time so saved for them, but they learned *no* psychiatry. Hence, the commencement of the Phipps men going throughout the general hospital and doing psychiatric consultation service, thereby endeavoring to teach resident staffs to recognize psychiatric problems, differentiate them from other difficulties and educate themselves to cope with them. This psychiatric liaison service is supplied "on request only" from resident staffs. One of its purposes is not to take the patients out of where they are, but to teach doctors — and students — to learn to manage them there; also, to make them comprehend that designating a person as "Phippsy" is merely a way of repairing one's own conceit. (I *have* to be sane to say he is crazy, formula.) There are times when a man may appear wacky and be so from heavy medication and not from psychosis and learning to recognize this, and teach other men to do so, is one of the responsibilities and duties of Phipps men.

Early in his Phipps training, the student is warned against the dangers of casual conversation regarding cases or patients and grows to understand the inadvisability of such discussions, even among students. In the 2nd year, he is trained in ways to talk to the patient and learns "A Guide to Patient Interviewing" methods.

When you talk to Phipps people now, they say, "We are so completely renovated, Miss Taylor would never recognize us!" (They are referring to Effie J. Taylor. When the Henry Phipps Psychiatric Clinic, the first of its kind in the nation, opened its doors she was named the Phipps Director of Nursing. Miss Taylor spent 17 years as a student and faculty member of the Hopkins Nursing School; later she was Dean of the Yale Nursing School).

Phipps now has a total of 77 beds, 9 of which are private and 68 semi-private. (10 years ago they had 104 beds, 19 of which were private and 85 semi-private). However, due to the intense increase in hospital cost, every effort is made now to treat as many patients as possible as outpatients. An inpatient pays $74.41 a day and costs the hospital $80.60 a day. The average inpatient stays 66.21 days. Phipps, like Marburg, runs 95% of occupancy, but the hospital loses on every Phipps patient $6.19 a day.

One really gloomy figure is that an outpatient pays on an average $6.90 whereas the general outpatient expense per visit is $22.05 and there were 20,637 such visits in 1971. Of the outpatients the clinic registers a year, about 3,000 of them are new.

They have abandoned the "Day Hospital," which used to exist and those patients now come in and are registered as outpatients and distributed to all the wards, one to four patients daily. They pay $40 a day and come 5 days a week.

In 1963-1964 $140,000 was spent converting 4 conventional wards into autonomous open ward units, and these were designed to accommodate patients of various degrees of illness without shifting them from one to another as their conditions improve or worsen.

One advantage of this system is that the patient keeps the same doctors who work on the British firm system. "A British firm is a senior doctor, a couple of associate doctors, several house officers and students who work together as a team. They are usually responsible for a ward of about 28 beds and also operate an out-patient clinic from which they take patients for admission or to which they discharge patients from the hospital."

This seems to give the patients more confidence in the care they receive and a mutual better understanding between the doctors and the patients and the patients and the doctors.

These units are coeducational and arranged so that there are private bed and bath areas for men and for women. Both groups seem to improve faster when they are in wards together.

Patients now decorate their own rooms, all areas are open, nurses eat with the patients, and they do not wear uniforms. Group meetings vary with each wing, so they are not all held on Tuesdays.

The rule has been changed that no medical student can become a member of the Phipps staff until he has served a one year internship elsewhere; now this is not always required, if the student seems promising. Phipps determines if it will require this year, although it may still be imposed, if they deem it advisable. He is a junior assistant resident, one year; an assistant resident one year and the senior assistant residency terminates the training. However, the Chief Resident has an additional year, and some fellows, of whom the chief is one, stay on for further study.

From Phipps since 1941 have gone out men, several of whom are full professors now; some say four. The work load per man is heavy, as the clinic now runs about 550 inpatients a year, the outpatients now number about 20,000, exclusive of the outpatient load handled in Harriet Lane.

Of the new open wards, on I East there are 13 patients and 1 Security Room; on I West there are 11 patients and 1 SR. On II West are 10 patients and 1 SR, while on III East are 12 patients and 1 SR and III West are 12 patients and 1 SR. IV East houses 10 patients and 1 SR and IV West 9 patients and 1 SR.

Occupational therapy is on the 5th floor and so is the dietitian's office.

The old Southern judge who years ago brought his son, who had studied too hard in law school and had a breakdown, to Phipps would never recognize the place, or much else about Hopkins, either.

They alighted from the streetcar at Monument and Broadway and the son, being vastly more agile than the judge, walked swiftly into the hospital and said he had brought his father to become a patient and the psychiatrist had to keep both several days before deciding which man to detain.

All Phipps PNAs, Phipps Nursing Assistants, are very carefully chosen and thoroughly trained, because their handling of and reports upon the progress of the patients are of great aid in affecting recoveries.

The 4-day-patients on each ward, who arrive at 8:50 A.M., have coffee and a friendly discussion or short group meeting with the nurse and discuss the problems which have arisen among them since 4:30 (the time they go home) the day before. Or, perhaps, another day, the floor group, of which they are members, will have their group meeting with the doctor, discuss and decide questions, and plot their ward events.

Each day from 9:30 to 11:30 A.M. they have in the following order, minor crafts, ceramics, carpentry, and recreation. The recreation they indulge in mutually; the other things according to their bent. Often a group paints tole trays or paper racks from number charts: a painstaking and rewarding occupation.

The midday meal is brought over from the central kitchen and eaten family style, and attractively appointed. Patients eat at tables set with place mats, 4 persons to a table. Mid-afternoon nourishment — juices, or milk and cookies — is served, as well as the 3 daily meals. (There is nourishment at night before-bed, too.)

The afternoon activities of the week vary; dancing is from 1:30 to 3:30 on one day a week; on another there is the group meeting with their doctor, and 3:00 to 4:00 daily, there are ward activities. One day a week, they watch a movie, in the early afternoon, then discuss it afterwards. Other days they have drawing, pottery, and recreation.

In case anything goes wrong with any patient, at any time, the nurse is free, using her own discretion, to call the doctor, and does so. The nurses in charge of these wards are highly trained, extremely gentle, genuinely kind, and the success of this type of treatment appears to be remarkable. As the nurse points out, the cures for mental patients must come from within.

Projects away from the ward, such as ice and roller skating parties, are also used as a means of group pleasure and fun; bowling too, which is done weekly at a nearby bowling alley, is increasingly looked forward to. The ping-pong table in the work room is in constant use, and the knowledge that co-ordination is possible there brings confidence for other and more strenuous efforts elsewhere. (After all if ping-pong can pierce the Iron Curtain, it can help in Phipps, too). A piano is frequently available, and TVs and radios abound.

Another cheering note is provided by the oil paintings, and other forms

A display in the Phipps lobby describes Dr. Adolf Meyer, the man.

Dr. Esther L. Richards (1885-1956).

of art loaned from the travelling collections of Art for the Hospitals of Maryland.

One of the most interesting projects in Phipps now is the outpatient craft group which use a room in the Phipps basement. Five days a week 40 of these patients work here making leather key cases, tile ashtrays, etc.

Twice a year they have a sale of their wares, spend some of the money on social events, and give the rest to charity. Last year they helped a local high-school band and bought supplies to make the Easter baskets for the CMSC children. They also help each other. And as their skill in crafts grow, they go out and teach other people, too; notably at Flynn House, Hopkins half-way house for alcoholics.

Until July 1, 1959, the University had no Department of Sociology; and since the tremendous increase in so many different types and groups of people for psychiatric help, it is fortunate that there now exists at Hopkins a large corps of psychiatrists and people trained in the behavioral sciences, too. The Behavioral Sciences research in Traylor, the new research in drugs and drug addiction, the Comprehensive Health Services in Columbia and East Baltimore, the Drug Abuse Clinic on Rutland Street, the Fellowship House on St. Paul Street — where recovering patients have a chance to experience community living, community responsibility, job orientation, under a controlled environment, are only *some* of the many projects and project-problems in which Phipps men are involved.

Two of their greatest laboratories have already been covered in the chapter on Neurology, which — who knows? — may shortly be adjacent to Phipps. In the mythical new building to replace Harriet Lane, there should certainly be ample quarters for Neurology, and perhaps, ENT, also.

If this were done "the entire head of man" would be housed, together, on the South Side of the Hopkins Complex.

This chapter should not close without recalling that the bronze bust and portrait of Dr. Adolph Meyer and the marble bust of Dr. Esther Richards are in the Phipps Common Room, on the first floor.

And Mr. Phipps' portrait is there, too.

Also in the lobby of Phipps, the Professor of Psychiatry has placed a collection of memorabilia relating to Dr. Meyer. Several letters to Dr. Meyer and his replies make especially good reading giving insight into the practices and customs of his day.

CHAPTER XVIII

The Unseen Hospital: I

FROM the minute you set foot inside the front gates of the hospital, you come under the care, one way or another, of the multitude of people who comprise the "unseen hospital." For instance, they paint the fence, keep the walks in shape, plant the flowers, trim the shrubs and lawns. Then, when you set foot in the hospital vestibule and observe the excellently polished brass, you may be surprised to know that an expert brass polisher, who learned his skill in the Army, is at work daily by 7:00 A.M. on this brass.

This vestibule and the lobby of the Administration Building are worked on many times in 24 hours, for the mass of humanity which passes through here in that period is practically impossible to estimate. Some say that 5,000 people a day pass Jesus; others put the figure at 10,000 or more. If you count repeat-passings, it is much more. Jesus is cleaned weekly, but He is dusted frequently.

Note: An interesting figure: The Security Office counted all the people who entered all the doors for several days last year. The average number of entries per day (includes repeat visits) was more than 30,000 persons.

If because of business interests you wish to see any of the departments

Polishing the brass in the main entrance vestibule of The Johns Hopkins Hospital.

The Hospital's copy of Thorwaldsen's "Christus Consolator" receives a thorough cleaning from a member of the Housekeeping Department.

mentioned in this chapter when you are well enough, talk to your nurse and doctor about such a tour and they will get in touch with the proper departments through which to arrange it. All the departments mentioned will be glad to show you about their "domains."

As soon as you enter the Administration Building lobby in winter you are grateful for the heat provided for you with the aid of the "unseen hospital." The building masthead board list, on the wall just beyond the information desk, will give you some idea of the whereabouts of the executives who run this portion of the hospital, most of whose offices are on the upper floors of this building. However to SEE where the work is done, one must take the elevator down, not up.

Underneath all of the buildings at Hopkins there is at least one, and in some cases two, complete subterranean floors where the real work of these departments is conducted. All the workrooms and offices are lighted with electricity and many are air-conditioned. Stairways from each building lead down to the corridor, directly beneath the Main Corridor, and all elevator shafts open on this corridor, also.

Even the Administration Building has a stairway to this corridor; it is the final portion of that iron, narrow back-stairway up and down which for 69 years interns and residents bolted to and fro from their quarters on the upper floors of the building.

Dr. Billings called the sub-corridor, the "pipe tunnel," because all hospital pipes for heating and ventilation (now air-conditioned) are overhead and exposed to instant view, and may be reached whenever necessary to be worked on.

Whatever you call it, though, this is a busy, busy place. One is reminded of the loading of a freight ship on the docks by the motor tugs scooting to and fro; here, however, the motor tugs are hauling food carts, laundry wire shoots, plumbing and carpenter requisitions, Central Supply orders, stationery orders, and clean uniforms.

Before you get out into this maelstrom of movement, as soon as you step from the elevator you see the offices and shops of the Maintenance Department, which employs 110 people, half of whom are busy all the time on repairs and alterations. The remainder maintain the heating, air-conditioning, ventilation, carpetering, painting, plumbing, electrical work, or are grounds keepers (there are 9 of them and they care among other things for 250,000 square feet of lawn).

At night 2 jacks-of-all-trades maintain the mechanical equipment of the hospital. Also, the Fire Brigade consists of maintenance men who volunteer to serve in emergencies and are trained to do so.

Racks of different sized plumbing pipes, nipples, plumbers' snakes, and all the accouterments of their trade are down here, too, as well as blueprints of every line in the hospital.

The carpenters still wear out more chisels than any other tool and their biggest annual purchase is lumber. In their way, they have always been historians of the Hopkins hospital, too. It was a man named John Thomas, who had worked for the contractor building the hospital, who turned the key unlocking the main door of the hospital in 1889, and afterward became a hospital carpenter. That key is now lost and the lock upon the main door of the hospital has been sealed. There is no working lock upon the "front door" of The Johns Hopkins Hospital.

Also it was a carpenter, William L. Woods, who put the false cornerstone up in the Dome, and Mr. Leeke, then a carpenter climbed, to place the weather-vane. The strange piece of writing done on wood and recently found when a wall was rebuilt during the placing of the air-conditioning ducts, was done by Chas. H. Shutt, a carpenter, in June, 1886, and hidden in that wall. He was then 32.

But the carpenter who had the greatest influence upon the history of this hospital was an uncle of the late Dr. Alan M. Chesney, who was born shortly before the hospital opened and whose childhood pleasure was listening to his uncle describe working on the Dome construction. Therefore ALL of his life, the Hopkins Hospital and its history were the most important things on earth to its great historian, Alan M. Chesney.

One final and amusing story about the carpenters centers around the statue of Jesus. Directly under the rotunda, obviously put there at the time the hospital was built, are 3 square, approximately 4' x 4' brick pillars. When the statue of Jesus was brought in, in 1896, He was placed in the rotunda, directly over the center pillar.

Several years ago, during one of these periodic face-lifting schemes which the hospital is liable to, a learned get-the-most-out-of-your-space engineer suggested that those brick pillars be removed as they were nowhere shown on the hospital plans. He ordered several of the old time carpenters to remove them and they just shook their heads and gave a flat and final "No!" and turned away.

After meeting this rebuff repeatedly, the engineer said, "Get me the tools. I'll do it, myself."

"Go ahead," said one of the carpenters, shrugged again and walked away.

"Why won't *you* do it?" the engineer persisted as he ran after him and tugged at his sleeve.

The old carpenter whirled around, his eyes flashing, and snapped, "Because Jesus will fall straight through the floor and the whole darn Hopkins Hospital will really collapse when that happens. That's why. Now go on and play with

The power plant is a complex maze of pipes and boilers.

something *you* can understand. Get out of here!"

All the assembled maintenance men roared, as the bright young man turned brick red.

Two other departments which are supervised by Buildings, Maintenance and Grounds (BM&G) are the Power House, between Rutland and Wolfe Streets, and entered through Rutland Street and the Housekeeping Department.

The powerhouse now burns gas, with oil as a year-round stand-by in case of emergency, and there are four 75,000 pounds per hour steam boilers. From this equipment they supply all of the hospital, and the other medical institutions and also the Maryland Hospital Service Laundry. There is no reduction in temperature in the hospital at night. They do not generate their own power; this is bought from the Baltimore Gas & Electric Company. The monthly gas bill is $30,000; monthly electric bill is $50,000 and the monthly water bill is $10,000.

Also in the powerhouse are three 3,000 ton per hour chillers which furnish Central Refrigeration for the entire hospital. Each is equivalent to the air-conditioning required to accommodate 600 large homes. The Johns Hopkins Hospital put in a 4th chiller in 1971 and the capacity of air-conditioning is now sufficient to accommodate 2,400 large homes. Fourteen people working 3 shifts, 7 days a week work the powerhouse and the equipment is manned at all times. The crew is composed of licensed boiler engineers.

A run down of the Hopkins Hospital air-conditioning situation in the summer of 1971 is as follows: the 4th chiller has been installed and the capacity therefrom applied to the new Edwards Park Building and some other areas.

The Administration Building, Marburg, Brady, and about 2% of Phipps have window units in use, as necessary. CMSC, Blalock, Osler, Halsted, Wilmer, and about 50% of the Dispensary are air-conditioned. So are the operating rooms in the Woman's Clinic. Pathology has no air-conditioning. Harriet Lane has no air-conditioning.

Both the School of Hygiene and the Welch Library are considered part of the university and not counted as a part of BM&G. However, the Welch Library is air-conditioned; and so is the new portion of the School of Hygiene.

This reckoning comes from BM&G and does not include the occasional unit in an occasional office.

The President of the hospital has taken the position that he will not air-condition the entire Administration Building, from the central supply of chilled air until *all* patient areas are air-conditioned — about 70% of these areas are so equipped, at present.

Incidentally, Dr. Billings' pipes were not disturbed when they put in the air-conditioning. There are two ways to get to the powerhouse, underground. One is to go CMSC tunnel past Kennedy, Turner, and exit across from the building through Traylor; the other is a small, almost crawl tunnel-space under Monument Street, no longer in use. Of course the easiest way is at ground level across Monument and half a block down Rutland, past the Pinkerton Agency house and into the powerhouse.

In case of a "brown-out," or a "black-out," auxiliary power is furnished by Diesel generators for operating rooms and other emergency areas. The hospital used to generate its own power, but the switchover to commercial source of electricity was necessitated by hospital machines which require large surges of power not available from the generator supply. Of course, the commercial use has upped the electric bill considerably.

One place where electricity is much more in use now than formerly is in the Housekeeping Department, also under BM&G. It has 240 employees whose job it is to clean the hospital; 34 of these people are supervisors and it is their duty to see that the people under them do their work and keep the hospital clean. All these 240 people work in shifts. Two hundred of them work from 5:00 A.M. to 2:00 P.M. From 7:00 A.M. to 4:00 P.M. and 9:00 A.M. to 6:00 P.M. the other 40, the second and third shifts, work.

Altogether these 240 people clean 2 million square feet of floor space including wooden, carpeted, asbestos tile and terrazzo floors; also walls, ceilings, furniture, and equipment; and included in this work load are 24 operating rooms. Everything in every operating room must be moved and thoroughly cleaned every day.

One worker in Housekeeping has been in the employ of the hospital for 40 years, and the women who clean the operating rooms are all specially trained. These are the most difficult rooms to clean, but the most exasperating portions are places like the Emergency Room, the outpatient departments, and the admitting office and Main Corridor, where there are always people and always some of the people are ungrateful litterbugs.

Not only must the whole hospital be cleaned every day, but the rooms to which patients are admitted, after former patients have vacated them, must be re-cleaned again.

BM&G are continually seeking advice of professionals in all fields and always buying new and improved housekeeping equipment and taking the advice of Community Systems Foundation, a consulting firm that advises hospitals of all types.

Every person entering the hospital affects the Housekeeping Department in wear, tear, and cleaning bills. It costs $200,000 a month to clean and maintain the hospital. The cleaning equipment for each building is housed in that building and each supervisor has an office in the building, also.

Leading out of the elevator corridor into the main subcorridor, one sees a door across the corridor, probably under the post-office entrance on the Main Corridor, saying "Tug-Scrub Room," and it is here that food tug carts are hosed and cleaned daily. They are also charged electrically overnight.

Further down the corridor, directly under the cafeteria is the hugh central kitchen of The Johns Hopkins Hospital. One enters it through an air-door which forms a barrier against outside tunnel air which might come into the kitchens. It has a whirring sound and will blow your papers out of your hand if you are not prepared for it, and it would delight Dr. Billings.

In the original buildings this subcorridor was kept entirely for service, it being thought then, that miasmas emanated from the ground and nothing which touched the sick should be placed at that level. No elevators were put in any of the old buildings because it was suspected that infections travelled upwards and would be carried via the elevator shafts from floor to floor. This is interesting to remember when the chairman of the Department of Environmental Medicine is advocating combining ventilation with ultraviolet radiation to disinfect the air throughout an entire hospital!

Before entering the kitchen, please take a look at those overhead heating pipes which are adjacent to the corridor ceiling. They are historic. Hopkins was the first hospital in America to have central heating. Dr. Billings insisted that the pipes be exposed, so that a leak could be discovered at any time; and he devised the insulation for them, now so widely used everywhere.

In the hospital kitchen there are several longtime service employees, whose service goes back to 1937. The Chief Chef, who formerly dispensed his superior efforts for the benefit of the clients of the now, alas, deceased Emerson Hotel is one such employee. He likes food, enjoys cooking, and has lived to see his dream kitchen come true.

The Assistant Director of Food Production, who is in charge of all the kitchen operations is also an Emerson Hotel alumnus, and has had great experience in hotel catering and allied fields. He likes hospital catering because "there is a sense of pride at the end of the day in catering to help to restore health. Also, there is a sense of challenge because no matter *what* happens, you've got to get the food out."

Chef Herman Prag, now retired, checks the taste of food before it leaves the kitchen.

There are 125 kitchen workers and their shifts vary; some work part time after school. However, there are still 19 cooks, 4 of whom are pastry cooks. During 8 hours of the 24 no cooking is done. The kitchen opens at 4:00 A.M. and closes at 9:00 P.M. (Hospital floors are equipped to house their special diets and emergency meals, for late arrivals, during those 8 closed hours.)

Kitchen food production exists from stove to consumption destination and everybody in the kitchen works a 40 hour week.

Green goods are bought fresh daily; milk powder is still used; margarine is used for special diets; butter for regular ones; meat is no longer bought by the carcass, but by wholesale cuts. Special treats for which the patient pays extra are newburgs, steaks of certain types, and chops. Meats are bought bi-weekly, fresh vegetables 3 times a week; dairy products, daily. All purchasing is now done through a purchasing department. Requirements are given and put out for bids; in some cases, like canned goods, orders may be for 6 months at a time. Mostly frozen vegetables, but some canned, are used; and everybody gets the same. No soft boiled eggs are served, unless on doctor's orders, because of salmonella.

All food preparation equipment receives a complete cleaning.

All equipment throughout the kitchen is stainless steel and there are four 100 gallon and four 75 gallon steel kettles — steam kettles — in which all soup, frozen vegetables, and braised meats are prepared. All bones from which roast meat has been cut are immediately put in the steam kettles, set at simmer, and commence their second usefulness as soup bones. The cooks also have 10 ovens, 4 warming ovens, and a microwave oven. No longer is any cooking done on the patient floors, except diet cooking. Each floor has facilities for warming deferred trays (patients off the floor at meal time), special orders, and also for serving between meal nourishments.

The kitchen is now conducting a survey for a new dishwasher. It takes one and one-half hours to wash up from every meal and 5 to 6 years of use have depleted the present equipment. As 6,000 to 6,500 meals a day are served through this kitchen, one can comprehend the use to which the present dishwashing equipment has been subjected. They still use commercial detergents for dishwashing, to which has been added a chemically sterilizing solution, and the water is 180 F. as recommended by the Baltimore City Health Department. Not only do they, but the School of Hygiene also, keep a careful check on the kitchen operations.

The purchasing of a new pot and pan washer is in the works, too.

Many labor-saving devices are in the kitchen, including one to slice carrots and another to slice potatoes.

All kitchen workers are X-rayed annually and they also have a physical examination prior to employment. They need to be healthy, for they are busy people; there is no slack time and they go from one meal to another. The busiest time, however, is lunch, for not only are all the patients fed but the majority of day workers eat in the cafeteria then.

Many of these people also eat breakfast in the cafeteria, and the hospital uses 210 dozen eggs in 24 hours, all of which are hand broken, which takes considerable time. It also takes time to slice the roasts; (all kitchen blades, as are all other blades belonging to the hospital, are sent outside the hospital to be sharpened). Precisely how many slices are to be had from a piece of meat of precisely how much poundage is well known to the expert carvers. There is a general meat refrigerator on the kitchen floor, a walk-in one, and supplies are brought up from the basement ahead of time and stored therein. There is also another refrigerator for juices, relishes, etc., and salad greens may be stored here. All salad greens are washed before they are cut up.

Hopkins is a teaching hospital in the kitchen, too. There is a classroom off this new main kitchen which holds 25 people, and to which an adjacent special experimental kitchen is attached. The students in this classroom work one half day in the kitchen and study the other half day. The project is paid for as follows: the Federal Government pays 50%, the remaining 50% is paid one-half by the Vocational Training Program and one-half by the Hopkins Hospital. So far 10 students have completed the training. They learn sufficiently varied things so as to permit them to get better jobs as food workers either here or elsewhere. When these funds cease, the hospital plans to continue the project.

Even Kosher food is prepared at Hopkins, for though there is no Kosher kitchen, Kosher meals are served on request.

Eventually, these students are ready to work in the "dish-up" line, under the ever watchful eyes of their supervisors and dietitians. Carts which carry food to the different buildings, called tray-trucks, cannot be replugged on the floors for which they are destined. There 54 such tray-trucks and 1 tug can pull 4 loaded ones, coupled together, and bring back even more empties.

The food on these trucks is kept hot by means of a "hot pellet" method. The pellet is about the size of an after-dinner coffee saucer and goes into the double-soup plate type stainless steel container on which the china (china is used) plate sits. The pellet is about the size of a flat doughnut and removed by tongs from a dispensing oven into the bottom of the steel soup plate before the tray loading commences. All hot food put on the trays is served from a steam table.

The dishing up is done with military precision. First, all menu-marked slips are checked as to diet correctness, and then placed in floor sequence, for the building in question. Then — because they bear in the upper left-hand corner a color-line (5 different ones being used) they are sorted as to placement. Regular diets first, specials, low protein, no salt, etc. follow.

Before any food whatever goes on any tray these computer-studied menu slips are processed. If a mistake has been made in the marking, the computer will throw the slip out for re-checking. So, by the time the tray commences down the moving runway, beside the steam-tables, all is in readiness for it.

It receives its paper placement, dinner-sized paper napkin (pleasantly colored) its cutlery and then its double stainless steel soup-plate, heat pellet, china plate over the pellet, and commences the trip down the dish-up line. The supervisor has re-checked its all important menu slip and the dish-up begins. If the diet is average, progress is easy. If special, each item goes on accordingly; all this being decided en-route from the corner-coloring of the menu slip by the quick-eyed dish-up workers.

Utter concentration accompanies their work.

Great effort is made to provide colorful, attractive meals; and whereas the under half of the aforementioned soup-plate covers the completed china plate when the tray reached the line-up end, en-route everything which goes on the tray, off that china plate, is covered. A milk glass has a plastic top. Celery, etc., is wrapped. Salads and salad dressings are topped; so are desserts, etc.

At the end of the dish-up line are the waiting dietitions and supervisors to check the tray contents; a regular supervisor and a special diet supervisor place their knowing eyes upon every item. Okayed, the trays get their soup-plate tops replaced and are then put in the steel slot racks and thence into the food tray-carts. The doors of those carts are then closed and the carts moved into their 4 cart positions, hooked to their tugs, the lines form and Brady and Wilmer (first to be fed) move out of the kitchen into the pipe corridor under their own power toward the elevators of the two aforementioned buildings. (OHH, Brady carts go to CMSC elevators.)

Dishing up for the whole hospital takes about an hour plus, beginning at 11:30 for dinner and being over by 12:45 to 1:00 P.M.

It is a highly intricate, very exacting process, requiring great skill; and the tension in the kitchen during it is sort of like that in an operating room while a critical operation is in progress.

Only CMSC has slot, self-expelling elevators for single trucks, which are put into the elevators loaded in the kitchen and after proper button punching on the elevator panel expel themselves on the designated floor. This is a great help and possible because CMSC was so recently built. The trucks may also be returned by the same method. In all other buildings the tugs take them to the service elevators.

Other things prepared in this main kitchen are all liquid diets, which may be

Empty train of food carts returns.

200

frozen and called for as needed. They are made fresh every 24 hours. All infant formulas are prepared fresh each morning and taken to the floors as required. Box lunches for CMSC (served on Tuesdays) are prepared here, too.

The major preparation of all the meals served in Turner and elsewhere for special meetings and groups throughout the hospital is done here, also.

The Nutrition Department, which plans the menus of all food prepared in this kitchen, is a huge department, having in the Hopkins' phone directory 41 listings. Each building has a dietitian and the GOR cafeteria and Corridor cafe are also part of this telephone complex. The annual departmental budget is $3 million, over 59% of which is personnel cost, and food alone costs 36%. In a year's time the department served over 1,800,000 meals of which 51% were patient meals and 49% were patron meals. Under the latter heading come all the meals served in Turner. Among the big events is the luncheon served during the bi-annual Medical and Surgical Meetings when 700 to 800 persons are served buffet. In a recent year in Turner there were served 24,782 cups of coffee, 7,164 luncheons per person plus the coffee, 1,167 dinners, and 6,992 persons at receptions.

Turner is excellently constructed, space-wise, for food service, forming a large U-shaped area, with a central concourse and side ambulatories. Each ambulatory will seat 125 persons for a meal. The service area for the whole consists of 1 large pantry, where the salads are sometimes fixed, 1 storage room; but there is no dishwasher. However, this has been very well circumvented by these ingenious ladies of the Nutrition Department. They use green- and gold-edged dinner-sized plastic plates, with napkins to match; sometimes gold napkins, sometimes green. Each round table has a bud vase of flowers in the center, if it is a small one; for a large dinner they buy flowers as needed, and put them in the refrigerators between events, if the second event comes the same day. All cutlery is silver from the hospital sets.

For a REALLY big party they use the large concourse and both ambulatories. The main courses are always brought over from the hospital and for such an especial occasion there is roast beef or newburg. For such a party a typical menu consists of: shrimp cocktail, roast sirloin of beef or roast young tom turkey, salmon in aspic, devilled eggs, potato salad, sliced tomatoes, assorted relishes, parkerhouse rolls, vanilla ice cream slice imprinted with the Dome, and coffee.

In October and May, Turner is used almost daily. During medical seminars 300 a day for 3 days straight come to lunch there, while 300 a day for 5 days come

Employees gather for the annual Hospital Christmas party.

for coffee. Turner began operating in December, 1968, when the Faculty Club in the Welch Library was closed.

The Hopkins Christmas Party for *all* Johns Hopkins Hospital and affiliate-adjacent personnel is "Total Hopkins"; there were 2800 present in 1971. In two hours they consumed 48 gallons of fruit punch; 61 gallons of eggnog; 155 pounds of pound cake; 125 pounds of cookies; 60 pounds of petit fours; 60 pounds of mixed nuts; and 15 pounds of mints!

Turner is also used during the meeting of the Wilmer Residents Association each year in April. Then the fountains outside the large concourse play. They are lighted at night, and the fountains beside the second-story ambulatories play also. For the Turtle Derby dinner, a dance band may be put in a corner of the large concourse and a portable dance floor laid. There is a whole generation of young people around Hopkins now, whose memories are all tied up in this new building, already. Patron Food is a big part of the Nutrition Department's work.

But all of those patients and other people who never attend any event in Turner also have a special place in this department.

The menus for the corridor cafe and the buttery (Women's Board projects) are made by the people who run them. However, in the staff cafeteria, the corridor cafe, and the buttery there are grills which do a steady trade in grilled cheese sandwiches, hamburgers, and frankfurters. Besides the doctors' cafeteria and the staff one, there is a small cafeteria in GOR for the doctors and staff serving the 17 operating rooms of GOR; and those menus are all the responsibility of the Nutrition Department. All these menus which come under Patient Service are planned for 3 weeks ahead on a 5 week cycle, and planning is seasonal, too. Treats like fried oysters or fried onions are sometimes served.

As regards special diets for diabetics, low-calorie and low-protein patients, they are planned as needed and based on the diet therapy policy stated in the *Manual of Applied Nutrition,* 5th edition. Dietitians go on doctors' rounds 3 times a week and each day visit patients on their own.

The tube feeding area in the main kitchen is under diet supervision; and diets are frozen, lasting for 24 hours, and dispensed from floor pantries as needed.

Marburg salad and dessert cart lists are made up weekly, and these trays consist of tossed salads, molded salads, relishes (sometimes), as well as various desserts. There is no extra charge for this service.

The hospital still provides birthday cakes — and sometimes wedding anniversary cakes. Again, no charge.

Guest trays are served on holidays. They are charged for. Also on Christmas, Thanksgiving, and Easter, patients average 1 or 2 such trays.

Coffee service in CMSC for parents is free (hostesses from Special Services take care of this). Coffee is served to the relatives in the Waiting Room outside GOR, too.

Nutrition clinics are conducted by dietitians. There are 3 of these in which patients on special diets are taught how to measure, weigh, and prepare their meals for later consumption when they are discharged. This is done with food models, etc., and patients, after discharge may return for more instruction if they so desire. They are taught to look forward to their future and enjoy their clinic trips.

In the last 10 years there have been many advances in diet. People who formerly died now have a chance to live, thanks to proper nutrition. Kidney cases now have low-protein diets to keep them alive until the transplant occurs. People on diet heart studies, now eat diets modified in fat content. Those with genetic conditions can't digest certain protein or certain sugar; and they, too, continue to live, thanks to special diets.

All the kitchen employees are members of the 1199E Union, and it is the consensus of opinion in the Nutrition Department that employee attendance has not appreciably improved since the workers were unionized. One asset, though, the wise Director of Nutrition points out is the improvement in supervision; and all employees are insured consistent supervision and interpretation of contract clauses.

The plaque in memory of Miss Phyllis Dawson Rowe (OHH), who was Director of the Dietary Department and the School of Dietetics from 1922 to 1949, which refers to her gracious counseling, to which many people can testify, is on the wall beside the entrance to the office of the Director of Nutrition on the 3rd floor of the Administration Building, now.

If you will accept the premise that the doctors, nurses, and the medical students are the brains of the hospital, the patient is the heart, and the unseen hospital is the lungs, you will immediately grasp the total importance that the 19 women comprising the telephone operators of the hospital play. They are now located in the basement of the Marburg Building, to the left side of the tunnel leading toward Hampton House; and they have been in that location since Johns Hopkins Hospital went on Centrex in April, 1964. They are also visible behind the glass windows from the sub-corridor.

There are 19 operators, including 3 night operators; and although these ladies work a 5-day week, the office is in operation 24 hours a day, 52 weeks in the year. It is never closed. All these operators are hospital employees. They are chosen for compassion, for they must be able to understand that people call from all walks of life; and the operator must have some feeling for their needs. They are chosen for intelligence, for they must be able to pick up medical terminology. They are chosen for coolness in crisis, for they must be able to handle all types of emergencies, including initiation of all fire equipment notification.

The lady in charge of Centrex has worked for the hospital 17½ years. Some of her operators have been there many years. One recently retired and plans to

The Hospital's Centrex operators are ready in emergencies and help thousands of callers daily.

tour the U. S. visiting her "famous boys," who were interns and residents when she first knew them — included among her favorites is the Hopkins graduate who transplants hearts in Houston.

When the telephone system was changed from switchboard to Centrex, it obtained a capability for direct inward dialing. Daily calls have increased to well over 100,000 including incoming and outgoing. Out of this total the incoming are approximately 12,000; 85% of all calls are dialed direct.

To handle this very complicated system, the C. & P. Telephone repair men and installers work as needed. The 5 or 6 such men are there all day and some are kept constantly in the hospital during any emergency. They, too, work around the clock as required.

The 3 basic services in this JHH phone center are answering incoming calls, answering and assembling all patient information, and paging.

One thing which most people do not realize is that every patient arriving via the Emergency Room, admitted as an inpatient, is subject to patient information care reporting, too.

The patient information service covers admissions, condition, and death or discharge. When the patient is admitted, the Admitting Office, via teletape, sends the phone operator the patient's name and designated bed space as to building and floor. By means of a lazy susan wheel the patient's whereabouts and his condition information are immediately filed. The next day, admissions sends around a card with his complete data; and this, too, is filed in the susan.

As soon as the admission data arrives via teletype, the operator types the patient name-and-condition slip and pastes these tapes to the floor plan of the susan. These floor patient charts are alphabetically listed and are photographed at midnight, after the hospital census is taken. Then, they are delivered to the floor by the security force.

After she receives them, the charge nurse (when the floor quiets down) checks the patient's condition again; and by 8:00 A.M. via the routine hospital messenger service, all of these daily condition sheets are safely snug in the susan file. Sudden patient changes are reported to the phone operator within 30 minutes and she whirls the susan, finds the patient, and tabulates the change. Patient information notifies relatives when the patient is put on the critical list, if requested to do so by the floor on which the patient lies.

In case of death-verification calls from outside, the operator says, "Have no information on patient. Suggest you contact the family."

Various floors notify families of patient deaths.

Incidentally, there are approximately 600 patient phones in the hospital; and patient calls, except long distance, are included in the room rate. Long-distance calls are extra. A patient can by-pass Centrex on referred calls from his home phone, but this is arranged through the C. & P. Telephone Company, not the hospital. However, it requires prior knowledge of patient room Centrex number.

The Johns Hopkins Medical Institutions has a telephone book of its own listing all the necessary departments and people, and a copy is in every office in the buildings. Therefore, persons having this book may dial direct, as they see fit. It is a time saver for many people, but others, whose eyes are getting dim, curse it and say the whole thing is worse than the Paris phone system!

The Telephone Office ladies have their own lounge and restrooms adjacent, and are always available in case of emergencies. They are certainly an unseen blessing and tower of strength to many persons.

If you are in the hospital and MUST talk to a person who can only be reached through the Centrex system, go to a pay phone, dial 955-5000, explain your problem, and ask the Hopkins operator to CONNECT you. If you haven't the dime to make the call, then go around to the phone beside the information desk, at the front entrance, where there is a permanently kept Centrex book, look up your party, and make the call from there. Also, there are Centrex books at the Hurd Hall and Womans Clinic Information booths. Centrex books at other locations are steadily stolen.

Two parts of the basement complex which are repeatedly seen by patients are not covered here, but in the chapters on Wilmer and on radiology. The primary purpose here is to acquaint the patient with some of those portions of the hospital which constantly affect him, and which he does not see.

The largest of all of these is Central Supply, under a former Air Force supply colonel, whose office is on the 3rd floor of the Administration Building, and whose most capable lieutenant in the basement is a former Air Force nurse: she is in charge of all the technical supplies throughout the entire hospital. Between them, they know everything worth buying in the United States to maintain a first-rate hospital and who has what, when, where, and how soon they can put it on a plane, if need be. Both of these wonderful people have had extensive battle experience and if the goods cannot be purchased, but is necessary to save a life or make a patient more comfortable, they devise it themselves!

She operates from the Osler Basement in an office not much bigger than the vestibule of the hospital, one corner of which has been appropriated for the computer operators and their boss. But via the telephone, constant trips, and constant thinking, thanks to her the Hopkins Hospital performs its technical equipment duties splendidly.

One of the places she checks is the Clean Up Room, which processes 1,600 pairs of rubber gloves on an average day; and they are washed in superlarge washing machines with mild soap. Tubes and catheters are put in mesh bags, and also done in similar machines, but they get a mild bleach, too. All are dried in steam heated dryers (hospital steam), which is best for rubber and cheaper to operate and has no repairs.

Adjacent to this equipment is a distilled water still, about the size of 2 average steel oil drums. At 4 zig-zag steel sinks (easier on turning, leaning over of people performing the task and JHH designed) all tubes and catheters are rinsed

An employee in the Central Supply Department washes catheters, which then will be sterilized and packed for later use.

An employee heat-seals a clean-catch tray in Central Supply. The tray contains two specimen bottles, an aluminum cup and six cotton balls.

under pressure in distilled water; also there are air jets in each sink. Rubber deteriorates from heat. This method gets 10 uses out of a rubber catheter. Then, they are gas sterilized, after the washing.

All glass tubes, bottles, and medicine glasses are washed in a dishwasher-type detergent, then subjected to ultrasonic waves. These have implode, not explode pulls; they loosen the dirt, but don't remove it. Dirt is rinsed off under pressure. Tap water is first used, second, distilled water, and the dirt floats away.

All contact openings with the adjacent Issue Area are under negative pressure causing germs to remain in Clean Up Room. The glass-washer eventually delivers completed loads into Issue Room. The Hopkins-engineered utensil washer cost one-fourth as much as a "Hospital Equipment" one would have cost. Available space at Hopkins would not take the Hospital Equipment model.

The Issue Area has a center section with down-slanting ball-bearing shelves (a chain-store idea) allowing one-third greater shelf space for the room. "No rubber bricks at JHH so expansion comes from using your heads," the Air Force nurse explains. Everything mentioned in floor station consist (explained in Data processing) is stored here, and remains in cut cartons making more storage space. Each item is given a colored computer tag before being stored. The oldest material is used first, therefore storing is from top down roller-coaster shelves. (Orders are filled from the lower end.)

Also in this room are seated the many capable women, in uniforms, who pack the female catheter trays, all equipment treatment trays, and all sterile heart catheter and radium trays for X-ray and special treatments. They do exact, fascinating work, using, among other devices, a high powered electron magnifying glass (about the diameter of a standard saucer). Incidentally, while many plastic items are now used in hospital care, the trays on which all this special equipment is packed — catheter trays, etc. — are a paper product. It is the same type tray also used by fried chicken carry-outs which will hold water for 40 or more hours, and up-chuck pans are also made of this.

Some interesting items are 4,000 to 5,000 catheters are gone over daily and this department is open 24 hours a day, 7 days a week, and employs 72 people. Everything is supervised or checked and re-checked before it is finally sealed and given its computer tags. All the above catheters are put in double-sealed, heat-sealed long-paper sacks. Everything is sterile and all trays are *right* when sealed.

Among the most interesting items in this department are the cardiac resuscitation carts, for pediatrics and for adults. Every floor has one. They are housed in what was originally designed as a Sears tool chest. They contain a Resus bag, drug kit, syringes, drugs (labelled), IV solutions, tracheotomy tray, gloves, gown, cut-down set, IV things. Also they house airway equipment maintenance fluids, and are *locked* with a disposable padlock which once opened cannot be reclosed. When once opened, the whole cart is returned to Issue Area for re-stocking, and re-checking.

These carts make all the difference between life and death, again and again; and their care, both on the floor and in the Issue Area is one of the most serious duties at Hopkins.

Emergency Department thermometers are shaken down in the Issue Area. Two sterilizers are used for the old gravity type and they take 35 to 45 minutes, but the 2 others are high-temperature vacuum and take only 17 minutes.

All bed pans and urinals are dispensed from here, after sterilization, and are now blue plastic. One little boy, who thought his urinal was *so* pretty, couldn't be persuaded to leave it, and carried it around the whole time he was in the hospital.

All the items above mentioned except the resuscitation carts, which are sent by special messenger, are serviced by computer; and every item, every bottle, every solution, every single piece of equipment bears its computer tag.

Also sent out from the Issue Room are the EKG machines, the monitors, all the sophisticated electronic patient-care machines and the orthopedic carts. These were formerly laundry carts; there is something of everything an ortho-pedist needs upon them (a standard new cart would cost $400 to $500 and since the hospital uses 3, the improvised cart represents a true saving as it cost only $36 to convert into its present usage. Each one carries all equipment an ortho-pedist requires, including stockingette and rope and horizontal traction bars.

The Treatment Equipment Room has a multiplicity of "patient helps" in it. The amazing thing is that everything listed here is kept in shape by a single super mechanic, who constantly does the impossible.

Among the equipment items are stainless steel commode chairs (all cleaned, washed, and then squirted with high pressure water line to rinse), patient lifters, hypothermia units, bed jackets, heated bed cradles, walker with wheels, walker without wheels; also, two G suits (anti-gravity), suits, same principle as ones astro-nauts wear; used on the lower chest on down to help maintain blood pressure).

There are cold steam vaporisers; plueral, constant, low pressure, intermittent suctions. The room contains, too, 3 extra-long beds, which are used in spells, then remain strangely idle! Here, too, are hypothermia blankets, and two-piece-each hinged collapsible wooden bedboards, with each section cracked to meet a Gatch bed breaks. Also, one sees a sitz bath chair of stainless steel; Sims heat lamp; circle electric bed which revolves a full 360 degrees; Stryker bed, which revolves on itself; and a Foster bed, in which the patient may be angled.

Everything to make life bearable for the desperately ill patient is here, too, including portable bath tubs, which are used to prevent bed sores and for patients who can't be turned to bathe.

These are indented stainless steel slabs on wheels inset with vinyl tops containing bottom drains. Patient is laid in the vinyl cap, so to speak, and the sides of it are lifted about him and attached to an upper frame. Water is then turned on and the patient is bathed in comfort — sort of. They come in child sizes, too.

Also, there is a floating bed which has a sculptured mattress for a patient with back sores, which takes the weight off him. Scott Paper devised this and a baby one, too, and gave their first models to the hospital, then sold the idea to another manufacturer who now supplies Hopkins.

One pitiful, and odd, story is that of the sea-sick baby in the floating bed. People came to admire the contraption, jiggled the mattress and the baby promptly vomited, but when the ingenuous people from Central Supply made the baby a foam rubber neck contour pilow, she promptly and permanently recovered. The mechanic here not only does the impossible but he also sees that it comes to you in perfect condition and ready to work smoothly. He contributes greatly, to patient recovery throughout the entire hospital.

Also, in Central Supply is the Gas Sterilizer Room, which currently is used Monday through Friday, and does 3 loads every 24 hour period. It is the largest gas sterilizer in use in any hospital, and it is called an Ethylene Oxide Sterilizer. Heat and moisture regulated temperature are 120 to 130 degrees, and it takes 5 isoletted (isolation-packed) or 2 big truck loads. Then there has to be a 48 hour aeration period for the material so sterilized.

The only exception to this is PVC (polyvinylchloride) which take a 7 day aeration period. Therefore, if any equipment so designated is used by a patient once, the hospital must have a supply of the item to last 8 days. This is one of the reasons hospital costs are so high.

The finished loads are put in sealed paper bags, labelled and set about the room to "season."

There is also a smaller sterilizer in GOR. Exposure time to gas is 4 hours. First a vacuum 23 PSI is drawn to remove air, then the gas is released and builds to a plus 7 pounds P.S.I.; at the end of 4 hour exposure the gas is vacuumed out. The load goes through 6 entire cycles and is exposed, to vacuum out, then flushed through with fresh air.

For items requiring gas sterilization, these 2 sterilizers serve the entire hospital, university, and medical institution labs; the latter 2 have the service free of charge, but must bring and get their own loads.

Just to give you a look-see on how vast and important all of these Central Supply operations are, now might be as good a time as any to take the reader to the General Recovery Room, where vast quantities of the equipment here stored, here sterilized, here serviced, are used. Anyhow, as far as the patient is concerned GRR certainly qualifies as part of the "unseen hospital," for you are too sick to know what is going on or you wouldn't be there.

GRR is on Carnegie VII, and receives 30 to 45 post-operative patients daily. The staff works three-8 hour shifts and consists of 5 to 6 R.N.'s by day, 3 evening shift, 2 to 3 night shifts, which is 11:00 P.M. to 7:00 A.M., also technicians (4 corpsmen). Combat men are preferred; the Army is mostly O.T.R. — trained in the field — while those of the Navy and Marines were trained at Great Lakes. At present 3 Navy and 1 Army are on duty in GRR. They work 3 shifts, too, and the team consists of 3 day men, 1 to 2 at night. There is always room for more corps-men. Please apply.

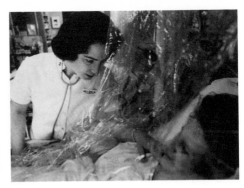

Bedside nursing remains important for patients who need intensive care.

The bed consist is 22 regular, of which 8 are narrower and to maintain the original number, beds are listed 1 through 21, the extra bed being numbered 3½. When GRR is crowded it is possible to raise the bed consist to 30 beds.

Everything on those beds but the patient, including the beds themselves, is supplied through Central Supply.

Also in GRR is one "floating" anesthesiologist assigned to this area. Nursing assistants here transport the patients to GOR (there are now 17 operating rooms in GOR) to GRR or back to the floor, from whence they originally came. These people help with patient care, make beds after each occupant, etc. Here, too are nursing auxiliaries, grade #2 experienced, and grade #1, technical — a total of 3 in all in each shift.

The general factotums of this forever exciting, endlessly busy, life-and-death-and-recovery ward are 2 ward-clerks. They keep the books on the Recovery Room patients, on *everything*: patients' condition, and number of beds available at any given moment. They can *never* lose their heads and they can *never* forget what is in them. There are 4 telephones and 3 extra phones, and sometimes all are in use simultaneously.

All mattresses are rubber-covered; all pillows are plastic-covered. Among the work machines available for each bed are blood-pressure, 3 kinds of suction, oxygen, monitors, oscilloscopes, defibrillators, special respiratory and inhalation equipment, pacers, electric thermometers and hypothermac (for warming or cooling patients). Also, there can be brought in portable X-ray machines (there is a developer in OR and viewer boxes. Picture available in 5 minutes); electroencephalograms; E.K.G.; IV therapy also comes up here and own lab work can be done up here, too.

Besires those 30 to 45 post-op patients, others who need intensive care are adult open hearts, pediatric open hearts (to be moved to their own unit shortly), chest trauma cases — car accidents; kidney transplant patients, donors, and recipients. Interesting insert: kidney recoveries are good now because of careful matching of tissue type. Kidneys are sent wherever needed, if available; those on hand are put on the kidney "ticker-tape" and some have gone from here to Atlanta and Roanoke, Virginia.

The Baltimore Police Department helicopter transports the kidney to a waiting plane at Friendship Airport. The helicopter lands and takes off from the top level of the parking garage, always to the excitement of the neighborhood children.

CHAPTER XIX

The Unseen Hospital: II

MEDICAL and Surgical Intensive Care Units recently opened on Osler VII and Halsted VII, are connected, and each has 21 beds, under 1 joint nursing staff. Part of the GRR work passes on through to them, as recovery becomes feasible.

Work in GRR is very grueling and there is a very rapid nurse turnover; some stay a year, but most stay 2 years. Rapid pace is too exhausting for many people. The head nurse is a slight young woman, who is pretty, unhurried, and yet very fast moving, and completely unflutterable.

Anything she needs from Central Supply, she needs NOW always, and it always must be ready NOW, too.

IV fluids for pre- and-post operative patients are pretty much standard practice now, and the vast majority of those beds above mentioned are being so serviced. Eleven of the best groomed and most attractive nurses at Hopkins are the "Scooter girls." They ride around the entire hospital on a small white scooter; and everybody gets out of their way, everywhere, all the time, for they are always on a "hurry up" mission. Their shoes glisten, their uniforms are spotlessly clean, they have no do-dads or ribbons in their hair. They come from all over the U.S. and Canada and they are an asset to their profession. Nine of them are regular scooter

An I.V. Therapy nurse scoots to the bedside of a patient.

riders, 1 is the supervisor, and 1 is the department head; but they, too, take their turn at scooter-riding, when necessary. Also, working with them is 1 corpsman and 6 medical students. That corpsman, too, has been around. Once when the girls were talking about how hard it was to get the needle in some patients — to stay — he said, laconically, "Particularly in a rolling sea." "What do you mean?" one of the girls asked scornfully. "Just," he explained, "that you've got to hold on to the ladder, balance your tray, swing onto the bottle, and your patients are lying in tiers of 6, in bunks one over the other."

That shut them up! He'd seen duty on a hospital ship, off Vietnam and never told them, before.

The IV shifts at Hopkins are 7:00 A.M. to 3:30 P.M.; 3:30 P.M. to 11:30 P.M.; and 11:00 P.M. to 7:00 A.M. Five nurses work the day shift; 3 the evening; 1 the night. The service is based in the sub-corridor, directly across from Central Supply, in the Osler base.

Intravenous therapy service was begun at Hopkins in July, 1967; and it means that intravenous fluids and medications are given to the patient through the veins. They are fluids which are made isotonic enough to go through the veins and give nourishment and medication to the body. Through the IV method the patient can receive antibiotics, anticoagulants, electrolytes, e. g. KCL which is potassium choloride.

Medicine, surgery, genecology, obstetrics, Marburg, Brady, CMSC, Phipps and Wilmer all will use this service when service is throughout the hospital. Intravenous feedings are also given when oral (by mouth) difficulties exist or rapid absorption of a medicine is needed.

Via the scooter the girls can get anywhere in record time, at any minute. Between the handle-bars there is a shelf on which they carry their IV tray. If fluid balance in the patient is improper, it can be corrected by intravenous feedings even though the patient can take nothing by mouth.

A nurse on a floor may call for an IV nurse when a problem exists with a patient's intravenous therapy. An example of this situation is an extravasation. (This means the needle has come out of the vein, causing the fluid to infuse into the surrounding tissue), and the patient may experience discomfort. An IV nurse answers these emergency calls and replaces the device.

An attractive nurse who answered such a call, approached the patient, an 80-year-old man and said, "I understand you are leaking." "No ma'am," he replied, "I did that right before lunch!"

People even get fat on IV fluids which, in some instances, produce 900 calories or more. Poorly nourished babies who cannot maintain oral feeding or for some medical reason need the intestinal tract put at complete rest are given hyperalimentation treatment.

Vitamins can also be injected via IV fluids. However most people are inclined to lose weight, unless, of course, the feeding contains a lot of calories, as related above.

Isotonic fluids are fluids chemically created to be within the normal balance of body absorption, so the body can absorb them without difficulty. They are never just water or distilled water, as it is not suitable or isotonic. To make it suitable sugar (dextrose) or salt (sodium chloride) must be added in carefully prepared amounts.

Bottles are prescribed according to patient's different conditions by attending doctors. Pharmacy can add medication or prepare any mixture and the patient is still guaranteed of getting a sterile bottle, made up especially for him — "custom made," so to speak.

There are 20 items in the plastic baskets from which the IV nurse draws her equipment. Bottles have a plastic tubing with flow control clamp which can be used to regulate fluid thereby to last specified lengths of time. There is a data notation on final taping, after insertion, as ordered by your doctor. Tape is put on the patient's arm with device.

If you are new at IV care here is what is done to you: the nurse finds a healthy vein, if hairy she shaves the area over with a disposable plastic razor, puts on iodine from individual plastic cachet, rubs it off, scrubs the area with alcohol. Next she removes the pastic tubing from sterile container, inserts the needle, also removed from plastic container, connects tubing thereto and adjusts the flow control (attaches bottle to tubing, raises it to rack, and you are ready to go.) Fluid begins to flow. In cases where a chance cannot be taken on the needle coming out, a plastic catheter is used in its place and this cannot dislodge so easily.

The nurse checks everything to be sure it is working correctly. The whole procedure takes approximately 15 minutes. Then she tells her patient, "If this starts burning, like vinegar in a cut, or if blood appears backing up in the little tube or if your bottle has gone dry, be sure and call the nurse." She leaves the patient comfortable, secure, and informed.

Then she goes and charts on patient's record and "goes home again, out again." Referred calls en route are answered immediately, through pocket-pager. Patients are daily re-dressed and check and tape is again applied-dated.

If patient is having IV for first time, procedure is explained carefully and patient is queried as to whether he is allergic to adhesive and told always to remember the bottle must stay at a level above the heart. Also, things to remember are patient can never get air in veins through the sets used at JHH "Saftiset" prevents this and solution and flow will stop, as needle will clog first.

If an indwelling catheter is to be inserted, the area is anesthetized first and there is only a little sting. These catheters are made of teflon and move with the vein.

The only things which can damage a vein are trauma, some medications, indwelling catheters remaining too long and not cared for properly, and poor sterile technique. No one need fear the latter with this team of nurses and corpsman.

IV baskets are all restocked 6 times daily. One nurse has taken as many as 48 calls in an 8 hour shift. During the week, they have more patients because of major surgery and tests. Most patients get pre-operative fluids and majority have post-operative fluids, too.

These people are where the action is and you can rest at ease when getting your IV's started or restarted by this team: they know their job and all it entails. They care about you. Watch and see if they don't!

Of course you have been wondering where the IV bottles come from and where and how they are made ready for you. So this is probably as good a place as any to describe the pharmacy, which is an up-and-down proposition. The part the patient sees — the ambulatory patient — is in Osler, just behind the elevators, and extends through into the Carnegie Outpatient Building. There is also a satellite pharmacy on Osler II and another in the Osler basement.

In all 3 there are 70 employees; in 1965, there were 30 people. Over $1 million annually is spent on drugs, containers, labels, and related packaging and marking. It is not unusual, now, to fill 1,000 outpatient prescriptions a day (in 1965 they ran 200 a day).

The outpatient clinics are closed on Saturday and Sunday, but the pharmacy still fills 200 outpatient prescriptions then. If the refill time is reached, the patient comes in any time he or she is not working and gets his refill, regardless. Outpatients are 60% on prescriptions from Medicaid (under title 19) and those patients pay nothing, and the hospital is re-imbursed for them by the State. The State pays on such a prescription normally $1.75 plus cost of ingredients. To pay-outpatients the normal charge is $2.00 plus cost of drugs; therefore there is a $.25 loss on all Medicaid prescriptions to the hospital.

Of that other 40% of the prescription load which is supposed to pay, a portion are employees, who get a discount, while university health service patient-bills are sent to the university for collection.

So due to financial leakage, the pharmacy is always in the red; nevertheless, is stays open 24 hours a day and is NEVER closed, and has a staff adequate for the demands placed upon it.

They also fill about 1,000 inpatient prescription orders per day. It is the busiest pharmacy store of Maryland for outpatients in the State of Maryland. To become a pharmacist now takes 5 years university training, in addition to high school; for the training has become much more complicated. In the pharmacy library alone, 600 to 1,000 world periodicals a month are abstracted, mostly from German and French.

The medical staff policy now is that the name of the drug be on every label.

The director of the pharmacy services at Hopkins is the fifth Chief Pharmacist in the history of the hospital, and every pharmacist — female and male — working for him is licensed. There are 29 such employed here now; there were 11 in 1965.

Two-thirds of all patient-doctor visits in the U.S. now result in at least 1 prescription for drugs, which costs on a average of somewhere near $3.70. It is ironic to learn that 66 to 67% of all patients have some adverse reactions to drugs, while 5% of all emergency admissions are due to a drug reaction. Therefore, the pharmacist is steadily in consultation with the medical men as to the whys and wherefores of patient drug difficulties.

Osler, CMSC, and Marburg are the largest drug users, per patient, in the hospital.

One new area of the pharmacy is where preparations not available commercially are added to the bottles containing IV solutions. It is an additive service, where 350 mixtures a day are used; and in 80% of the bottles 1 or more drugs are added. Each bottle has an expiration date on it, and among the things which are added are vitamins and antibiotics.

This compounding job is uniquely taught now in pharmacy school.

The bottles used in Brady, CMSC, and Wilmer are not yet prepared by this method; there, nurses still do it. However, when they, too, get on the computer, they will be so prepared.

As every patient who is operated on now routinely receives IV fluids, the prescriptions for the bottles he will need are sent down to the pharmacy in advance;

Pharmacists prepare medications
in the satellite pharmacy.

and therefore when the time comes for him to be hooked up to his IV fluids, the bottles he required are available to him, wherever he is.

To add to these bottles and still have the contents remain sterile, modern pharmacy practice is indebted to a space industry development which is called a Laminar Flow Air Unit, which is dust-free. It is really a filtered air screen under which the bottles are prepared and sealed. This is all accomplished in the part of the pharmacy in the Osler basement.

The second sub-pharmacy, on Osler II, is referred to as a satellite Unit Dosage Pharmacy. This service replaces the nurses' traditional function of preparing medicine for the patients. The computer takes the doctor's orders, pre-estimates the work load; and as each patient receives on an average of 16 doses of medicine a day, through its exactitude it precludes medicine-mix-up as each dosage bears the patient's name, whereabouts, history number, and dose-time. Here, again, pharmacists work in a sterile atmosphere; and delivery can be made 30 to 60 minutes in advance of dose-time, if necessary, around the clock. If it is changed and wanted immediately, immediate preparation is made and the dosage is run up to the floor.

In fact, in some hospitals now all medicines are given by pharmacists who travel on a close schedule with their medicine baskets on routine routes throughout the hospital. Ohio State University Hospital now uses this method and finds that it frees all nursing personnel for other duties and makes the pharmacist completely responsible for not only preparing, but administering drugs. These unit dose dispensing trays carry carbon copies of the doctors' orders and the pharmacist checks each previously computer checked packaged dosage before administering it.

Osler and CMSC are now on computerized dosages, and it is expected that eventually the entire hospital will be, too.

Again, in the satellite pharmacy all dosages are prepared and packaged beneath the Laminar Flow Air Unit, and are dust-free as well as sterile.

The present Chief Pharmacist teaches not only at Hopkins, but also at the University of Maryland.

Frequent mention has been made of the computer throughout this chapter; and the part of the Osler basement portion of Central Supply in which the ticket reader and print out are located is called the Data Processing room. The master file in the computer memory is in the Turner base computer room, and the Osler base is hooked up with that.

Here, in the simplest terms is how the Osler base works: certain editing of computer contents from time to time is required. They now cover 188 nursing, reception, and LPN stations, and later will cover the whole hospital.

As is well known, a computer is only so good as what you put in it. "If you put in valid information, you get out valid information: machine can do two things — say yes or no; plus or minus."

The man who said this programmed the one used at Hopkins Hospital which is programmed to cover $1.5 million in supplies. (The interior of his head is in such constant operation that his conversation is terse and to the point.) Thanks to the computer the patients get more accurate bills. It is now set-up for outpatient billing, only. Inpatient billing remains a future hope. It can add 10 times more nursing units and many catalogue items (explained later). It is rigged to cover 1,260 beds, eventually.

The total number of items on a surgical ward is 150, more or less; on a medical ward, 100, more or less. Halsted IV is the second largest listing; GRR, the largest; Woman's Clinic the smallest (plus 80, more or less) and Research, where there are 2 or 3 patients runs plus 12 items, more or less.

Special purchasing is done through the computer, too (which means you go outside and buy). All is done with one catalogue, though, and including the number 9 on an item ticket identifies 'special purchase'; NS means non-standard, while LU indicates limited use.

Loss throughout the computer-covered supply stations throughout the hospital can be reckoned accurately and runs to 15 to 20%. Scissors, particularly, go. CSD spends approximately $100,000 replacing items — but this is not all from loss — scissors and other small instruments, though, have an annual loss of $80,000. Again, the thief.

One charming story accentuating this occurred in another Baltimore hospital where the supervisor found so many scissors disappearing that she went onto the ward and actually began taking them out of the employees pockets. One of them protested, hotly, and said, "Those aren't . . . Hospital scissors. They belonged to Hopkins. My mother works there and she gave them to me. And you give 'em back right now! Hopkins buys the *best* scissors. We don't, here!"

The largest thing which has ever been 'lost' from CSD was one orthopedic bed!

The most used thing in the computer catalogue is suture scissors. They have a bin-number of their own, which aids in "pulling supplies," which means filling orders.

Loss, however, will hopefully diminish as monthly ward summary listing of all items and cost of same goes to each ward nurse in charge, Assistant Director of Nursing, and Administrator of the building in question. Plainly stated thievery can be pinpointed with a computer.

The very smart young man who developed the catalogue and set-up the JHH computer now has 90% confidence in the information upon which the computer memory works.

The computer keeps books on its inventory for nursing and Central Supply. It can figure the lead-time (which means from the time of order until item is on shelf.) One of the inventions of this department is a clean catch tray in which the cotton balls and specimen containers are in sterile bags of their own. The computer also keeps track of components.

It takes 5 hours a day now to do the hospital (arrange and check the tickets, again, later explained). However, the actual time of processing the tickets, or cards if you prefer, through the card-reader is about 15 minutes, daily. Twenty-five hundred cards a day go through the whole system. Remember, these figures are for one half of JHH only.

Two very exact young women sort the tickets, arrange them in spindles, and set up the operation. Prior to running the cards through the machines, they do a test-run to be certain there are no "bugs" in their instruments.

To get out of the fancy language and simplify. Suppose you set up, completely, a stocked kitchen — canned goods, gadgets, cutlery, pots and pans, detergents etc. — and each of these items has a specific number tag attached to it, corresponding to the catalogue numbers for that kitchen housed in the computer memory.

Every time you use an item you tear off the number tag and drop it in a plastic bag (each bag has a code number). Translate all of this idea to the items on a surgical ward. At the day's end, the plastic bags from each so set-up station go down to the computer file room, and next morning the two aforementioned young women put the tickets on the spindles and process them through the card-reader to the computer memory. These tickets are white, blue, and red. The first two indicate station-reporting and restock and the third (red) means charge — "you are in the red."

If the supply of the items listed is below average level in the Issue room, (already described) the memory bank electric typewriter automatically types out a requisition to rebuy; if the item comes by cases, the purchase slip so states.

In other words, the computer keeps books against the ward, for the ward restocking — a steady, daily, flow of replenishment items. It also keeps the books for the hospital-cost-sheets and for the patient billing, too. (Every bottle in every case bears a separate ticket, so you couldn't be charged for a case when you've used a bottle.) No, they do not come that way; that is attached in the Issue Room, before

Tags help inventory control for Central Supply.

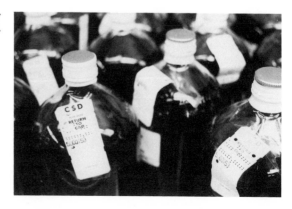

they are shelved.

Your special medicines, however, come down on other slips and they are run through the computer only after they have been checked and rechecked. This is the only thing in the entire procedure which is not automatically done by ticket-tearing on the ward. With the exception of this one duty, the nurses, through the ticket system, are obviously released from making endless, daily, restocking lists, as they were formerly required to do. They, therefore, have much more time to devote to patient care.

If you put garbage into a computer, the saying goes, you get garbage out, but if you put intricate common sense in — as the hospital has done — you get efficiency, accuracy, and a gigantic saving in paper and people worktime. Again, also, the hospital can get an accurate check on its thieves: particularly, drug thieves.

This remarkable supply system was started in April, 1970, and the "bugs" are now out of it, the confidence developed. However, in case of an emergency, the hospital has a back-up arrangement with Hutzler's (a large Baltimore department store complex), which will take them over on their machines temporarily. An auxiliary machine set-up is now being prepared for JHH and power in case of a "brown out" exists.

The master inventory file records all items; each has a number; each a catalogue number key; each a fixed unit of issue and a date of purchase.

Also, each nursing unit has a code-bag number and the patient an accurate access to how much in the "red" he now is.

One thing Hopkins has never lacked is brains, and when its own go out and inaugurate a computer system in a hospital half across the world which WORKS, as a former Assistant Director at JHH, now Director of American University Hospital in Beirut has done, there isn't any reason why Hopkins can't do the same. In fact in Beirut, "each day at noon every account is put through the billing machine and the days charges for room are automatically entered. On the back of each bill is a magnetic tape for recording data concerning the patient and for printing out the bill any time the billing office wishes to do so."

Get ready for it! You may die of surprise when it happens, but it is coming at Hopkins, too.

You will still pay your bills on the 1st floor of the Administration Building, though, before you are discharged from the hospital as a patient.

Hospital Post Office workers handle mountains of mail each day.

Another place on the 1st floor you can get rid of your money, which has unseen employees, too, is the post-office. The amount of outgoing mail is not known, but as much as 300 to 400 pieces of junk mail come in on Mondays, and incoming straight mail averages about 111,300 pieces daily, while inter-Johns Hopkins Medical Institutions mail averages 126,000.

It is difficult to judge the busiest month in the year, but the mail does seem to be less when the academic staff departs. However, this is quickly followed by the arrival of the new house staff, so relearning commences immediately. The post-office ladies insist there is never a slackest month.

They sell on an average of $9,000 worth of stamps, monthly, but how many stamps are used is impossible to judge because JHH uses business vending machines; however, the out-going meter mail averages $133,084.99 monthly.

One-fourth of that 111,300 pieces of daily mail is patient mail, and one has to be patient, indeed, to sort it. Some years ago a letter came to Hopkins addressed to a patient at Osler 503, U.S.A. The New York P. O. figured Osler might relate to Baltimore so they sent it on down, and the husband of the Hopkins post-mistress was a post-office employee and he of course knew where to send it.

Another time, during a terrible snowstorm they received a package of fire engine parts addressed to Hopkins Hospital Post Office and saying in the corner "To be collected." It was collected by a nearby fire engine house shortly: the mails got through in those days!

There are 8 employees in the JHH post-office and the movie projectionist works with these ladies in his spare time. From 8.30 A.M. to 5:00 P.M. the post-office is never closed and like the "Mississippi River the mail never stops." The employees work 8 hour shifts, and among other things, sort and put the mail into the 342 separate boxes which the house staff use. Amusingly enough, many house-staff couples want separate boxes! Romances flower and fade under the repeated gaze of these astute ladies. Phipps therapy patients help out in the post-office and the ladies report that schizophrenics and alcoholics do excellent work.

Among places receiving mail service inter-departmentally are: Medical School, School of Hygiene, Homewood Campus, 550 Broadway, Columbia Clinics, and Good Samaritan Hospital.

Much of the Hopkins mail comes from and goes to foreign countries and the post-office ladies are most gracious in aiding people with language problems to ship packages and post letters. The amount of parcel post passing through here is hard to estimate; every 48 hours it is removed and most of it is strictly U.S.

The stamp window is a very busy place, serving the hospital side of Monument Street, Broadway and all employees and visitors. The efficient lady in charge has been here 19½ years, and has been in post-office work an overall 26½ years, having started in Italy before she came to the U.S.

Another section of the unseen hospital which affects everybody almost as much, perhaps even more, than the post-office is the laundry; for not only does it serve the patients, but also the employees. The hospital supplies 3,500 employees with 5 uniforms apiece, therefore the hospital has 17,500 uniforms which cost approximately $11.00 each, or $192,500.00 in all. They are made of dacron and cotton and the laundering is done completely free to the wearer. The personnel put in uniforms includes all persons whose personal clothing would be put at risk by their duties; when an employee leaves, the hospital takes back the uniforms.

Thousands of pounds of laundry are processed daily.

The doctors' uniforms are stored in a room in the basement of Marburg. The other employees change daily or as needed, and receive their clean uniforms 5 days later, after sending dirty uniforms to laundry. No registered nurse receives her uniforms free, but they are all laundered free, as are those of all other hospital employees. The doctors' uniforms are bought in Philadelphia; all the others in New York.

No laundry is actually washed in the hospital. It is all sent through the connecting underground corridor to Maryland Hospital Laundries, next door behind the JHH garage. Nothing is counted and goes out by pounds of weight, except uniforms which are counted by pieces. (Those uniforms for Hampton House for the student nurses are delivered 2 days a week).

On an average day 20,000 pounds of soiled laundry has been delivered by 11:15 A.M. from JHH to MHLS. Seven men deliver and return to JHH both the dirty and the clean "shoots," which is what the wire cages in which the laundry travels are called. Returns to JHH from MHLS are delivered by 9:00 A.M. daily, except Saturday and Sunday when neither the laundry nor the hospital laundry-service works.

The hospital laundry-service is really a folding, counting service. A regular patient uses 40 pounds of laundry daily, an incontinent patient, 80 pounds. Nothing is hand ironed at JHH now; all ironing is done by machine at MHLS.

The clean storerooms contain all kinds of interesting items, including artificial sheepskin squares, which are used to put under patients who are in bed for long periods and which help to prevent bed-sores. In an average week 40 to 50 of these squares are used. They require special handling in their washing so that they will return fluffy and soft.

This department, whose correct title is Linen Distribution Center, contains a uniform room, sewing room, clean linen room, packaging room, sterile pack room, and soiled linen room.

It has 32 employees and 1 manager; the women work from 7:30 A.M. to 4:00 P.M. and the men from 6:00 A.M. to 2:30 P.M. There are no night workers and no night orders are filled, because each floor has an emergency closet from which to draw in an emergency.

The women are very expert in their work and it takes about 3 minutes to count 100 sheets after they are put on the clean shoot. Each floor's consist is tabulated and listed and the shoot-packing is a highly intricate performance. All laundry for the weekend is packed on Friday; and on Monday morning, the weekend dirty laundry shoots are lined up on the side of the basement corridor ready to go to MHLS. Not only the sheepskins are given special care, but also difficult to wash are the cubicle curtains and fishnets, which go over cribs.

The heaviest sheet user, daily, is the Emergency Room, which averages between 300 to 350; the next heaviest is B-5 (Woman's Clinic) where 150 to 300 sheets are used daily; the lightest user is Phipps.

Four girls pack the whole hospital daily; as already explained, the 7 days are packed in 5 days and the 7 days are delivered in 5 days; not only do these people work 8 hours regularly, but if someone is sick, the crew turns to and works until finished, for which they receive overtime pay. As is the case for all union workers under the contract, they receive time and a half for overtime.

The Johns Hopkins Hospital is the first in the line-up, daily, at MHLS, which serves 6 voluntary hospitals in Baltimore, including the Hopkins affiliates, among which are Kennedy, Hampton House, and lots of the university accounts — the Medical School, School of Hygiene, Traylor and Turner, Welch, and all the clinics of the hospital.

All linen at JHH is marked as to purchase month on every piece. Also, all operating room gowns, etc. are marked by color; therefore it is easy to pack Wilmer (blue), GOR (green), Woman's Clinic (purple), fenestration (circumcision towels —white with different-edged colors), and CMSC (pink), while, yellow means isolation.

Thievery can be laid to hospital visitors, as well as to employees, taking items off the dirty work trucks. Ten percent of the sheets and pillow cases "walk" off annually: between 4,000 to 5,000 items. Thievery alters with seasonal changes. More sheets and pillow cases are taken in summer; more thermal blankets in winter.

The hospital is experimenting with paper sheets, and now uses entirely disposable pillows.

The pressure upon the people who work down here is enormous, as to counting, remembering, checking, sterile-packing, and oft times they work in intense haste. They do a fine job. The 7 men who "pull" the shoots in Halsted, Osler, the 2 who "pull" them in Woman's, Dispensary, GOR, Brady, CMSC, and who collect from the floors in Marburg, Wilmer, Phipps, Harriet Lane and Kennedy, are very adroit at manipulating their cages and trucks. Their routes go in and out of elevators and then to their proper stations in the sub-corridor, and later into MHLS.

One group of volunteers down here, though, are women who are senior citizens, members of Amalgamated Garment Workers Union who work in the sewing room, helping with the mending, insignia sewing, and general linen repair.

All the regular employees, except supervisors and the manager, are members of 1199E of the Hospital and Nursing Home Employees Union.

Wherever you are in the hospital, whatever you are doing, somehow, some way, Central Stores is involved in equipping you. It is housed in the 11,360 square feet of the Quonset hut, near the Phipps Building, on the Wolfe Street side of the

Central Stores are located in twin Quonset huts behind the Hospital on Wolfe Street.

hospital. Here are delivered for storage all JHH supplies, except food, and some specified supplies such as oxygen tanks. (Food and those items are delivered on the driveway between Brady and CMSC, and the food is stored directly below the central kitchen, being carried down there by elevators.)

The trailer trucks for Central Stores are backed into the hospital backyard and up to the hut doors; items are usually carton-boxed, and removed from the trucks by means of a collapsable roller-bearing sectioned conveyor belt. Then they are checked off by the truck-crew, JHH-checked by two end men beside the conveyor belt, the one adjacent to the truck being the foreman.

Visibly damaged goods are refused at truck-tail.

A single tractor truck recently arrived carrying 2,500 cases of sterile solutions and infusion sets. (This cargo originated in Chattanooga, Tennessee.) Packages off the conveyor are stacked in similar stacks according to size and kind.

Everything is stacked *off* the concrete floor, either on wooden pallets or metal ascending shelves. The hut contains a sprinkler system, 6 fire extinguishers, and smoking is allowed everywhere except in the broken-bin stock-shelving aisles.

The crew of 21 people work 8:00 A.M. to 4:30 P.M., 5 days a week; and their jobs cover receiving, storage of stock items, and special order-room stock and issuing. (The print shop is also housed in the hut.)

From this storeroom go supplies to the hospital departments known as Matron (dishes, cutlery, soaps, cleaning supplies), Surgical Instruments, Bulk Pharmacy, Dressings, Linen, and the Print Shop. The dog food for the university experimental animals is received here, too. Recently 24 white mice somehow got their container lid disloged and went on an unguided tour of the hut. All female employees removed themselves and 22 mice were recovered Two are still at large.

All bulk stock is put on wooden pallets adjacent to the receiving entrance, then broken down, carton contents counted and stored, still in cartons — still on pallets — in areas listed as Matron, Surgical, Laboratory, Bulk Pharmacy, etc., and these pallet rows form the main hut corridor. Behind them come the broken-bins (metal shelves).

Stock is "pulled" all day from the broken bins and one half hour each day their shelves are restocked. Every shelf in every bin bears a number and a metal name tag. Therefore since pallet rows are also numbered (odd and even sides) everything in the hut should be readily found at all times.

221

Among the many items which catch the eye are disposable pillows — only kind the hospital now buys — fiilled with shredded urethane pure foam flakes. They are non-allergic. Disposal sheets are also purchased and so are disposable diapers. The diapers, called Pampers, come in two sizes: overnight and new-born. Non-disposal diapers are still used, too. An average purchase being 3,600 every 3 or 4 months.

Other miscellaneous items are soap, steel wool, safety matches, oxygen tanks, pens, bags (paper and plastic), disposal cups, bottles, syringes, also glass bottles, paper towels, toilet paper (2,500 rolls every 2 weeks) floor wax, soap, specimen bottles, urine collectors, and safety pins.

There is a catalogue of listed, numbered, named items, similar to a mail order catalogue, only without pictures, which lists 1,225 different items bearing the same number from bulk storage to broken-bins. This catalogue is used for ordering by every building and department storing in this hut.

The stock control clerk does all ordering. She gets the day out, then orders the day in. Books are kept on inventory and the hut is always 1 day ahead of orders in stocking.

Loss is minimal per year, according to the Central Stores manager, a long-time hospital employee, who has also seen much of the world, done military service, and been employed in the Quartermaster's Department of the Army.

There are 2 main delivery men, working out of Central Stores; one delivers to one-half of the hospital, the other the other half, and a 3rd man delivers what they miss or special requests. Each man has a log book which the receiver of the goods signs.

Pending-orders from purchasing, waiting for incoming-goods-for-completion, remain in a special section near the truck entrance.

In winter many things come in heated trucks. These are items affected by weather and low temperature such as ether, formaldehyde, acetates, and ditto fluid. They stay in an air-conditioned store room.

Beds are special orders. Animals are, too. All hospital furniture is received here also. The most interesting trailer truck load the manager remembers was the one bringing radiology machinery and supplies.

All worn-out linen is brought here and torn into rags for use in JHH and dispensed to Matron as necessary. Incidentally, Matron was one of the original designations of titles when the JHH opened its doors.

No eating is allowed in the storeroom and the exterminator-man comes every two months to eradicate paper fleas, and when necessary, flying ants and, perhaps, 2 mice.

In one year $2.5 million worth of supplies pass through Central Stores.

As you remember, the Print Shop is also in the hut — in the hottest corner, in summer, and the coldest one in winter. It has no printer's devil and the 3 experienced printers do all printing for JHH and part of the university. Three printers (the head one learned his trade at Bendix) work a 5 day week and are always 10 days behind. However, priorities are gotten out right away. Daily they print the nursing exams, Wednesday and Thursday they do menus, and monthly they do the financial statement, Trustees' minutes, and Medical Record Statistical Reports.

They have 5 presses, print approximately 1 million pieces of copy a month. A five months recent total came to 4,606,390 pieces of copy.

There are two ways to get from the hut to Medical Records, one is to retrace your steps through the basement corridor to the Osler corridor exit, on Monument Street, and the other is to go out to Wolfe Street and walk back to that exit, down Monument. By this route you descend a half flight of steps, turn abruptly right and the Medical Records is at the end of that half corridor, to your right.

There are many listings in the Hopkins telephone book for Medical Records, covering locations other than the one in the basement corridor. Among these are history numbers, known and unknown, history numbers, old and new and 12 different satellite record rooms, in various buildings. In the basement corridor department, the great mass of records, though, are housed. Among the changes, there, in the last 12 years, are more use of microfilm records, and computer output of lab reports in case histories, which now include a summary data of such reports; the same thing is true of the medication rendered, which also goes through the computer.

The right to see a case history is as follows: a patient may authorize that his record may be seen by another physician (than the one attending him) or by social agencies. He may also authorize it be seen by lawyers, insurance agents, etc.

Monday is a slow starting day in the record department; and speaking of activity, if there has been none in a case history in the past 18 months, it may be microfilmed.

The microfilming is being done by years. By 1950 there had been microfilmed all records since 1889 and these were destroyed through 1940. By 1960 there had been filmed all since 1950, including 1940 to 1950, and they are now in their 3rd microfilming. Present records have a huge increase in the volume of paper, because now more is done to a patient which has to be documented; therefore it is advisable as soon as possible to get them into a condensed form, where they will need less space for storing.

Because of the great increase in malpractice suits against doctors, hospitals, and hospital personnel, in the last 10 years record employees have become very knowledgeable to the legal aspect of medical records. Unauthorized reading of records is ground for dismissal of any employee. Any doctor affiliated with JHH may read for research only. Anyone else wanting to review records for research purposes

The Medical Records department keeps track of 1.5 million patient records.

Blind workers at
work in Medical Records.

must get administrative approval.

The most famous loss of any record in the history of the hospital is that of Thomas Wolfe. Its present whereabouts are completely unknown.

Records are filed by terminal digit order, last number being used and they stay in open shelf files, and requests therefor must be on requisition slips. Records may *not* be taken from the hospital. All records of patients discharged, whether dead or alive, are processed. All case histories, except those of Phipps and the affiliates are kept here. Those are kept in the basements of their buildings.

Thirty percent of all medical records are now on microfilm. The Medical Board gives authority to the Medical Records Committee to microfilm certain groups of records. The actual supervision of the program is carried out by Medical Records personnel under the direction of the Medical Records Librarian.

In the Medical Records Department there are 180 employees. The facility is open around the clock, 7 days a week, and works 3 separate shifts, although the same people work the same hours. The oldest employee has been here 30 years.

The Blind worker in
Pathology; also there are
blind workers in Radiology
and in Phipps.

Interestingly enough, blind typists are the nucleus around which the whole transcription pool revolves. Their output is greater, their knowledge is outstanding. They are excellent teachers and a great source of help to new employees. Their hearing is superior, they rarely make mistakes, and are splendid spellers and cheerful workers. There are 2 separate groups of blind typists; in the basement of Blalock, 2 are completely blind and 2 partially blind; also there is 1 worker in the Phipps basement and 1 blind worker in pathology and 1 in radiology. The oldest blind worker has been here 27 years.

Hopkins has 1,500,000 case histories.

Annually outpatient case histories (not new case histories) handled number about 500,000.

The third Director of The Johns Hopkins Hospital, Dr. E. L. Crosby, came to Hopkins as a statistician in the Medical Records Department.

At the other end of the cross basement corridor from the Medical Records is the Personnel Department. Here are some interesting facts gleaned there:

The Johns Hopkins Hospital has approximately 4,400 employees, including nearly 600 registered nurses. A new graduate nurse, with Maryland registration is classified as a General Staff Nurse with an annual starting salary of $8,528.00. If a nurse elects to work the 3:00 P.M. to 11:00 P.M. shift, she gets an additional $100.00 per month; if she elects permanent night shift (11:00 P.M. to 7:00 A.M.) she receives an additional $75.00 per month.

All hospital applicants receive a physical examination which includes rubella screening for females who will work with children, as in CMSC and the Harriet Lane Outpatient Department.

References and background checks are completed on all applicants. Historically turnover has been about 40%, but improved hospital wages and benefits have reduced the figure by approximately half.

Benefits* offered all employees working at the Hospital include: *Medical Insurance* — All eligible employees may elect individual or family coverage under the Hospital Blue Cross/Blue Shield plan which is fully paid for by the Hospital. Each employee is also entitled to a 20% discount on any inpatient or outpatient bill he or his dependents incur.

* Certain employees of the Hospital are represented by a Union, and are provided insurance benefits under a Union Health and Welfare Plan, as distinct from those outlined herein.

Life Insurance — Eligible employees are covered by a life insurance policy in an amount equal to their annual salary, at no cost to the employees. The policy automatically increases in value as the employee's salary increases. Terminated employees are covered through the month during which their resignation is effective and they may convert the insurance to a private policy without medical examination. *Vacations* — Hourly employees are entitled to two weeks per year during the first five years of employment. One week may be taken after six months of employment. Those with 5 to 10 years of service receive 3 weeks, 10 to 20 years receive 4 weeks and 20 or more years of service entitles them to 5 weeks. Salaried employees (including nurses, dietitians, social workers, members of the administrative staff, etc.) receive 3 weeks' vacation per year during the first and second year of employment, 18 days per year from 2 to 5 years of service, 21 days per year from 5 to 10 years and 27 days for more than 20 years of service.

Dr. Edwin L. Crosby (1908-1972). Director of The Johns Hopkins Hospital, 1946-1952. He was appointed Assistant Director of The Hospital in 1940 and so served until the retirement of Dr. Winford Smith in 1946. At the time of his death, Dr. Crosby was chief executive officer of the American Hospital Association.

Sick Leave — Employees earn 10 days of sick leave annually and may accumulate sick leave up to a maximum of 65 working days.

Workman's Compensation — Benefits for employees injured on the job are provided in accord with Maryland State laws.

Income Protection Insurance — Eligible employees may elect to join this insurance program which provides 60% of salary to an employee who is totally disabled by a non-job-related illness or accident, beginning after 13 weeks of continuous disability. Payments will be continued while so disabled to age 65.

Pension Plan — Hospital employees are eligible for retirement benefits under the Trusteed Pension Plan established by the Hospital in 1955. The Plan includes "basic" benefits, financed by the Hospital, and "supplemental" benefits, for which eligible employees share in the cost. The Normal Retirement Date is age 65, and provisions are made in the Plan for early retirement, disability retirement, and other optional forms of retirement, all of which are independent of Social Security Benefits.

Holidays — The Hospital observes 9 paid holidays per year: New Year's Day, George Washington's birthday, Good Friday, Memorial Day, July 4th, Labor Day, Thanksgiving, Chirstmas, and a floating holiday of the employee's choice. Hourly employees who work on a holiday receive time and a half plus an alternate holiday.

Tuition Refund — The Hospital offers 100% tuition reimbursement to eligible employees who successfully complete preapproved job-related courses at accredited educational institutions.

Hospital Attorney — One employee of the Hospital who was purposely saved to be mentioned right here, although his office is on the 4th floor of the Administration Building, is the Staff attorney. Every contract, every accident, every injury, every theft, every suit, threatened or instituted against the Hospital, every loss, every insurance policy the Hospital has, are all reported to him and brought under his scrutiny.

He gets a daily report on any or all of these matters, in both the Seen and the Unseen Hospital, *every day,* as they affect *everybody,* and advises upon all of them. He has to be astute, aware, alert, fair, calm and wise. He is.

CHAPTER XX

Hopkins Is a Fighting Hospital

IT is hard to realize in this grasping age that there are people and institutions in this country who still consider it their proud privilege to volunteer, at great professional and personal sacrifice to themselves, then — and later, to defend Their Country. When the wars are over and the hogs get into the Government trough, everything is always done to belittle such men.

Both "Base Hospital 18," which was composed of nurses and doctors from The Johns Hopkins Hospital and sailed from Hoboken on the 9th of June, 1917, on the *Finland* for World War I under Major J. M. T. Finney, and "18th General Hospital," composed of 45 officers, 60 nurses, 275 enlisted men, 7 Red Cross workers, dietitians, and physical therapists, which sailed on the transport *General James Parker* from San Francisco, on May 24, 1942, under Dr. Finney's son, suffered this fate. Also embarked into the Pacific that spring the second Hopkins Unit, another 500 bed hospital, the "118th General Hospital," which went straight to Australia and remained there.

"Base 18" in World War I had a horrible commanding officer, a Regular, whom they finally succeeded in getting rid of. Eventually "Base 18" got listed in the "Tables of Organization" and received better pickings thereafter. The "18th General Hospital" eventually achieved this rating also, which seems to hinge on some type of Army red-tape regarding time.

The above paragraphs are a gripe and intended as such, for skill to a doctor is a thing which can only be kept through doing.

As regards "Base 18," when they were in dire straits for equipment during the Second Battle of the Marne, the Army still wouldn't find them "on the tables," and Dr. Finney, who was Colonel in charge of the hospital, went to the Red Cross for supplies, and got them. He was later detached from this job and made Chief Consultant in Surgery to the A.E.F. and acted as a personal messenger from General Pershing to President Wilson requesting that General Ireland be made Surgeon General, and this was done.

Dr. W. S. Thayer experienced World War I as Director of General Medicine for the A.E.F. and it was Osler's friends who operated upon Sir William Osler's only son and only child, Lt. Edward Revere Osler of the Royal Field Artillery, trying unsuccessfully to save his life after he had been horribly wounded by shell fragments.

Among the complement of "Base 18" were 97 nurses and 32 medical students; 30 of them were in their 4th year, 2 beginning their 3rd year. The 2 were sent home, at the end of 1 year, to continue their medical schooling, the 30 received their diplomas while in France. They are the only Hopkins doctors ever graduated at the front. And, they had a weekend leave in Paris, which even as old men makes them weak to describe!

The late Lawson Wilkins, who was one of those medical students, later —
years later — gave this description of their experiences: "We enlisted April 3, 1917,
and graduated May 30, 1918. There were 32 medical students enlisted as buck
privates, 2 of whom died: one of scarlet fever, one of typhoid.

"After enlisting we completed the school year here, then to Camden Station,
to Hoboken, to a flophouse in New York for 3 days, back to Hoboken, sailed aboard
a transport June 10, landed in Saint Nazaire about June 30. Were in New York
harbor several days awaiting convoy.

"In France, we scrubbed floors, washed wards, worked like troopers. One
morning we were ordered by the Adjutant (Harvey Stone), 'Put on your blouses,
boys, and come up for inspection. This is going to be something 'special.'

"We did so and Stone read us a cable which said:
     'You have this day been granted the degree of Doctor
     of Medicine from The Johns Hopkins Medical School
     by order of the President of the University.'
                              Signed   Williams

"Dr. J. Whitridge Williams was 'Bull' Williams, you know, Dean of the
Medical School and we were all, automatically, First Lieutenants.

"Dr. Stone then said, 'That's all. You can go back to work now.' So we
went back, took off our blouses and it was a month later before we had our celebration in Longe — a walled town.

"Ethel Dunham, class of '18 at JHMS, had given us some money with which
to adopt a French war orphan. We added to it our own savings and bought cham-
pagne and sparkling burgundy which we mixed in a bucket and drank all dressed up
in our uniforms. First we toasted the deceased, and then we had a royal celebration.

"As a result at reveille next morning, the old sergeant gave us a knowing
glance, scarcely any setting up exercises and said, 'You boys, lie down under that
tree and rest yourselves for 20 minutes,' and we did just that!"

When that "Base 18" Unit got out of the backwash, they were busy, 24
hours a day busy, and the conditions they lived under, in France, of no heat, no
plumbing, much mud, made life ever after seem a sweet affair. Incidentally, the
way they did get themselves out of the doldrums hinged upon the influence of a

grateful patient, a Colonel who was a Regular, and had been ill and cared for upon the transport going over. He, in the interim, had become a Major General and made good on his offer to help them if he ever could.

The first time Dr. J. M. T. Finney participated in the military life of the Hopkins Hospital was related to the Spanish-American War. The Fifth Maryland Regiment, United States Volunteers, was encamped at Huntsville, Alabama, after the end of hostilities (they had been stationed in Tampa hoping to embark for Cuba), but came down with what is graphically described as "Southern fevers," and were moved to Tampa Heights, where they got worse, and then to Huntsville, for a cooler climate. There they became much worse and it was decided to send 2 trains of 5 pullmans each to bring the ailing soldiers to Baltimore. When the first train arrived, at the request of Dr. I. R. Trimble, Sr., who was Assistant Surgeon of the Regiment, Dr. Harvey Cushing and Dr. J. M. T. Finney met the train at Camden Station (Dr. Cushing later wrote his fiancée a vivid letter about it). In all 47 patients were hospitalized, 1 of whom was admitted to Hopkins. He had typhoid, finally recovered, and 31 years later became President of the Board of Managers of the Harriet Lane Home. He was Mr. Charles H. Baetjer.

On the second train, 2 Hopkins doctors, Harvey Cushing and Eugene L. Opie, accompanied the train. Later Dr. Opie wrote a splendid description of that trip for Dr. Chesney, from whose magnificent history all of the above Spanish-American War data was gleaned. He sums up as follows:

"Such then, was the contribution of The Johns Hopkins Hospital as an institution . . . during the Spanish-American War, — the partial manning of a train to bring 76 soldiers of the Fifth Infantry . . . back to Baltimore . . . and the reception and care of fourteen members of that regiment who had contracted typhoid fever, and of one who had contracted malaria. . . . Viewed in retrospect and in comparison with what the Hospital did later in World War I and World War II it cannot be said to have been a great contribution. . . . After all, it was a short war, for hostilities continued for only 109 days altogether."

The Baltimore station which figured in both the great contributions which the Hopkins made was the Pennsylvania Station. It was June that first time the wives, and mothers and sweethearts went there to bid the unit good-bye; it was April 20, 1942, when the same scene was re-enacted and the volunteers set off again, for then, they knew not where.

There had been a wonderful farewell reception, given by the Board of Trustees and the Women's Board, at which each of the two units had colors and atlases given to them, and $5,000 with which to "pleasure themselves" when and where and how they wished! The atlases and colors were the gift of "Base Hospital 18" of World War I, beautifully bound and marked with the unit's number. Before they sailed from San Francisco, the colors were returned to the hospital and the inscriptions on the atlases amputated: Army orders, censorship.

When the men and women left Baltimore, that rainy April, many an older doctor, who hadn't the heart for it — who literally hadn't — went over to the hospital and commenced shouldering the duties which he knew would kill him. They took up the teaching jobs of the men now gone, they saw the patients, and in cases where younger men had been declared "essential" and not permitted to go, those men scrupulously kept books on the patients of their colleagues they did see and remitted to the wives of their absent comrades.

The Director, who had been in charge of the hospital 31 years and planned to retire, changed his plans, and his steady hand guided the hospital through World War II, as it had done through World War I.

The "18th General Hospital" under the command of Dr. Finney's son, landed on June 12, 1942, at Auckland, after nearly 7,000 miles through "hot" waters. Six rumor-packed weeks in Auckland and then they embarked for "Fan Tan," the code name for Fiji; on August 3 they arrived at Suva, from which a Marine convoy — destination unknown — had sailed on August 2nd. Everything was done which could be done by the local authorities to help, but they were not on the "Tables." Supplies were nonexistent and you couldn't set a hospital up without them in what had been a school for 90 boys. Supplies trickled in.

Dr. R. Carmichael Tilghman states in his excellent little book, *L.O.D. — YES:* "In advance of the Army's confirmation of the expected arrival of casualties, however, the 18th General Hospital had begun its own program for expansion of its facilities. Ward tents were pitched while cement was being poured for floors. Medical officers transformed themselves into carpenters and assisted in erecting prefabricated buildings. Ward 4 took shape as three Dallas-type prefabricated huts were joined to form one long ward for sixty patients. The roof of this ward actually being joined overhead as ward beds were being set up. Nurses washed the beds, arranged the ward linen, stocked makeshift medicine cabinets, attended to countless minutiae for the care of patients. So urgent was the need for equipment that the Medical Supply Department was unable to keep tally on the innumerable small items withdrawn. The Registrar arranged for records, so vital in the Army. Mess facilities had to be increased. Toward nightfall the engineers began to pour cement directly onto the grass to make walks, over which litter patients could be rolled or carried. The rolling ground of Nasinu with its thin eroded top soil and slippery soapstone base made navigation precarious without some form of walk. Work proceeded to a late hour and as midnight approached two hundred and seventy beds were ready for occupancy. The hospital capacity had been increased fivefold in less than 24 hours!

"The U. S. Navy Hospital Ship "Solace" reached Suva at daybreak on October 27th, 1942. Her passengers were the Marines from Tulagi and Guadalcanal and the Navy survivors whose ships had been sunk.

"By noon two hundred and sixteen patients from the 'Solace' had been admitted to the 18th General Hospital."

Research went on in the South Pacific too, and much was learned by this Hopkins Unit about atabrine and its use in the treatment of malaria. An operation was devised, by a Hopkins surgeon, for those poor sailors whose heel-bones had been crushed by concussion as they stood on the steel decks of ships which had been hit.

Eventually, the war moved on and this unit came home via a wild and woolly trip, "Kiplingesque" in the extreme, across India. When they got to Ledo, with typical Army snafu, they found there was already a large hospital, with too few patients, in good working order.

Some time in the Fijis, two ex-gynecologists — Doctors Edmund B. Kelly, and C. Bernard Brack, both now deceased — who had taken a quick course under Dr. Young, in Brady, did a prostatectomy on a Fiji chief. He survived, but was pretty sick, so they had a consultation, via cable, with Dr. Young, followed his orders and the chief perked up right away, and recovered.

During both of these wars, there were other Hopkins men requisitioned to important positions in Washington. Among them is Dr. John T. King who in World War II became Colonel King, Chief of Medicine at Walter Reed. (In World War I, he had been a Lieutenant on duty in several General Hospitals.) By one of those queer quirks of history, a patient he had on his mind much of World War II had been commander of the American Armies in World War I, General of the Armies John J. Pershing.

Among the persons whose health was cared for by the Hopkins Unit stationed in Australia in World War II were General MacArthur and his family.

In World War I, when the Hopkins Unit was in France, and again in World War II, when the two Hopkins Units were in the Pacific, thanks to the intelligence system maintained via Mrs. Barker's Sewing Class, both the men with the scalpel and the women with the needle had a remarkable knowledge of how-who-was-where-when. All the medical wives who were eligible brought their husbands' letters, read pertinent portions, pooled their inquiries, and subjected different men to different questions.

A vast amount of comforting knowledge was so gathered and dissembled. Frequently a friend knew a baby had been born before its own father received the word!

Among the benefits which Hopkins received from the Pacific, two of diverse nature stand out. Then, as now, Baltimore was the bone-setting capital of the athletic bone-setting world, and working with the units in the Pacific was a young doctor, whom they "picked up in the Pacific," brought back to Baltimore, and now wears the crown which so long sat upon the heads of Doctors Bennett and Johnson. The other benefit was the first permanent Chaplain for the hospital. The Chief Nurse of one of the units married a chaplain she met out there, while out there; later she became the successor to Miss Wolf, as Director of the School of Nursing at The Johns Hopkins Hospital, and her husband became all-time chaplain. Until then, there had been no paid clergy in the hospital.

It certainly should be mentioned that Hopkins profited greatly by World War II and the later "Police Actions" in that many among its employees are veterans of those conflicts, with military and executive training and excellent persons to have around in crises.

One such was the late Captain Herman E. Schieke, USN (ret) who graduated from the Naval Academy in 1921, was in on the planning of the original landings at Guadalcanal and Bougainville and saw much action in World War II. He retired in 1955 and 6 months later was appointed administrative engineer of The Johns Hopkins Hospital. He remained in that position until he died in 1965. He was a magnificent person and did much to reorganize and update the unseen hospital. Through him, many other retired officers came into the employ of the hospital. If Dr. Billings could have, in Captain Schieke's generation, picked his administrative engineer, he would have undoubtedly picked Schieke. They both believed in demanding excellence, from everybody in everything all the time. Captain Schieke walked the entire unseen hospital every day, everywhere, and looked at everything. She was his ship and he loved her.

Fine men like to come back to this hospital and work; one such retired officer came in 1934, left for military service in 1942, did his 20 years in the Air

Muster in photo of the combined 18th General Hospital and the 118th General Hospital taken at The Johns Hopkins Hospital on April 18, 1942. Originally patterned after Base Hospital 18 of WWI, this single, Hopkins-affiliated unit voluntarily split into the 18th and the 118th General Hospitals. The 18th, originally under the command of Lt. Colonel Amos R. Koontz, and after December of 1942 under the Command of Lt. Colonel George G. Finney, was sent to the South Pacific area. The 118th, originally under the command of Lt. Colonel Allan W. Dawson and, after April 1944, under the command of Lt. Colonel James Bordley, III, was sent to Australia.

A Marine Honor Guard participated
in March 1970 in the dedication
of a seminar room in the Turner
Building to Lt. Samuel Stockton
Miles, M.D. At left is his widow.
At right is his classmate,
Dr. R. Paul Higgins, Jr., who made
the dedication address.

Force and is back again as Assistant Administrator in charge of Materials Management. He, too, walks the unseen hospital daily.

Another bonus from the Wars is the use of medical corpsmen in key emergency positions. By 1969, 3 medical technicians (former corpsmen) had completed a 30 hours in class study program and total 6 months on the job training program, supervised by a professional nurse. Some of their previous medical corps experience ranged from 17 months to 20 years. The group has grown enormously so that as of 1971 there are now 104 former corpsmen working at Hopkins. Approximately 146 corpsmen have come to JHH for advanced training following military discharge. Those not at Hopkins are working in other hospitals.

Not all Hopkins nurses went to war in units. One, who had graduated from the Nursing School 2 years before the Spanish American War joined the Red Cross during World War I, and after being turned down because of her age, paid her own passage to Paris. There she spent 18 months aiding wounded soldiers, and earned 2 citations for exceptional service although she was then past 50 years of age. In 1967, she was 100 and lived in Columbia, South Carolina. Her name on the graduate list of the Hopkins nurses is Virginia Lee McMaster Foard.

As you see from the picture used in this chapter, taken at the time of the didication of the Samuel Stockton Miles Memorial Room, the Marines came to Honor Their Own. The lady present is his widow.

Since the conclusion of World War II, no Hopkins Units have gone to war, though, many Hopkins men have. Believe it or not, there is no official record of them. BUT do not despair, in wonderful and devious ways, the truth is always preserved. You may recall the description of the brilliant study being conducted by that eminent Professor Emeritus of Medicine on Medical School classes. She began her study in 1948, and therefore will eventually be able to provide absolutely accurate information upon this subject. The Korean War lasted from June 27, 1950, to July 27, 1953, and that began our involvements after World War II.

The Professor Emeritus began her study with the class of 1948 graduates of The Johns Hopkins Medical School. On September 14, 1971, she reports regarding "A Brief Summary Of Military Service By Johns Hopkins Medical Students and Graduates", as follows:

> "In the classes of 1948-1964, 26.1 percent, or 296 of 1,130 white male medical students, are known to have served in the Armed Forces *before* entering medical school. The great majority of these young men (92.6 percent) were in classes graduating between 1948 and 1958 inclusive.
>
> "A steady stream of young Hopkins doctors has entered military service *after* graduation. Although there has been variation in terms of military demands from year to year, a provisional sampling of the classes graduating in three successive years (1962-1964) suggests that almost all serve in some way (over 90%). Nearly 60 percent have entered some branch of the Armed Forces, while another third were in the Public Health Service, either going to the National Institute of Health to do research, or serving at a variety of other posts. Only seven percent of those reporting to date have not served in some capacity."

As far as is known, none of these doctors, so far, Thank God, has been killed.

CHAPTER XXI

"A Woman's Work, Grave Sirs, Is Never Done"

PROBABLY the strongest arm the Hopkins Hospital has ever had around it — many people think *the* strongest — has been the organization now called The Women's Board. "The Women's Auxiliary Board of The Johns Hopkins Hospital was organized in 1925, and appointed by the Board of Trustees in 1927, for the purpose of making the work of The Johns Hopkins Hospital better known to the people of Baltimore and to render such aid to the Hospital as lay within its power." The above is quoted from the "Forty-First Report of the Director of The Johns Hopkins Hospital" (1930).

The Board was organized by Mrs. William M. Manly, who acted as President until her death in 1929. By the time of the 1930 report they had given the hospital $81,176.09. It went for such various things as $60,081.25 toward the current expenses of the hospital; $2,000.00 for transfusion in Harriet Lane Home; $1,800.00 to cover the increase in the salary of a Social Worker in the Surgical Department; $3,000.00 to pay the salary of a Social Worker in the same department; $8,000.00 to cover the salary of a Social Worker in the Medical Department; $1,750.00 to cover the salary of an Anaesthetist in the Woman's Clinic; and $3,600.00 to cover the salary of a Social Service Worker in the Gynecological Department. They also paid for a Diathermy Machine and Alpine Lamp which cost $594.24.

They ended up the year with a balance of $7,245.21 according to Mrs. Louis P. Hamburger, Treasurer. They accomplished all of this with 42 members.

They had a guild for each building; the furnishings committee redecorated 11 rooms in Marburg and the first patient occupying one of them was so pleased she gave them $500 towards renovating additional rooms. They ran a cafeteria, which served hundreds of patients in the Dispensary for a nominal charge. They gave cakes and candy for the Nurses' Christmas Sale. They had rummage sales, arranged concerts, decorated the hospital for Christmas, gave patient-children presents, and even got the Towson Nurseries to give 30 Christmas trees for the wards!

Two members of that original Board are still alive and are sustaining members of the present Board, now called The Women's Board of The Johns Hopkins Hospital. They are both still vitally interested in the affairs of the Hopkins Hospital and contribute constantly in their time, their strength, and their influence to its well-being.

By the time the hospital reached its 50th anniversary, the Board was composed of 49 members, making $10,000.00 a year from the Carry-On-Shop and $2,742.25 from Conveniences; taking in $12,744.00 from its mail campaign; paying $9,295.00 toward Social Service workers salaries; giving $4,000.00 toward the Outside Obstetrical Service; and they ended the year with $41,716.50 in the

This historic picture is of three Hopkins stalwarts — Dr. Russell A. Nelson, Director of The Johns Hopkins Hospital 1952 to 1958, Executive Vice-President and Director 1958 to 1963 and President from 1963 to 1973. Mrs. Albert D. Hutzler, (center), and Mrs. Harry R. Slack, members of the original Women's Auxiliary Board organized in 1925.

banks!

That year Mrs. Hamburger retired and the lady who is still working for The Women's Board, and has worn many hats upon that Board, became Treasurer.

It has ever been the duty of the Women's Board to raise money for the Hopkins Hospital, although many of them have given thousands and thousands of hours of service within its doors. One such member, who has now retired because her husband became an invalid worked in the hospital 3 days a week for 20 years. She is a very astute business woman and it was she who remarked, "The Women's Board raises for the hospital each year the equivalent of the income of $1.5 million and each of the 50 Board members considers herself obligated to assist in the Board's money-making projects. Beyond our hospital obligations, the Board gives to medical and nursing scholarships. So we need every single cent we can come by."

Through calm and storm, all seasons, all hours, everywhere they go and are, these ladies are ever ready to use their brains, your money, their energy, your influence, their charm, manners and wit, and your TOTAL conscious and unconscious talents in behalf of The Hospital.

You can be completely across the room from one of these ladies and it can cost you plenty if she smiles and bows! Their best fund raisers often appear too frail to lift a powder puff and if at the same time they walk with a cane, you are likely to be out more than your money, too. Men tremble for the very clothes on their backs, for if one of these ladies says, "The lapels on that suit are too narrow. I'll send for it tomorrow and put it in the Carry-On-Shop," the man in question

The Corridor Café is a
project of the Women's Board.

knows there is no use to carry on! He's got to acquiesce.

The Carry-On-Shop at 531 North Howard Street now makes about $25,000.00 annually for the Women's Board; these ladies stock and run it; and in it, of course, among other things, are the clothes of all the Women's Board husbands sold long before their owners were willing to abandon them. Also books, some antiques, and children's clothes are there, too.

What used to be called the canteen is now known as the Corridor Cafe but it remains still on the left hand side of the corridor going toward Monument Street, which veers off the Main Corridor, to the left of Halsted. The Corridor Cafe is now open from 7:30 A.M. to 5:00 P.M.; all the help is now paid and no volunteers work there anymore. It serves about 1,200 meals a day and nets about $7,500.00 a year for the Women's Board. What it does for the hospital is beyond financial estimate: a quiet haven in which to rest a few minutes, peruse a book, or have a good conversation with a friend.

The Buttery is still to the left of the Monument Street corridor, near the Monument Street door, and it, too, is still a Women's Board project. Coffee still costs 12 cents a paper take-out cup, 2 cents of which is the cost, wholesale, of the cup. The Buttery is open from 11:00 A.M. to 3:00 P.M. and is still mostly a stand-up place. It nets the Women's Board $12,000.00 annually. All the help is paid and it is the quick-quickie eating place of the hospital. When and if the bank moves across Monument Street, it is to move into the bank's present location and expand.

The gift shop which has to be traversed to enter the Corridor Cafe, does a rattling good business particularly around Christmas and holidays, is manned in part by volunteers, and makes approximately (including the adjacent flower shop) $40,000.00 annually for the Women's Board projects.

The bank still does big business on pay-day and is engaged in the usual pursuits regarding that necessary evil—money.

Two members of The Women's Board continue to hold private sales in their homes annually, by invitation only, of their own and their well-dressed friends' clothes for the benefit of the Board, and there is also a waiting list for mink coats and stoles which may be donated to the Board.

It has been a long time since anybody has left the Board any jewelry. There used to be a friend of a member, who lived away from Baltimore, who had a satisfaction in fine jewelry and an income which permitted her to indulge her taste. From time to time, through her friend, she gave the hospital pieces which were latr sold through the Parke-Bernet Galleries in New York. At one sale, through her generosity and that of others, the Women's Board netted between $7,000.00 and $8,000.00. (Anybody who reads this and desires to give a piece of jewelry should contact the hospital or the Women's Board and they will collect it.)

The lady who made that astute statement about The Women's Board giving the hospital annually what would amount to the income from $1.5 million made it in 1962. Now The Women's Board budget, overall is about $125,000.00 so they have to scurry around considerably more than they did in 1962 to raise it.

At Evergreen House on the John W. Garrett estate, which was left to The Johns Hopkins University in the diplomat's will, the ladies have renovated and made most attractive the old Carriage House. Each fall they hold their 3 day Christmas sale there, which makes them about $20,000.00, and each spring, they hold a 3 day Antique Show and Sale, there too, which nets them about $18,000.00.

They like to keep their budget down to around $75,000.00 but so many many times something comes up where the hospital turns to the ladies and the ladies never fail. For instance, in 1968 they gave $150,000.00 toward the construction of the new intensive care units on Halsted/Osler 7th floors.

Those murals upon the walls in the corridor, outside the bank, as mentioned elsewhere were a gift to the Women's Board from the famous Richard Q. Yardley, who is the prize winning cartoonist of the *Sunpapers* and affectionately known

One of the Yardley cartoons displayed in the Blalock Arcade.

throughout the newspaper world as "Moco" Yardley.

As to when the name of The Women's Board was altered, this is the situation in a nut shell: when Dr. Winford Smith (OHH:JHMS, 1903) became Director of The Johns Hopkins Hospital, in 1911, the volunteer Social Service aides began to work throughout the hospital. Over the years, of course, the group grew, the work grew, and 12 years ago the Volunteer Service office was staffed by "one and a half paid workers, the half being a part-time typist, and sundry volunteers. The Women's Board paid the salaries."

In 1953, the astute lady previously quoted, who had been a member of the Women's Board since 1941, was given the job by the Board of organizing The Auxiliary To The Women's Board of The Johns Hopkins Hospital; and it was at that time the name of The Women's Board was changed. By 1962 the Auxiliary had more than 800 volunteers as members, and that year they obtained, as Director of the Volunteer Services, a lady, a Canadian, who had been volunteer director for the Royal Victoria Hospital in Montreal, where she arranged the first training course for volunteers ever presented in Canada. In 1968, she became the first President of the American Society of Directors of Volunteer Services and has done and is doing a splendid job for Hopkins.

Over the years, one of the goals of The Women's Board has been to "Start it. Get the men interested in it. And get out." In elegant language they mean slip Social Service into the hospital budget, eventually,—which they have done —get the Child Life Program to functioning so that it is practically indispensable, get the hospital to take it over budget-wise—which they have done—it goes on infinitum. In the meantime, every time the men get ready to get mad, the ladies give them something they need desperately. For instance, the first heart-lung machine, the cineradiography equipment for neuro-radiological diagnosis, the electronic monitoring devices to be used in the premature nursery of CMSC.

Then, if they have a little money left over, before the stunned men can think up something else they *really* need, the ladies have started the new-born baby photographic service or the gift cart for patients, or quickly gotten rid of the money to the scholarship nursing or medical student funds!

And it all starts over again, right away, somewhere else in the hospital in some new manner.

One of their recent developments is what they call Public Relations, but don't let the term throw you off. What they really mean is that they have an appoined Board member who sits in on the disposition by the different divisions and departments of the hospital meetings, and makes up her mind whether she thinks the men are wisely spending the money which the ladies have just given them. Consequently they have their fingers all over the hospital now that the liaison member serves as kind of an ombundsman between the department in question and The Women's Board.

Twenty to 30 ladies serve on these committees and they provide their hardworking confreres with an "unpaid, accurate ear" regarding the use made of their largesse. They ask men, they ask women, they ask children what they think. The private results of these "public relations" are awaited with trepidation by some and interest by all. As one lady said, "We worked hard for those funds. We don't want a penny of them wasted!"

To return to the Auxiliary, by 1963, 250 active members gave 38,400 hours

Mrs. Ralph G. Hills, former Vice-President of the Women's Board, who has given over 5,000 hours of service, assists at her regular Friday station in the operating room.

annually to the hospital. In October, 1971, the Auxiliary had 1,660 members, of which 609 were senior volunteers and 117 junior volunteers, and the combined groups now give 34,056 hours annually.

Innumerable volunteers have worked 200 to 500 hours, but there are 3 active volunteers who have worked 1,000 hours; 16 who have worked over 1,000 hours; 14 who have worked over 2,000 hours; 1 who has worked over 5,000 hours is a physician's wife and the former vice-president of The Women's Board; 5 have worked over 3,000 hours including the daughter of the second Professor of Obstetrics of the Hopkins who is a retired judge's wife. And there is 1 lady who has worked over 5,000 hours who is a retired anesthestist, a graduate of the Hopkins Nursing School and the wife of a retired doctor.

Last summer, 1971, among the Junior Volunteers, 20 boys worked a total

Mrs. Harold E. Loucks, at the Hurd Hall information desk, is also among the several volunteers who have given more than 5,000 hours of service to The Johns Hopkins Hospital.

of 10,565 hours during July and August. The Junior Program is aimed at interesting them in health careers, or as orderlies in GOR, for instance. There is a large contingent of Junior Girls, too, and teen-agers love the "meeting people" jobs.

As for the adults, a number of whom are men, they are in a thousand different places. Sales clerks in the Carry-On-Shop, filing and general clerical help clerks, answering the telephone, receptionist in GOR, taking care of medical observers, taking the gift sales cart through the buildings, gift sales clerks in the gift shop, medical staff rounds aides to answer the phone and notify the doctors during rounds, and those endless hours of helping in the registering, making appointments, doing clerical work in the out-patient clinics, working in the patients' library, packaging drugs in the pharmacy, liaison workers in the Recovery Room between relatives and the staff, Red Cross Nurses Aides, tutors to children. Many volunteers give 10 to 15 hours a week, at great personal sacrifice.

And let no man tell you that people do not love the Hopkins Hospital. In November and December, 1969, when the employee strike seemed imminent, the stack of special delivery letters, telegrams, and letters from all over the United States of persons offering their services in any capacity in which the hospital needed them, for as long as necessary, was at least two feet high. There were literally thousands upon thousands of them. The telephone calls, which came over the lines after the President of the hospital asked for volunteers to man the hospital on radio and TV, continued for days, hours, and weeks. Everybody in Baltimore and much of the State of Maryland was perfectly willing to forego their Christmas festivities and help the hospital. To uncountable people their greatest treasure on earth was threatened and their hearts and their hands were at its disposal 24 hours a day, 7 days a week, for long as need be. The grateful people in Baltimore, Maryland, and the Nation who have been patients there were—and are—available any time the hospital wants or needs them.

Two services which are under the Volunteer Department and have proved useful to so many patients at Hopkins are the Patients' Library and the Patient-

A volunteer loads the book cart in the Patients' Free Library with help from the librarian, a member of the Patient Staff Services Department.

Staff Services. The former receives $1,000 a year now from The Women's Board and has 2 workers (paid by the hospital). Except for them it is manned entirely by volunteers and usually has 1 volunteer a day, one of whom is a gentleman who has been pushing the book cart around the hospital for 10 years. The library now has 10,000 volumes (but—alas—the thief takes 400 books a year). They load cart with the best-seller list for Marburg and comic books for children. They have volunteers who read to the patients in Wilmer, and they also have a goodly supply of records and record changers, including show-tunes, books, and poetry. Talking books can be secured from the lady who handles them on the 2nd floor of Wilmer. Every now and then the ladies come upon a practically permanent patient, like the seaman who read everything in the entire library. He was on Osler 5 for 2 years and when he came to the hospital, he had to be weighed on the meat scale because he weighed 400 plus pounds. When he left he weighed 190 pounds.

The library is donation minded and they want, please, non-fiction, history and biography, particularly; also timely, current fiction. To get to the library, you go in Main Residence from the Main Corridor, turn left and it lies dead ahead through the doorway, open, so that you see the books on the walls.

The other library in this building is the Nurses' Library to the right and which is mentioned in the chapter on the Nurses.

In the smaller corridor just beyond the Patients' Library is Patient Staff Services, which has 9 employees and a very fine lingual cross-section. The interpreter speaks Spanish; the hostess, French; the secretary, Greek; and they have volunteer interpreters in all languages, including the sign language. The police call upon them for help from time to time.

They see all sorts of things which would break your heart, too. Like the patient who requested a recording, done on a tape recorder, because he wanted to record his own voice, before the radical neck operation which removed his speaking box. The ladies took it to him, worked the machine for him, and later secured a record of the recording for him.

These ladies mail all packages left behind after the patients go home—including false teeth, of which they have mailed 4 or 5 sets. And they will even take an artificial leg for adjustment. They have no idea how many people they have helped, and they usually have 6 volunteers a week working with them. They always keep a hostess in the family lounge near GOR to keep the patient's family informed, and these ladies serve tea and coffee to the relatives. Also they serve coffee to live-in mothers in CMSC. There is a hostess in Marburg, Brady, the Woman's Clinic, and the head of the department takes care of Halsted and Osler.

They have amusing times, too. Once a Marburg patient demanded to see the hostess right away because "something terrible" had happened. She rushed to his room and found him in dreadful distress, the source of which was his picture tube had ceased to function on his TV during the World Series. He missed some innings but she got him back on the diamond again.

Charity has not disappeared entirely from the United States. For as one volunteer in The Hopkins Hospital said, "I can work over here all day and be so tired I can hardly stand up, but at the same time I feel as fresh as a daisy and happy in my heart. It does something to you—something good—I'll never give it up as long as I can walk!"

A Hopkins Nurse

A Hopkins nurse is a serious girl,
One of the seriousest in the world.
Her cap is lined with frilly ruff,
But she won't stand for any bluff.

When Dr. Halsted took his cook some flowers,
A pupil nurse said, "It wasn't visiting hours."
And she told him plain and she told him flat,
He couldn't go on the ward—and that was that!

Oh, a Hopkins nurse can tell the spring,
She knows when the robins sing,
And without a word and without a reply
She can make a man want to catch her eye.

It must be that Broadway air,
That can make her make you care.
For she can marry the best of the crop
Without ever going to a single hop!

A Hopkins nurse is a world-wide treasure,
She's helped mankind beyond all measure.
Salute her, wherever you happen to be,
She's always a welcome sight to see!

The Johns Hopkins
Hospital
School of Nursing
pin.

The Johns Hopkins Hospital School of Nursing opened its doors, October, 1889.
The Johns Hopkins Hospital School of Nursing will close its doors, June, 1973.
As of June, 1971 the School had graduated 4,615 nurses.
The Class of 1972 had 52 members. The Class of 1973 has 53 members.

The Johns Hopkins
Hospital
School of Nursing
cap.

To Nurse The Sick

THERE are five things which a teaching hospital must have to function: patients, nurses, doctors, medical students and money—and not the least of these is the nurse. When you get sick, you want to be made comfortable and *then* you want to be made well.

In the 83 years of its existence (it began its first term in October of 1889) the School of Nursing of The Johns Hopkins Hospital has had a distinguished list of Superintendents and Principals, now called Directors.

May, 1889 to September, 1889	Louisa Parsons was acting Superintendent of the Training School for Nurses
September, 1889 to June, 1894	Isabel A. Hampton was Superintendent of Nurses and Principal of Training School
1894 - 1907	M. Adelaide Nutting, held those positions
1907 - 1908-1910	Georgina Ross, was acting in those positions
1910 - 1940	Elsie M. Lawler was Superintendent of Nurses and Principal of Training School
1940 - 1955	Anna D. Wolf, Director of Nursing and Nursing School
1955 - 1970	Mary Sanders Price, Director of Nursing and Nursing School

After Mrs. Price's retirement (she was the first of this group to be married), the position was split and there is now a Director of the Nursing Service and also a Director of the Nursing School.

The first permanent Superintendent, Miss Isabel Hampton, a graduate of Bellvue Hospital, was a Canadian, as was the third, Miss Elsie M. Lawler. Incidentally, the present Director of the Nursing Service is also one. The school owes much to these three fine Canadian ladies and the superior group of Maple Leaf girls they have attracted to Hopkins.

Miss Nutting, the second Superintendent, Miss Wolf, the fourth, and the fifth, as well as the present Director of the School of Nursing were all Hopkins-trained. The present Director also has her Ph.D. from The Johns Hopkins University in philosophy and therefore is entitled to be called "Doctor" as well as "Director."

Portraits (OHH) of Miss Nutting, Miss Wolf, Miss Hampton, Miss Lawler, and Mrs. Price all hang in the drawing room of Hampton House, the nurses' residence, which is upon the corner of Broadway and Monument Streets, across from the hospital. The portraits of Miss Nutting and Miss Lawler were moved from the Old Nurses Home, now called Main Residence because of vandalism. Miss Nutting's

Hampton House dedicated in 1925 as the residence for student nurses at The Johns Hopkins Hospital School of Nursing.

portrait had to be restored, so Miss Lawler though undamaged, was also moved to safer quarters.

Even though the portraits are gone and the girls now live elsewhere, the old lobby of the Old Nurses Home is one of the few places in the hospital which still reeks with its past. One can stand in its lobby, look over at the old iron grated radiator, with the wide marble slab top, and then turn and see all those hundreds of pupil nurses, doing their literal very best climbing and descending the wide stairway, with its iron treads and iron filigree railing. So earnestly they tried; so hard they worked; so well they did once they had reached that grand decision to be a Hopkins nurse.

There are, including the class of 1970, 4,568 graduates of this school. And if the three classes now in training all graduate—48 in 1971; 52 in 1972; and 53 in 1973, there will have been 4,721 graduates of the diploma School of Nursing of The Johns Hopkins Hospital when it closes its doors.

Recently two of those Hopkins nurses, one a graduate, the other her daughter, in training, were standing in that historic lobby of the Old Nurses Home together. The mother kept looking at the tiles of the floor and the very pretty daughter (who bears a marked resemblance to her) asked, "What are you thinking about? When you used to scrub those tiles?"

"No! We never scrubbed them. I was thinking about how cold they used to be when we knelt on them at 6:30 A.M. during the winter in the war, and Miss Lawler led us in our daily prayers and then asked the Lord to guard the Hospital Units in the Pacific and to give us, at home, enough sense to care for our patients as we should, to mind ourselves and learn, do our duty, and at all times conduct ourselves with the decorum and dignity befitting a Hopkins nurse."

"Was *she* kneeling on those tiles, too?" the student nurse inquired.

Her mother answered, rebuke and scorn lining her every word, "Of *course* she was!"

In the hallway, adjacent to the Nurses Library, are the graduating pictures of all the classes in a glass-framed, hinged contraption; and it is most absorbing to see one's friends, so fresh, so young, so eager. Over and over again, with each group, of course, sits the Superintendent of Nurses. The years go on and on, while

Miss Elsie M. Lawler
(1874-1962) after a
portrait by Harold Knight.

Miss Lawler changes from black-haired to grey-haired to white-haired, but always she remains the epitome of what a splendid trained nurse should be. Regal, dignified, expecting and demanding—and getting—excellent performance from "her girls."

Miss Lawler was ill for several years prior to her death in 1962 at the age of 88. She was bed-ridden much of the time and was cared for day and night by "her girls" in a room on the 3rd floor of the Marburg Building until she died.

In the Nurses Library, adjacent to the class pictures above mentioned, hangs a portrait of Loula E. Kennedy, who graduated from Hopkins, was director of theoretical nursing, and insisted that the library become a professional tool for the nurses.

Dr. Billings, in his address at the opening of the hospital, had plenty to say about what he intended the Hopkins nurse to be. The nurses he had seen at St. Thomas' Hospital in London, trained under the Nightingale system, he felt were "of a class from which the better kind of English domestic servants are obtained"; his desire for Hopkins was that it have a nursing school of "refined, educated women, fitted to move in good society." He, also, insisted that the Superintendent of Nurses be subordinate to the Director of the hospital.

It is interesting to know that the same year that Hopkins opened its nursing school, the University of Maryland opened theirs; and Baltimore became aware that the days of the untrained nurse were over, hereabouts.

However, in the last 10 years, the whole picture of nursing at Hopkins has altered. The nursing shortage became so acute that the now retired Director of the School of Nursing and the Nursing Service developed an in-service educational program for the nursing department, which has helped prepare nursing assistants, technicians, unit clerks, licensed practical nurses, and registered nurses for larger responsibilities.

Nursing stations are the action
centers of the patient units.

Nursing stations are the action centers of the patient units.

Under her directorship it no longer became obligatory to have 2 years of college prior to entry to the school, and effort was made to recruit bright high school graduates into the school as pupils; in 1968 men were admitted to the student program. Under the recruitment program, the class which graduated from the school in 1964 consisted of 125 young women from 26 states and Mexico.

In the basement of the Main Residence are the class rooms in which the nurses spend the major portion of their 1st year of basic training. Here are hospital beds, life-sized dummies of men and women, wheel chairs, and all the equpiment incidental to patient care.

Adjoining these classrooms are others equipped with ingenious mannikins from which the organs may be lifted, the tops of heads removed, and the student instructed; many of the organs are sectioned, as, for instance, is the spinal column. These laboratories contain, also, microscopes and bunsen burners, and over them hangs the air of years and years of infinitely hard work.

The 1st year of study is a jammed-packed 42 weeks learning such subjects as biological and physical sciences, psychology, microbiology, nursing I, and nursing I lab; sociology, writing, nursing II, and nursing II lab, human growth and development, nursing III and nursing III lab.

Beginning with the 2nd month, the student nurse spends some time in the hospital proper. As part of the unseen hospital, there exist many nurse-classrooms, at least one in each clinical department, where the nurse is taught what she is seeing in that department; the teaching staff of the nursing school has 45 full-time instructors of nursing, and in it, as in the Medical School, every person is either a teacher or being taught.

The 2nd year of the course, which is 48 weeks, she studies medical-surgical

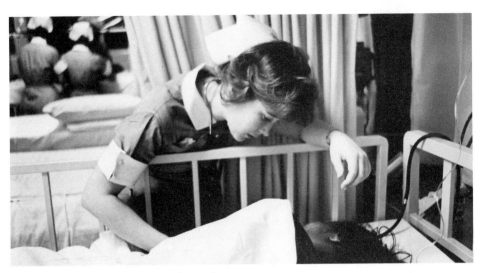
A student nurse comforts a recovering patient.

nursing, medical-surgical nursing lab, and maternal-child nursing, maternal-child nursing lab.

The 3rd, and last year, which consists of 36 weeks, she studies psychiatric nursing, psychiatric nursing lab, historical and current trends in nursing, community and outpatient nursing and lab; also leadership in nursing and leadership in nursing lab.

Upon graduation she receives a diploma and has the right to wear the ruched cap and the Maltese cross pin, which are distinctive badges of a Hopkins nurse around the world.

The cost of the 3-year nursing course now is $2,440.00, with the additional Blue Cross Student Plan fee which ranges around $70.00 annually. There are 126 weeks of instruction and work in the 3-year course and in the modern world a graduate can immediately step into a nursing job which will pay her over $8,000.00 annually.

Due to the current methods of working up patients, whereby the patient comes into the hospital directly before surgery and goes out very shortly afterwards, the turnover in really sick patients who need nursing care is about 3 times what it used to be. The work is, therefore, vastly more interesting, but is also demanding of great skill and judgment.

As regards the nursing aides and orderlies before referred to, they have many ratings to which to climb, through additional study, after their preliminary 6-week practical nursing course. Every effort, too, is made to inculcate into them, among other things, the knowledge that manners are the axle grease of life, and "thank you" has the longest echo of any sentence in the world. Hopkins aims to train these aides so that they will not be open to the criticism which Dr. Billings made of the nursing staff of St. Thomas' Hospital.

Again, regarding the closing of the Nursing School at the end of the 1973 term, Mr. Hopkins specifically stated in his Letter of Instruction to The Trustees,

"I desire you to establish in connection with the Hospital a training school for female nurses. This provision will secure the services of women competent to

247

care for the sick in the Hospital wards, and will enable you to benefit the whole community by supplying it with a class of trained and experienced nurses."

The desire of the Alumnae of the Nursing School repeatedly and plainly expressed is that The Johns Hopkins School of Nursing become a degree nursing school, and the supplementary courses be given on the campus at Homewood and the degree be granted by The Johns Hopkins University. (Some of the courses now taken by students of the diploma school are given there, and the girls are bussed from Hampton House to Homewood.)

The whole distressing situation has caused much anguish, disillusionment, and disgust among that fine body of ladies—Hopkins nurses—who have given their lives to working in the Hopkins Hospital, and for it.

Five million dollars would be sufficient to accomplish this purpose, and it seems disastrous that when the hospital exists, the nurses residence exists, the nursing faculty exists, that the university remains so obdurate; particularly since a petition signed by 371 Hopkins doctors has been recently handed to the President, asking for such a school.

Ironically, the other teaching hospital in Baltimore, whose nursing school opened the same year as Hopkins has had for many years such a school. All the hospitals of equal or superior rank to Hopkins, throughout the nation, now have such a degree school, with the degrees granted by the university with which they are connected; in fact, some of them have both the degree and the diploma school. The degree nurse generally goes into administrative work, and the diploma one into bed-care nursing.

It now appears that this dilemma may soon be resolved, as the Trustees of the University have authorized a School of Health Services. A Dean has been appointed, an advisory board formed, and hopefully the school, which will have a status similar to other schools within the University, will open in 1973. A nursing program will be a part of the new school and nurses will be able to work toward both baccalaureate and doctorate degrees, to be awarded by the Johns Hopkins University.

Historically, it is peculiarly interesting to note that Miss Nutting, who had been a member of the first graduating class of The Johns Hopkins Hospital School

Student nurses' shoes on the Hampton House fence at graduation time bespeak of the many miles walked.

248

Miss M. Adelaide Nutting
(1859-1948) after a
portrait by Cecelia Beaux.

of Nursing and the second Superintendent of Nurses and Principal of the Nursing School, left Hopkins to go "to Teachers College, at Columbia University, where she was the first nurse in the country ever to hold a professorship and where she developed the first program in collegiate education for graduate nurses."

Now housed in Main Residence but formerly in that odd and charming little museum on the first floor of Hampton House, referred to as "The Nightingale Room" is the desk Miss Nutting used at Hopkins and at the Teacher's College at Columbia University; also there is her graduation certificate (1891) from The Johns Hopkins Hospital Training School for Nurses signed by William Osler, W. S. Halsted, Howard A. Kelly, Francis T. King, Henry M. Hurd, and Isabel A. Hampton.

Here, too, are the first certificates ever issued by the Maryland State Board of Examiners of Nurses; number One was issued March 3, 1905, to a "certificate as Registered Nurse to Mary Adelaide Nutting," and Maryland Registered Certificate number Two was issued on the same date to Elsie Mildred Lawler.

In this museum, too, is Dr. Kelly's original gift letter addressed to Miss Lawler on September 18, 1920 offering to give the nurses his unique and fabulous Florence Nightingale collection, and the library he had assembled concerning her. The library is now in the Florence Nightingale Room at the Welch Library. However, a colored lithograph of Miss Nightingale's home, 3 lovely drawings of her (as a girl, as a nurse, and as an old lady), and a small statuette of her done in marble are here.

Her wheelchair, from Sir Harry Verney's collection, with written assurance to Dr. Kelly of its authenticity, is nearby, as are 4 chairs and 1 rocker from Miss Hampton's office, used from 1889 to 1894. A bookcase, where the certificates are, also contains 4 dolls dressed as nurses: a street uniform, 2 nurse JHH-style uniforms, and one matron (superintendent) uniform.

In this room, too, is a full-sized figure of a nurse dressed in uniform. She wears the long skirt, elbow cuffs on a blue uniform, with a long white apron, and a Hopkins' cap sits upon her head. Miscellaneous other photographs are upon the walls, concerning the nursing school, and several other certificates.

There was a silence in this little room, of accomplishment, work well done and a magnificent heritage.

There has never been a war since the school was founded, in which Hopkins' nurses have not served. Some were in the Spanish-American War; 44 of them went to War with Base 18 in World War I, and the 18th General Hospital, which served in the Pacific in World War II, had a complement of 60 nurses, while 118th (the second unit) had a varying complement. The Head Nurse of that unit and later Director Emeritus of The Johns Hopkins Hospital School of Nursing, recently wrote: "When the 118th General Hospital was activated in April 1942 we had a roster of 58 nurses. Before sailing from San Francisco the following month 5 more were added to our personnel making a total of 63.

"The number varied greatly during our years of service in Sydney Australia and Leyde P.I. At times we had as many as 118 nurses when our bed capacity tripled in the Philippines."

It is impossible to trace the service of Hopkins' nurses in the later wars to which no units have been sent.

There is the story of a nurse, who was a Major, assigned to cross the continent by mistake upon a train whose entire complement otherwise was male. After several treks to the dining car, through coaches wherein the males were in increasing dishabille, and steadily reprimanded by the male officer running interference for her, she suggested that her meals be brought to her, and she remain fixed in her permanent quarters. This was done, much to her relief and to that of every man aboard!

Another nurse, now an old lady, claims that the worst thing which happened to her in World War II was the time a desperately wounded man she was endeavoring to care for looked up at her and said, "Lady, what war was you young in?"

Their training has always been rigorous and administered by ladies Who Meant What They Said. A case in point was that of a new pupil nurse who had been instructed to admit *no one* to the ward after visiting hours. When a dignified gentleman tiptoed up, carrying a bunch of flowers for his cook, who was a gynecological patient thereon, the pupil nurse caught up with him, informed him of his crime, and relieved him of the flowers, promising to deliver them to the cook. When she did so, the cook said, "Dat's jes' like Docta Halsted to bring me dem dahlias he done raise hisself."

Another pupil nurse, a pretty little girl, was always in trouble with her plain supervisor. Eventually, the altercation sifted upward and Miss Lawler sent

A Hopkins nurse supervises the learning experience of the Hospital's Student nurses.

for the pupil nurse and after some preliminary rebukes, said, "Now, see here, what *is* all this trouble about?" Miss Lawler was not a lady one could answer evasively, hence the student's reply, "It's plain 'jealousness' and there isn't *anything* anybody can do about it."

In spite of their stern discipline and arduous training, Hopkins nurses, from the first, have been noted for marrying The Medical Catches of their respective generations. The first superintendent, Miss Isabel Hampton, resigned, after five years, to marry Dr. Kelly's assistant, Dr. Hunter Robb; her operating room head nurse, Miss Caroline Hampton, resigned, after one year, to marry Dr. Halsted. The lady Dr. J. M. T. Finney chose was a member of the first graduating class, as was the wife of Dr. Cullen. Even the present — and first — President of the hospital takes his home orders from a former Hopkins nurse.

Going off the service corridor beyond the Marburg Building is a tunnel under Broadway to Hampton House, at the end of which one must ring a bell, whereupon the telephone operator looks down through a glass window, and if one is of the satisfactory sex and uniform, she releases the catch on the door mechanically. Then one may enter the sacred precincts of Hampton House, in which each nurse has a separate room; it also contains a recreation room on the roof and numerous small parlors on the first floor, now known as "dating" rooms. Affiliate student nurses from Church Home and Hospital, Maryland General Hospital, St. Joseph Hospital, also live in Hampton House.

They all have more leeway in their free hours than did their predecessors; and youths with hair to their shoulders sit long hours in the Hampton House lobby waiting for girls who had waited — and waited — for them to phone and are now washing and drying their hair (unbeknownst to their swains) so that they will look "sharp" for their exasperated dates.

But these local flames may fade for as one nurse said, long ago, "Hopkins nurses come from everywhere, they go everywhere. I've been around the world two and a half times, and worked on five continents."

CHAPTER XXIII

The Hopkins Anniversaries and Current History

THE 25th anniversary of The Johns Hopkins Hospital was in May, 1914. Already that year startling things had happened. One of the most upsetting was that the Ford Motor Company had raised its basic wage from $2.40 for a 9 hour day to $5.00 for an 8 hour day. Well, there were still carriages and horses!

Also there was trouble on the Mexican border. U.S. Marines had been arrested in Tampico and the Mexican president refused to make formal apologies, so President Wilson had ordered the Atlantic fleet to Vera Cruz. On the 21st of April Vera Cruz was taken. The losses of the Marines and sailors were slight; and being hipped on sanitation, the Americans began to clean up the city. They had to do something to get rid of their venom, for 3 weeks before, the Secretary of the Navy, Josephus Daniels had banned the use of liquor in all ward-rooms. His son (OHH:JHMS, 1924) and grandson (OHH:JHMS, 1948) are Hopkins graduates.

In 1914, Dr. Osler was a resident of Oxford, being Regius Professor of Medicine there, but all the other great three were still at Hopkins.

And so many new faces were seen at Hopkins, then: young faces, too. The new Director, Dr. Winford H. Smith was only 37 and 11 years out of the Hopkins Medical School, while Miss Elsie M. Lawler, the new superintendent of the School of Nursing, was 39 and she had graduated at Hopkins 14 years before. Also, there were some right promising boys who would graduate from medical school this year. Their professors thought highly of them; among them were Stanhope Bayne-Jones, Alan C. Woods, and the now Associate Professor Emeritus of the Medical School, who is the senior doctor on the manuscript committee for this book (both editions).

In 1914, three wonderful, modern new buildings had been opened in the last two years — the Henry Phipps Psychiatric Clinic, the latest word in hospital construction. It was under a brilliant man named Dr. Adolph Meyer. He had been appointed Professor in 1909; Psychiatrist-in-Chief, in 1910. But he was *very* old, being 48. The Charles L. Marburg building was also up to date in *every* way. While the Harriet Lane Home was really almost too advanced in planning. The Professor of Pediatrics, however, was only 41, had been an Army surgeon in the Spanish-American War, and later practiced with Dr. L. Emmett Holt, whose *Care and Feeding of Children,* was the Spock-book of its time.

Something else new, which nobody was quite sure would work, was the full-time system, which had just been inaugurated for the Departments of Medicine, Surgery, and Pediatrics. Also, there was a new Professor of Medicine, because Dr. Lewellys F. Barker had resigned and Dr. Theodore C. Janeway was to take his place. He, too, was young, 42, and had been a member of the Board of Scientific Directors of the Rockefeller Institute for Medical Research.

Everything was so modern and even the people who had fought going on the full-time system so bitterly "hoped for the future." There was even talk that the last transcontinental telephone pole might be set by mid-June and there would be a direct line connection between New York and San Francisco. Automobiles were becoming much more prevalent and "Get Out and Get Under" was a song everybody was humming. Also, the young people were going to the dogs with their wicked dances, of which the bunny-hug was the worst, *by far*. Ladies, too, were wearing slit skirts and colored face powder!

Still, everything seemed so serene, really, for the anniversary. Hopkins looked so beautiful, the street-cars ran so regularly, the nurses looked so pretty, and it was a shame that Dr. Osler didn't come, but anyhow, he was coming in the fall for the medical school reunion.

By the first of August, all of these thoughts seemed as far away as childhood dreams. The shot that was heard around the world had had its effect. World War I had commenced, and Dr. Osler wrote a long letter to the first class which had graduated from the Medical School, but he did not attend their reunion.

And they whistled in the corridor, "It's a Long Way to Tipperary."

If the great wars in Europe always start after the harvest, then Hopkins is indeed fortunate to have its anniversary in May.

Again, in 1939, the anniversary weather was beautiful and among the events, which needed good weather was an out of door reception in a tent in the front yard of the hospital. Also Dr. Chesney hoped for good weather for his play "The Flowering of an Idea," being a capsule of Mr. Hopkins' life and the beginning of his hospital. Mrs. Chesney had painted all of the scenery for it and the play was presented at the Eastern High School.

In the second 25 years of the Hopkins Hospital much had happened. Dr. Osler had died; Dr. Halsted was dead. Brady had been opened (1915); Base Hospital 18 had gone to war and come home again; Dr. Welch had died and Dr. MacCallum succeeded; Dr. Kelly had retired as Gynecologist-in-Chief, and Dr. Cullen had been appointed; the Woman's Clinic had been occupied; the Carnegie Building had been opened; the new Pathological Building had been completed; Wilmer had come to Hopkins and the Institute opened; Hampton House had been built and was occupied; the Woman's Auxiliary Board had been begun; the Welch Library dedicated, and Osler and Halsted had been built; Hurd Hall completed; the Thayer Wards inaugurated; Dr. Woods appointed Ophthalmologist-in-Chief, and Hampton House had its addition.

Again people looked to the future. There *couldn't* be a better hospital.

Everybody was so proud of Hopkins and so grateful to the Rockefellers for all the buildings they had aided in building or built.

Dr. Kelly was still as chipper as ever. Dr. Smith and Miss Lawler, too, appeared ready to last forever, and so did Dr. Chesney, Dean of the Medical School.

By September 1, all of these facts seemed as far away as childhood dreams. World War II had commenced. That was the day the Germans marched into Poland and on September 3, Britain made her reluctant and unavoidable entry into the war.

The movie to see was *Gone with the Wind;* the commentators to listen to on your radio were Dorothy Thompson and Elmer Davis. And what a song-bird that Kate Smith was. Some people thought the British should ask Winston Churchill to serve in the War Cabinet, but everybody knew the fizzle he'd made at the Dardenelles in the first World War. Forget about him!

By 1945 they were whistling in the corridors, "Lilli Marlene," and "A White Christmas."

Nobody any longer remembered that the great speaker at the 50th reunion of the Hopkins Hospital had been Dr. James B. Herrick of Chicago, the discoverer of sickle cell anemia, who admired greatly Hopkins and the work which had been done at Hopkins on that abnormality.

Again, in 1964, the weather held and Hopkins had a lovely week of sunny, clear, and not too warm days. Dr. Parks had retired and there was a new young Professor of Pediatrics, 44 years old; there was also a new building for pediatrics, CMSC; and this was the *very last word* in construction. A new Basic Science Building adorned the Medical School; it, too, was a skyscraper, and Wilmer had an additional building, named for the just-deceased Dr. Alan C. Woods, which was to be devoted to pure research; the School of Hygiene had grown two wings; a new dormitory for medical students had been put up and had an addition to it, too, while down the hill, behind it, off McEldery Street, there was now a garden-type housing development for married interns and residents; and on the corner of Broadway and Monument there was to be built a handicapped children's hospital, Government financed, and named for the late President, who had been assassinated the previous November.

Again, the old familiar faces had altered, for Dr. Winford Smith, Miss Lawler, Dr. Charles R. Austrian, and Judge Henry D. Harlan, who had served on the Board of Trustees of The Johns Hopkins Hospital from 1895 until 1941 were dead.

The two hospital units had gone to and returned from World War II, both being stationed in the Pacific. The Women's Auxiliary Board of the hospital had given each a going-away party before they left. In these years, that group had changed their name to The Women's Board, and their previous name was now used by a group which had been formed to aid in the hospital as volunteers. Shortly after the War, in 1952 to be exact, a member of the Class of 1937 JHMS, who from 1937 to 1944 had been intern, assistant resident and resident on the Osler service, and served as Assistant Director of the hospital and Director of the medical clinics from 1945, was made Director. At the time of the 75th anniversary he had been in that position for 12 years and everybody was delighted with his work and so pleased that he was to receive the Distinguished Service Award given annually by the American Hospital Association this year.

He was young, he was Hopkins, and he'd married one of the prettiest of all the Hopkins, nurses, too.

Just a year ago, in 1963, the title had been changed and he was to be known from now on out as the President of The Johns Hopkins Hospital.

A lot of people snorted at the idea, but other things were changing, too. Nurses' aides, as well as practical nurses now served in the hospital, working under the direction of registered nurses; interns and residents got a stipend; the medical boarding houses were going or gone; and the medical students no longer had to toe the line. The post-doctoral program had been reformed and was growing rapidly. The Civil Rights marches in the South had already begun and everybody had opinions about them. Winston Churchill, who had saved the English speaking peoples throughout the world, was 90 years old, revered and adored. General of

254

the Army Douglas MacArthur had died in April; and Americans attended their second great television funeral. President Johnson had come out for medical care to the aged; John Glenn and Alan Shepherd had already been up and come down; two new communication satellites were fired off at Cape Kennedy, Relay II and Echo II; Cuba stopped the Guantanamo water; and the Associate Dean at the Medical School, (OHH:JHMS, 1940) everybody felt was a great asset to the future of Hopkins — "Hang on to him," the OHH said. "Don't let him get away from us!" Secretary McNamara re-affirmed "United States determination to give South Vietnam increased military and economic aid in its war against Communist in-urgency." In October, the U. S. Defense Department announced that 204 Americans had been killed in combat in South Vietnam since January 1, 1961.

But in May, at Hopkins, nobody had any information on that, and if they had had, it probably wouldn't have made much impression.

One of the nice things which had been done — deservedly done — was that in 1963 the Board of Trustees of the Hospital amended their by-laws to permit Mr. Walter F. Perkins to remain active through the 75th anniversary. He had been a Trustee of the Hospital since 1942, and was full of wit, wisdom, and vigor. He said, "You can delegate authority, but you can't give responsibility away to anybody. You have to *bear* that, and be equal to it. We give the doctors the authority to run the hospital, but we are RESPONSIBLE for the mistakes they make. So I tell 'em, don't make any." As chairman of the Board of Trustees, he had no office in the hospital, but he said, "I have given nobody any instructions, ever, but the place has been on my mind seven days a week." He had the hospital humming like a top, walked every foot of it, week in and week out, and knew the names of all the obscure and all the great, thereabouts. He was a brilliant engineer who had been a vice-president of the Koppers Company.

When he became a Trustee, the hospital budget was about $8 million. In 1965 it was $20 million *and* there was no deficit *and* $500,000 was plowed back into plant improvement. He was the guiding star in getting the money for CMSC, and many, many other things, too.

He was the 6th person to ever receive The Johns Hopkins Distinguished Service Award, but more about that later. The other recipients are:

> Mr. W. Frank Roberts, Trustee 6/7/1955
> Alan C. Woods, M.D., Director of Wilmer 6/7/1955
> Miss Anna D. Wolf, Director of Nursing 6/19/1955
> Dr. Lowell J. Reed, President J.H.U. 10/2/1956
> Alfred Blalock, M.D., Surgeon-in-Chief 4/2/1960
> Mr. Walter F. Perkins, Pres., Board of Trustees 6/2/1964
> Mrs. Mary S. Price, Director of Nursing 6/7/1970
> Mr. J. Crossan Cooper 3/7/72

One final thing which had been accomplished by the 75th anniversary: Dr. Chesney had completed the third volume, thereby bringing the history of the hospital up through 1914.

Now to begin at the beginning. For many weeks all the OHH and other invited guests had been in lively correspondence with the Public Relations Department of the hospital, as to how many tickets they wanted and what they could attend. The tremendous amount of paper work was beautifully handled, and very few mistakes were made. The hospital had received a severe face-lifting under the constant scrutiny of Mr. Perkins, who was completely a no-foolishness-man, and it looked *magnificent:* clean, spotlessly so, and filled with courteous employees.

The grounds had been completely manicured, all the flowers held their heads up, the grass was almost an emerald green, the fence was repainted, not a sprig of grass was visible in the brick driveway, the brass in the entry was glaringly polished, and even the people who did not approve of the rearrangement of the front entrance walk, sundial-wise, were impressed.

On May 10 THE SUNDAY SUN had devoted its entire magazine section of 31 pages, 53 photographs and a map to "Johns Hopkins Hospital: 75 Years Old." The colored photograph on the cover was by A. Aubrey Bodine, as were many of the interior shots also. The text was by Hervey Brackbill.

The TV listings of THE SUNDAY SUN, then the same dimensions as the magazine, stated that Tuesday, May 12 at 9:00 P.M. on Channel 11 there would be an hour-long documentary entitled: THE HOPKINS: Story of a Hospital. (Film study of the hospital's facilities and future, produced by WBAL-TV.)

Every OHH in Baltimore watched it, too, and all thought it excellently done. In their research, they credited their information to the following books for which they thanked the authors: *Cushing's Life of Sir. William Osler* and *Miss Susie Slagle's* and *It Happened At Hopkins.*

Their greatest aid and criticism had come from one of the most Hopkins-wise couples who have ever lived, the senior physician reviewing this book, and his wife. The producer was fortunate enough to be their son.

This film study of the hospital's facilities and its future still exists and should certainly be shown, again, as should also the film put out in the 1930s on which the late R. A. Rayner Downey, who was an assistant director of the Hospital used to lecture.

The official party leaves the Hospital's Board Room for the ceremonies which will dedicate the new Children's Medical and Surgical Center and commemorate the Institution's 75th anniversary.

To return to the 75th anniversary: the documentary took place at 9:00 P.M. on May 12, and on the 13th at 2:00 P.M. the invited guests came for the dedication of CMSC. The invitation said Wednesday, May 13, 2:00 P.M. but by 1:15 the faithful had begun to gather. They came up the front walk slowly, impressed with the momentousness of the occasion. Many of them had been born in the Hopkins Hospital; all of them had some emotional, mental, or marital ties with Hopkins. And they thanked the Lord for giving them such a beautiful day in which to return, remember, and refresh their souls, for to each, in his separate way, climbing that hill, for this occasion was truly a proud moment.

Then they entered the lobby, saw Jesus and the beautiful vases of flowers and received the courteous greetings. The President's pretty wife, and Mr. Perkins, the President himself, many of the Board of Trustees and their wives were welcoming and greeting the guests. Countless eyes filled with sudden tears at the sight and many an old lady said, "I lived to be here!"

As the crush became too great and one moved courteously out into the Main Corridor, many a person caught his or her breadth at the lovely sight.

The hospital was decorated precisely as it had been at the opening 75 years ago. Hanging baskets of pink geraniums were at every window and over the doorways; it all looked so pretty and so gay, and winning, that many an old guest, as one watched, discarded her years and walked among her memories again.

As far as the eye could see, up and down the corridor, the beauty continued. Many a person present was so old that he or she knew they would never live to attend another anniversary; and they had no intention, whatever, of forgetting *anything* concerning this one. The "meetings, greetings and voices of women talking with men," filled the corridor as the crowd slowly made its way to the large tent, which had been set up in the courtyard, behind the Administration Building. More than 1,000 people were gathered in and around it. The ceremonies began at 2:00 P.M. The Rabbi of the Baltimore Hebrew Congregation gave the invocation; Mr. Perkins welcomed the guests; the Episcopal Bishop of Maryland gave the dedication; there were short statements from the Trustees of the Robert Garrett Fund, the Harriet Lane Home, Hospital for the Consumptives of Maryland, and the President of the Hospital.

The main address was given by the Pediatrician-in-Chief and Director of Department of Pediatrics; it was an excellent speech entitled "The Biological Advantage of Man," but it was getting hot in the tent and people fanned through it without realizing how good it was.

Mr. Perkins made a statement of dedication on behalf of the Board of Trustees, and the benediction was given by the Roman Catholic Archbishop of Baltimore. The patients had been moved to the new building since the 17th of March and the guests were invited to take a tour of it, after the reception, which was held in the "new" cafeteria.

The invitation to the dedication stated: "The placement of flowers on the speaker's platform duplicates a ceremony which took place at the Opening Exercises of The Johns Hopkins Hospital an May 7, 1889. Immediately following today's ceremony these flowers will be taken to Greenmount Cemetery and placed on Johns Hopkins' grave."

Many people were pleased about this and said so at the reception, which, when time came to tour CMSC, boiled down to the hearty leaving to tour and the faithful OHH sitting around at the tables chatting.

And what did they talk about? Hopkins then — yes. Hopkins now — yes. Who had come for the celebration — mercy, yes. "Aren't you pleased that Hattie Alexander, who is now professor of pediatrics, at P. & S. came down and is one of the chief speakers in the three day symposium on 'The Child.' And did you know that the Nuffield professor of surgery from Oxford is here? And young Denton Cooley is back, too, you know; so is Henry Bahnson. And Bill Longmire — mercy, I remember when he was just an intern — is now Professor and Chairman of the Department of Surgery at UCLA. Mercy, how old I am!"

They all met the new Administrator of the hospital, who was going to take over the business end so the President could be free of details; international medicine demanded that Hopkins assume a larger role in global affairs. Just look at the speakers for the celebration; one of them is an M. D. from the American University at Beirut and he has been professor and head of the Department of Microbiology at Vanderbilt!

They looked over the various programs and decided that wonderful things lay ahead this month at Hopkins: 41 scientific papers on "The Child"; Topics in Clinical Medicine from May 18-23; Ministering to the Sick, June 1-5; and the Wilmer Residents were meeting, too, for the dedication of the Woods Building!

"Food's gone downhill!" one old lady said as she sipped fruit punch and ate a cookie. "Downhill from where?" her daughter asked, scornfully. "From the 50th anniversary, from the 25th anniversity and from the *opening* of the hospital," her mother said, emphatically. "How would you know about the opening? You're only 72, Mamma." "I know," the old lady snapped, "because Margaret Billings said so, in that piece she wrote about the opening of the hospital. They had strawberries, and cream and chicken salad." Her daughter chided, "This isn't dinner. It's a reception. Will you have a slice of ribbon ice-cream?" "Certainly not," the old lady answered, "I never eat slab food."

Nevertheless back in the corridor, on the way out, when everybody around her was saying, "Doesn't it look beautiful? Aren't the geraniums lovely?" She nodded, in spite of herself.

But her daughter didn't pay much attention to her, for somebody nearby had said, "I do hope Dr. Blalock can make it to the banquet tomorrow night. He's determined to come." In answer to the inquiry as to why he shouldn't make it, the reply was "Don't you know? He was operated upon for an obstruction 6 days ago." "Six days ago! He shouldn't be there." "You know Dr. Blalock when he makes up his mind. We'll see."

At the Lord Baltimore Hotel on the night of May 14 "800 distinguished guests" were present. The ladies wore evening dresses and long gloves, the gentlemen tuxedoes, and cocktails were had in the lounge before dinner. Everybody who was anybody in American medicine was there, and many internationally renowned guests, too. The words "Will Dr. Blalock make it?" were on everybody's lips, and when the guests were all seated, the word flew around, "He made it. I told you he would."

The old lady who had found fault with the refreshments at the reception enjoyed her meal thoroughly. As THE SUN described it the next day, "800 distinguished guests plowed through lobster thermidor, filet mignon with burgundy sauce and cherries jubilee." At each guest's place, too, was a bronze anniversary medallion bearing a replica of the dome and the bust of Johns Hopkins, these being the elements of the official anniversary symbol, plus the watchwords, "Advancement of Knowledge — Relief of Suffering."

Silver medallions were given to the Carnegie Foundation for the Advancement of Teaching and the Carnegie Corporation of New York, the Ford Foundation, the Rockefeller Foundation, The Johns Hopkins University, and the National Institutes of Health; the City of Baltimore and the State of Maryland were also honored with citations.

Dr. Blalock, who was retiring in June, was dying of cancer which either had already metastasized to his liver or would shortly do so. He knew it and many of the doctors present knew it. But the one thing he did not know, which many of them did, was that the Clinical Science Building was to be renamed the Alfred Blalock Clinical Science Building. His speech was very measured, very slow when he acknowledged the honor. But he recovered his composure and made an excellent address about the old days at Hopkins, two statements from which are very pertinent now. He said, "The secret of future success is to hold to the belief that quality is more important than quantity." The other statement was, "It is my sincere hope that the hospital will maintain its excellence and do so without becoming too big and too impersonal."

Many old movies of Hopkins were flashed on a screen, and Dr. Blalock noted that the total expense of running the hospital in 1911 was $358,000; also in early 1911, Dr. Hurd applied to the Trustees for permission to live outside the hospital. He was 67 and had been a professor of psychiatry as well as Superintendent. (His successor, Dr. Smith, lived in the Administration Building for many years after that.)

After Dr. Blalock had been surprised by the change in the name of the Clinical Science Building, the announcement of which had been made by Mr. Perkins, Mr. Perkins, too, was flabbergasted, for he received the Johns Hopkins

Dr. Alfred Blalock addresses
the 75th Anniversary banquet guests.

Hopkins' student nurses model old and new student nurse uniforms for guests at Hopkins' Anniversary dinner in 1964.

Distinguished Service Award. He had even more difficulty making his acceptance speech than Dr. Blalock had!

At one table in the Grand Ballroom taking *everything* in and certainly in a position, arithmetically, to remember it longer than anybody else who was present were 5 student nurses. They wore a probationer's uniform, vintage JHH 1915; a graduate uniform, 1963; a uniform of 1919; a uniform of 1920; and a uniform of 1970, a student nurse wearing a dress similar to that brought by Miss Lawler, class of 1896, when she entered the nursing school; another wearing her own uniform from 1942; another wearing the uniform of a pre-clinical student, 1942 to 1964.

They were adorable, and when they had moved around in the lounge among the guests, prior to dinner, had elicited many, many compliments. In the face of their youth, even the Diamond Jubilee replica of the Administration Building and Dome didn't dare to melt or wither.

Again, the guests realized they had been present on a momentous occasion.

Before the year was over both Dr. Blalock and Dr. Chesney were dead. And nobody will ever see Dr. Stanhope Bayne-Jones again, wearing his decorations and looking so *very* handsome.

The Wilmer banquet has held during the Wilmer Residents' Association meeting, which began on the 25th of May. The banquet guests numbered 600 and is described in the chapter on Wilmer.

A scale model of the Administration Building is carved from ice for the 75th Anniversary festivities.

Dr. Alan M. Chesney (1888-1964) author of *"The Johns Hopkins Hospital and The Johns Hopkins University School of Medicine."*

When summer came The Johns Hopkins Hospital had entered the last 25 years of its first century.

What lay ahead?

The first time it was necessary to show the mettle which those medals commemorating the 75th anniversary had depicted was February of 1966, when Baltimore had the Great Snow: *the* Blizzard, they called it. Due to huge drifts, the hospital's motorized snow removal equipment couldn't function. So plumbers, painters, and electricians moved the snow. How? With 36 shovels the hospital owned.

The President of the hospital couldn't possibly get from University Parkway to the hospital in his car, so he walked. Many, many ordinary people behaved in extraordinary ways. For example on Monday, 12 out of 90 people in BM&G got to JHH and 63 out of 250 people in Housekeeping arrived. So what did they do? They worked as long as necessary, as much as necessary until they finished the necessary work load.

The nurses worked a day and evening shift and then stayed overnight to help with the busy morning routine: they took 2 assignments. "The student nurses were really the salvation," the Director of Nursing said.

Everybody who could make it to the hospital stayed there and WORKED, and they slept in Hampton House, Halsted, and CMSC.

Fuel oil got down to a 24 hour supply Monday evening, then the first truck in 3 days made it through the snow. The hospital uses 20,000 gallons of oil a day in cold weather and it takes 4 trucks a day to keep it replenished.

The IV stock level got low — patients require 600 to 870 thousand bottles a month. The Thursday after the storm when a truck got through with IV fluid, the hospital was down to the bottles on patient floors, only.

There was enough food on hand, staples and such, and the hospital's milkman delivered his 180 gallons a day without fail.

By Monday evening walks and drives to the Emergency Room, Woman's Clinic, and main entrance on Broadway were passable. That "white Monday" the shoveling crew used 60% of its annual supply of salt on icy sidewalks and entrance ways.

A Wilmer patient came in by helicopter on Monday and there was space cleared for the landing on the parking lot.

As the President of the hospital said, "It's hard work, but everyone has been magnificent. . . . This big place becomes small. You can feel the ranks close around you, when the siren goes off, or, in this case, when the blizzard blows."

You don't forget things like that if you go through them, together. Esprit de corps cannot be bought: it must be earned.

The guard who had stayed in his guard-house outside Hampton House for 4 days and nights during the Great Snow said, "A foot-path was opened in front, so I could just see the heads and shoulders of the people as they passed going or coming from the hospital. Reliefs couldn't get here. I slept when I could. Food was brought to me."

The next time he was on duty so long it was April, and who knows, perhaps the snow of 1966 was a learning-time at Hopkins for the terror of 1968.

The assassination of Dr. Martin Luther King took place on April 4, but it was Saturday, April 6, before Baltimore began its baptism of fire. Crowds were gathering in East Baltimore and West Baltimore, but it was 6:15 P.M. on April 6 that the first major fire was reported on Gay Street.

Ever since the fires broke out in Washington on April 4, there had been an uneasy fright in the air around Hopkins; and this time and these riots are covered in this book because those 4 days from April 6 through April 10 are among the most difficult and heroic times which the hospital has ever experienced in all of its 84 years. Many points of view are given here, for those days are engraved in the memories of hundreds, nay thousands of daily workers at the hospital and other medical institutions in East Baltimore.

During that Saturday afternoon, the guards had told people that it was safe to go home, and some did, among them a woman who lives in Anne Arundel County and works for the hospital. She took a bus and when it got to Eager and Broadway, it was surrounded, all the windows were broken and the driver yelled to his 7 passengers. "Hit the floor. Cover your eyes. Don't look up. Don't move. Lie flat. I'm heading down Gay Street and I'm going to get through if I can."

He did and they did. When he got to City Hall, he said, "You can get up, now. We made it. God brought us through."

The woman eventually got home, near Glen Burnie. Presently the hospital called, "Come back soon as you can."

She did. At dawn the next morning, when the streets were deserted her husband took her back and she carried a suitcase. Neither of them spoke of her coming home. They both knew she'd be home — when it was over. This woman holds a very vital position, and is a splendid employee.

Another such woman got word to "come back." She had nowhere to leave her children; the neighbors couldn't take them. So she said, "Get your sleeping bags, boys."

They did. They got through and for 3 nights the boys slept on the floor of her office and ran errands for the hospital in the hospital, during the day.

After that fire started on Gay Street, at approximately 6:30 P.M. the Emergency Room received its first patient. At 6:45 P.M. The Johns Hopkins Hospital went on Operation Yellow, which means Hospital Disaster.

In the meantime, between Thursday night and 6:45 P.M. Saturday, all elective admissions to the hospital had been cancelled, patients had been transferred elsewhere, or not brought in; the people to be discharged were discharged early; the senior student nurses were kept; all others were sent home: The Hopkins Hospital was ready — as always — to do its duty.

After the hospital went on Yellow, all the key off-duty employees reported in, if it was humanly possible to do so. One such was a young Mid-Westerner, who had several weeks earlier come to fill an important position. Unfamiliar with the streets, he missed his turn at Broadway and came down Wolfe Street instead. He had his doors locked already, but his car was stoned, his windows were broken, but he kept going and finally made it to the hospital. The damage to his car was over $168.

His assistant, a young German recently emigrated to the United States, came down Broadway and when he got to Eager Street there was a large, loud ominous crowd blocking his passage, so he drove his little foreign car up on the parkway and got by it. Then he returned to the street and found the traffic light was red. Being law abiding, he waited, the mob started after him. Fortunately, the light turned yellow, then green, and because of the pick-up of the car he was able to speed away and make it to the hospital.

Off-duty nurses — many of them old Hopkins' nurses with no particular assignment at the hospital, who knew they would be needed — banded together, got in one of their cars, put on their caps, locked doors, and started across town. They had put a sign on their windshield reading, "Johns Hopkins Hospital Nurses." They were stoned, jeered, and hooted at; so they took off their caps, put them on the floor for safe keeping, buttoned up their coats to hide their uniforms, somehow managed to retrieve their windshield sign, and kept going.

They made it to the hospital, put on their caps and went to work. They did anything which was necessary: helped with patient meals, housekeeping duties, or filled in for nurses who couldn't get to the hospital.

All residents of the Compound were moved into the Reed Hall Annex, and lived there, for 3 days. Guards — soldiers by this time — were on top of Reed Hall, Hampton House and 550 Broadway. By Saturday night 5,500 Maryland Guard Troops were in Baltimore, on duty.

Saturday night all Chief Residents were phoned to announce that The Johns Hopkins Hospital was in an Emergency Situation and to make it back to The Hospital, if possible. At that time the Administration decided to evacuate the Compound of wives and children because, under present circumstances it was felt it would not be defensible and the occupants would be safer in Reed Hall.

A few residents, not on call, on their own refused to leave the Compound unguarded and set up their patrol among themselves to try and protect their personal property. They used their children's toy walkie-talkies to communicate with each other, and several of them carried hunting rifles.

One Chief Resident, who did not live in the Compound, but was across town when the call went out, against the advice of his professor, who was at the same gathering he was, made it back. He could get no police escort and when he reached North Avenue and Broadway, he saw the fires at Sears and the looting crowds. Still, he managed to get down Broadway, in his car, to his rooms in the 800 block, where he stopped to get his white coat. Afterwards, as he ran down the center parkway, he was chased by two men with knives. Fortunately, he reached The Hospital gates before they reached him.

Sunday morning — Palm Sunday morning — the word went out that there was to be a meeting of all the Chief Residents in the small doctors' office within the Emergency Room, at 1:00 P.M. and *to be there,* as the Chairman of the Board of Trustees of The Johns Hopkins Hospital, Mr. J. Crossan Cooper wished to meet with them.

Although the Chief Residents had been up all night and were bone tired, they knew that Mr. Cooper had risked his life to come all across the burning city, in his car. To a man, they were there to meet him. (Since this is an historic event, Mr. Cooper is here mentioned by name.)

The tall, robust, man entered and the residents rose. He motioned them to be seated.

Against the fierce hubbub of the Emergency Room, with the background of screaming sirens and hysterical people, Mr. Cooper's calm voice remarked, "Gentlemen, there is no asset which The Hopkins Hospital has that it considers as valuable as its house staff. We can build The Hospital again, if it is burned; we can start over, but we cannot replace the life of a houseman. Therefore, I beseech you, now that your wives and children are safe in Reed Hall, to STOP defending the Compound. Please get those few remaining doctors out of the Compound, immediately, I beg of you. Will you do it?"

One Chief Resident, who lived in the Compound, explained, "They are defending it, sir, because many of us have prized possessions there, while others have managed to buy brand new funiture. We do not want to have these things burned. Few, if any of us, can afford to carry insurance on anything of value which we have there."

"I understand completely," the reasonable, elderly lawyer replied. Then he squared his shoulders, raised his head and continued, "I give you *my* word that I, *personally,* will be responsible for *any* or *all* losses incurred by you from damage to your possessions in the Compound.

"Of course all of us know that certain possessions are irreplaceable, but I will try to do so, if necessary, as far as possible. And I am sure the Board of Trustees will back me up in what I say now. Under these circumstances will you order those housemen to come to The Hospital, immediately, and cease risking their lives in the Compound?"

The Chief Residents agreed and the message was sent by them for the remaining doctors to evacuate the Compound. Then the meeting broke up and they returned to their pressing duties.

No matter what happened that day, nor happens in the remainder of their lives, not one of those young men, who attended that meeting, will ever forget the magnificent courage, wise counsel and tremendous concern Mr. Cooper displayed. They comprehended his great love for The Hospital and for each and every employee in it, who was now serving and helping it. Mr. Cooper had been a Trustee 27 years and Chairman of the Board of Trustees 4 years, at that time.

One of the attending residents walked with him up the corridor, past Jesus, out of the front door of The Hospital and saw him into his car. The scream of fire-engines, the growing pall of smoke, the horrible fright which had invaded the air, were everywhere as that steady, quiet gentleman began his perilous journey

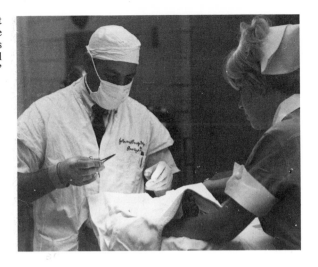

"Emergency Department doctor treats one of the many laceration cases brought to the Hospital during the crisis."

back across the flaming city. Angels accompanied him, though, for he arrived home, safely.

Between that meeting and the time the 3,000 troops from the 18th Airborne Division arrived in Baltimore Sunday night, the Compound remained unguarded. It was not burned, nor plundered.

Sunday evening the Governor asked the President for 1,900 more troops to re-inforce those already present. Within four minutes after the request was received 1,900 men from the 197th Infantry had been ordered to Baltimore.

By Sunday night more than 290 people had been injured, 380 fires had broken out, 350 cases of looting were reported. The curfew imposed Saturday night from 6:00 P.M. to dawn, was now 4:00 P.M. to dawn.

The first casualty in the Emergency Room Saturday night was received at 6:00 P.M. with major lacerations, and torn tendons, and had been pushed through a plate glass window. Before the night was over, the high percentage of laceration cases had made it advisable to use the medical treatment area of the Emergency Room as a surgical facility.

The medical and surgical men slept there; the nurses in Hampton House; everybody worked 12 to 16 hours. To help with the patient load, off duty people at home came back and ER was fairly adequately staffed. By Tuesday night 152 people had been registered and treated in the Emergency Room; before it was all over they had seen 250 to 300 emergencies. Fortunately there were no major traumas or life-threatening situations among them, but largely lacerations and injured eyes. The latter were immediately evaluated, registered, and sent to Wilmer, where those young men worked valiantly. You can remove the glass, or hope to, from the eye, but there isn't always too much you can do for the damage. Many and many a person will carry to the grave the visual scars of those 4 days in Baltimore, and struggle with impaired vision therefrom.

As always humor walked hand in hand with tragedy. One of the first patients brought to the Emergency Room was a great, big, fat woman who was moaning and groaning. Her distress seemed so intense they didn't try to undress her, but cut her clothes off her, got her on the examining table and the doctors went to work. They could find no abrasions, no lacerations, no tenderness, no gaping wound. Finally, a puzzled young doctor asked, "What seems to be your trouble? What kind of doctor do you want to see?" "A psychiatrist," she moaned. "I need a psychiatrist!"

One of the great troubles became that there was no place for the relatives of the injured or the ambulatory-injured to go. When martial law was declared, the busses and taxis had stopped running. Most of the injured were not hospitalized, unless with gunshot or stab wounds.

Hurd Hall was taken over for these people, who numbered about 100. "They were refugees, really," the Chaplain said. The hospital gave them coffee and sandwiches and provided blankets to cover them until somehow, somebody could come to take them home.

This service was provided around the clock.

"Baltimore City Fire Department ambulances were a familiar sight, although many patients were able to come in for treatment under their own power."

Three days and 3 nights, the Chaplain never left the hospital; he assisted the residents in patient care, and was the liaison person between the families and the patients. Many people "seeming lost," he says, "came in off the streets to bed down on the Dispensary benches. They seemed to feel safe, once they got to the hospital."

One thing all persons who were there describe is the eerie silence which descended, completely hysterical, and broken only by the sound of the ambulance sirens and the fire trucks. One night — Sunday — at 2:30 A.M. a couple of men attached to the administration of the hospital went out and stood in the center of Broadway to reconnoiter. They looked up at the hospital and knew they would never forget this night. They looked down toward Church Home and caught their breath with terror, for the whole place appeared to be on fire. They began to wonder how they could get the patients out, where they would put them, and then they realized that the reflection from the fires which were burning around Sears, on North Avenue, were glaring in all the glass windows of Church Home. Everywhere, the air was filled with acrid, thick smoke, and later they went up on top of CMSC and looked over the city.

"It looked like some city which had been bombed out in World War II. Dot fires everywhere. And after it was over, I didn't wonder. The fire loss and looting loss, in Baltimore, after it was over was over $10 million."

The extra feeding at Hopkins not only concerned the personnel, but the police, ambulance crews, and firemen, too. At 3:00 P.M. Sunday it was arranged to have a special dinner for the firemen from Engine House #9, 21 of them. They finally made it to the hospital about 5:00 P.M. reeking of smoke and grimy with dirt, and they ate and ate and ate roast beef and mashed potatoes. One man had 3 helpings. There are 4 fire-houses in the Hopkins neighborhood and many of the men came when they could and ate.

Thirty State of Maryland troopers, who had worked without sleep or relief Saturday and Sunday nights were served meals, too.

Sunday morning 745 breakfasts were served; normally there would have been 300 people in the cafeteria.

How was this done? Student nurses, nutrition students, volunteers (they had come in in droves, too, to work, anywhere, anyway) helped. Eventually 75% of the kitchen and nutrition workers got to work and one of the finest figures to come from the whole time is this: of the approximately 4,000 employees of the Hopkins Hospital, 2,500 are bus riders; and after martial law was declared no busses ran. Also many of these people's lives and property were threatened, if they came to work. They came, not knowing whether their homes would be burned when they got home, either.

As soon as the trouble started, the hospital set up cots in Main Residence where workers could sleep.

The telephone operators closed in on the hospital, and they all came. The head operator remained in the hospital and stayed awake all night for 3 nights and slept days. The service was as good as ever, thank you.

Nurses in GOR who had worked their usual shifts, and lived nearby, when called, came back as soon as the two Pinkerton guards sent to escort them arrived, and went right to work, again. The GOR nurses did, also.

As you know from the Hopkins' anniversaries résumés, The Johns Hopkins Hospital has seen many things in American history and participated in many things in American history. It has watched the City of Baltimore grow, be a mecca of learning and gracious living, deteriorate, change, be revitalized, continue, but perhaps the best description of those four days in April, 1968, is this:

A School of Hygiene research doctor fought back the tears as she said: "You know there is a place — a point — on the Jones Falls Expressway, coming into Baltimore, where for just a moment, you can glimpse the Dome of The Hospital. Each morning, during those terrible days, as I came over here, I looked for it, *because* I knew that if The Hopkins Hospital was safe, the City of Baltimore could be saved, too."

The Johns Hopkins Hospital was safe.

CHAPTER XXIV

To Make the Blind to See

PERHAPS the two most important parts of the Hopkins Hospital sit across the backyard in lonely grandeur now. To Mend The Mind is a *great* undertaking, but To Make The Blind To See ensures one a seat on the right hand of God, which only a person who has survived eye damage and difficulties can ever appreciate.

The children have moved, the nurses are gone, but these two buildings — Phipps, and Wilmer — remain serene and strong in their high callings.

By and large ophthalmology is the "silent service." An ophthalmologist examines one of your eyes, pats your arm, grunts, then says, "Let's see the other one please," as if to say, "first is all right" or "I'm counting on this second to pull you out of the rough." Then he looks forever in the second, makes no comment and you *wonder*.

They even succeeded in building a beautiful new building at Wilmer, adjoining the original building (OHH, where west wing old nurses' home stood) and made hardly enough noise to scare off a rat. During the air-conditioning installation in Wilmer, using the same techniques they had practised before, they'd stick their heads out of an examining room and say to a workman, "Lower that noise, if you can, please." Nothing scalds a workman's decibels like that approach!

Generally the patient suffers in silence, the ophthalmologist looks in silence and the improvement or disaster occurs in silence. Eyes are reality. You open them and whether you like it or not you make a judgment of what you see out of them *now*.

An ophthalmologist prepares
to test a patient for glaucoma.

Bob Hope, right, chats with the University President Milton S. Eisenhower, left, and Dr. A. Edward Maumenee, Director of Wilmer, at the dedication of the Wilmer Woods Research Building.

And because eyes are reality, ophthalmologists can even go out and raise money for buildings from people that nobody else would ever think of asking. Witness the fact that the largest single contributor of the Woods Building is a group which was organized in Baltimore in 1819, and has a monument on Broadway a few blocks below Wilmer commemorating that fact. They endowed a research chair at Wilmer which is named "Odd Fellow World Eye Bank and Visual Research Foundation Professionship." For this purpose they gave $200,00, but the overall gift of the Independent Order of Odd Fellows to Wilmer was $625,000. Matching funds to the private contributions were provided by the National Institutes of Health. A then newly organized (1961) voluntary health agency, Research for Blindness, in collaboration with the Johns Hopkins Fund, campaigned to raise funds from private sources. Among the large contributors were W. K. Kellogg Foundation, $115,000; Texaco Corporation, $50,000; and $115,000 from the Alcon Eye Research Foundation of Ft. Worth, Texas.

The building cost $1.5 million and was dedicated during the 75th anniversary celebration of the hospital in 1964. A patient and long-time friend, from his California days, of the Director of the department and Ophthalmologist-in-Chief attended the Wilmer banquet as a guest of honor. His name is Bob Hope and he is no mean fund raiser himself.

The principal speaker of the evening, Dr. Norman Ashton, Professsor of Pathology at the Institute of Ophthalmology, University of London, said, "This is the first time I have been on the podium with a comedian — that is, an intentional comedian."

Later when Bob Hope spoke, he remarked, "I have never been on with a funny eye doctor" and all 600 guests roared.

Unfortunately, Dr. Alan C. Woods, the second Director of the Wilmer Institute for whom the building was named, had died the previous December of 1963. Also, Dr. Jonas S. Friedenwald, for whom the beautiful library in the Woods Building is named, had died in 1955. Both of these men and their work are described in detail later in this chapter.

Suffice to say here that a medical student once said, "Research was Dr. Woods' soul, but patients were his life" and of Dr. Friedenwald, "Research was his soul and his life, but patients were his pleasure."

The Woods Building is devoted entirely to research and Wilmer is now "the world's largest unified center for research of the eye." Although the Woods Building is only 9 years old, it is looked to by ophthalmologists around the world as the North Star of Research in their specialty.

The present Director and Ophthalmologist-in-Chief, who is also the Professor of Ophthalmology, returned to Hopkins specifically to work with Dr. Friedenwald, and therefore knows how to create the mental climate so necessary to productive research.

This new wing of Wilmer was designed with 4 floors for research, containing approximately 5,000 square feet; and each of these floors was built to house an individual area of research. As the Director so cogently put it, "Few people realize that the eye is really a microcosm of the body and that practically any form of research work that is needed elsewhere in the body can well be applied to the eye, and because of the special structure of the eye much basic research work done elsewhere in the body has to be redesigned before it is applicable to treatment of eye disease. With these thoughts in mind I staffed each of the four research floors with a person who had a Ph.D. in a basic area of research and then he developed his research team as he saw fit."

The reason he chose a Ph.D. and not an M.D. was "when a person has had four years of undergraduate work, four years of medical school, a year of internship, two years in the service, and three to five years of specialty training, he is probably so out-of-date as far as basic research work is concerned and has spent so much time in the clinical field that he is not likely to return to basic research, and if he did his knowledge would be out-of-date. On the other hand, it would be much easier for a Ph.D. to learn something about the ophthalmic disease and be in the forefront of his area of investigation."

One of these research teams has done much work in fetal immunology, which concerns among many other things, the prenatal well-being of the infant's eye. This team of immunopathologists are making great progress in this field.

Another problem which is being studied — this time by physiologists — is the mechanisms of flow and secretion of aqueous that has to do with the production

The Woods Research Building
of the Wilmer Eye Institute.

270

of glaucoma. A second subject that this group is working on is the pharmacology of the aqueous flow and the transparency of the cornea. As the Director states, "Some of this experimental work is bringing us to an understanding and treatment of the causes of glaucoma."

On a 3rd of these research floors another brilliant young man is working in the field of neurobiology. He has been studying the functions of the retina and has been particularly interested in the wiring of the retina so that the coding mechanism of the central nervous system can be understood. Again the Director explains, "The retina is merely an extension of the brain and because of its accessibility and the fact that it can be stimulated with exact quantum of light, it is an ideal place to study the intricate mechanisms of the central nervous system. The Ph.D. spearheading this work has been offered a major chair at Harvard in the field of neurobiology in the undergraduate school. The chair is very comparable to the chair that was held by Dr. George Wald, a recent Nobel Prize winner."

The final floor — the 2nd floor — was designed for a biochemist, but the Director says, "We have not as yet found a person whom we would like to have join us." In the meantime it is being used by the Professor Emeritus for the study of neuro-ophthalmology and neuropathology, and the Associate Professor of Ophthalmology. He has done extensive work on the vascular supply of the retina; also on the treatment of diabetic retinopathy and macular lesions with the laser beam photocoagulator.

Also, integrated into the research work of the Woods' Building have been studies by the clinical staff, by 10 or 12 medical students per year, a number of postdoctorate fellows who are seeking Ph.D.'s and young research workers concerned with the activities already described.

A tool used for investigation in many of these pieces of research is electronmicroscopy. Wilmer now has 2 of these instruments and at one time in recent years 12 persons were there working with electronmicroscopy.

Much still goes on in the basement of the old building, too. The work in physiological optics and in visual aids for persons who have extremely low vision continues.

Also down there are the clinics (in the Wilmer Building) familiar to so many people with eye problems: emergency, glaucoma, low vision, minor surgery, orthoptics, strabismus, tonography, and physiological optics, to name a few; there, too, is the optician. Contact lens is now housed at 550 Broadway.

The basement of the new building, contains the laboratories of electron

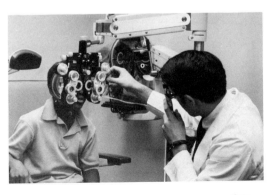

A patient is examined for new glasses by a physician in the Wilmer Institute.

microscopy and the Jonas S. Friedenwald Library, which is one of the leading ophthalmological libraries of the world.

Here are housed all the ophthalmological rarities which the Doctors, Jonas S. and Harry Friedenwald and Ernst Bodenheimer collected over many, many years: here, too, are the libraries on the same specialty, collected by Dr. William H. Wilmer, Dr. Alan C. Woods, and many of the books of Dr. Samuel Theobald, who was placed in charge of Ophthalmology and Otology when the Dispensary opened in 1889. He was a graduate of the University of Maryland who had studied in Vienna and London. He became clinical Professor of Ophthalmology and remained on the staff at Hopkins for many years. In 1912-13, he was in favor of appointing a resident ophthalmologist, but the Trustees rejected the request, on the ground that "such an officer should not be appointed until a room could be provided for him." Ophthalmologically speaking, Hopkins has come a *long way* since then.

The Friedenwald Library contains 9,000 to 10,000 volumes and subscribes to 97 periodicals, keeping up in Japanese, Spanish (including Mexican dialects), French, German, Korean, Portuguese, Russian, Chinese, Arabic, Scandinavian, although their journals are published in English, as are also those of the Dutch.

Perhaps the rarest book it contains is a *History of Ophthalmology,* covering the Arabic, Chinese, the Greeks and Romans.

The library is two-storied, really, this being accomplished by a gallery which circles the sides. Directly one enters on the right hand wall is a crayon portrait of Dr. Friedenwald, which was given by and done by Dr. Ernst Bodenheimer, who was also an artist of considerable note. It is very lifelike and much admired by Dr. Friedenwald's old students and friends. Then if one looks up immediately, on the wall of the gallery, on the second floor hangs a large, later portrait of Dr. Friedenwald, which does not always elicit the same reaction from his intimates as does Dr. Bodenheimer's drawing.

The large rectangular table on the main floor of the library was given by the Maryland Ophthalmological Society in 1963 in memory of Dr. Alan C. Woods. Studying fellows, residents, interns, students sit around it, constantly, silently reading. In the office to the right, also quietly, sits the long-time, and completely competent librarian, who came to this country and to Hopkins from Germany in the early 1930s.

In the two small rooms to the left, one of which opens through to the other, are many interesting things, from a patient's point of view; and they are described in detail here because this library is kept locked now, and one may not wander in at will to see them.

As in all other learned libraries throughout the hospital, the doors are locked unless the librarian is in. When she is absent, admittance is only allowed for persons who have been issued keys. For here, too, as they have also learned to their bitter sorrow in the Welch Library, comes the thief. Only here it is the knowledgeable, unscrupulous thief, who wants rare or valuable books. All Wilmer men who write, give a presentation set of their books to the library, naturally, and just recently the library had to buy another set of a recently revised Wilmer professor's work, which cost $105. The just published — just given — set was stolen in less than a month after it had been presented. Stamped in it, of course, was that it was the property of the Friedenwald Library.

Whoever stole it, wherever he takes it, he will never be able to look into it without being reminded of what he is: a thief. All the famous bibliophiles who ever lived and worked at Hopkins would turn in their graves at this degenerate, disgraceful situation.

The bust of the first Director of Wilmer Institute and Ophthalmologist-in-Chief is in the room with Dr. Wilmer's other personal belonging. For this bust, he is wearing his military decorations and ribbons, pinned on his Colonel's uniform. Many people credit him with being the father of American Aviation Medicine. He commanded Medical Research Board Number One, A.E.F. Among the research that board did in France was a "study of the effect of altitude on ocular functions."

In the volumes dedicated to Sir William Osler to honor his 70th birthday, Dr. T. R. Boggs (OHH:JHMS, 1901) who worked in France in Aviation Medicine then, too, describes the flight surgeon as the newest specialist in medicine. He says (1919), "The development of civil and commercial aviation may create in time ample scope for an interesting professional branch. But whatever the difficulties to

Dr. William Holland Wilmer (1863-1936).

Ancient spectacles from all over the world in a display case adjacent to the Friedenwald library.

be surmounted as time goes on, we must recognize now a sturdy neophyte in the Temple of Hippocrates, the Flight Surgeon, at once the foster-son of Daedalus, a disciple of Leonardo, and a votary of St. Elias."

To get your feet back on the ground, Dr. Wilmer returned to Washington, and here, in this little room is the old ophthalmolic chair in which he sat his patients. It is black leather, has no arms, has a back crank and a head rest with clamps. It can crank forward and backward, too. Getting one's eyes examined in those days was a no-foolishness business!

There are handwritten sketches of the lectures written by Professor Wilmer, while at Georgetown University here, also.

On the wall behind the aforementioned bust of Dr. Wilmer, is a case containing his many medals and honors.

In another case, nearby are rare medical instruments, including an old type retroscope found in the Old Cupboard in the Main Corridor of JHH and a Loring Ophthalmoscope found there, too. (Nobody seems to know what the cupboard was, nor where it was now). Here, too, is an artificial leech used by Dr. Nathan Ryno Smith and given by his grandson, Dr. Samuel Theobald.

In the smaller room beyond are two glass cases which cannot help but impress upon one the long history of optics. Opera glass; opera monocle; toy opera glass, shell and tortoise with inlaid mother of pearl; ivory opera monocle; silver ones; Georgian pocket glass; gold lachrymal tube worn by Miss Evelyn S. Thompson for 25 years (Estate of Dr. Theobald and presented by Dr. Jonas S. Friedenwald). Vinaigrette and opera glass combined (shaped like a snail with opera glass in center); old gold and silver quizzing glasses; lorgnettes all sizes, many shapes; (largest with a lens 1½ times a silver dollar and long tortoise shell long handle. Glasses worn by a squinting child 11 months old; silver frames and earpiece ribbons to hold top and back on skull. Old silver spectacles, 4 different kinds, presented by Simon J. Swartz; New Orleans ophthalmoscope, 1875, in velvet and leather case, size of large package of cigarettes. Shell holder with many colored test folding lenses.

Modern Alaskan snow glasses (wood with slits); war guard composed of metal links to protect the eyes; rock crystal snow glasses from village of Szechuan on Tibetan border given by Kermit Roosevelt, June 20, 1929.

Chinese spectacles, many over 100 years old; also types used by a wealthy family — given by Dr. Eugene Chan. Other carved and beautiful frames, also from

Dr. Chan. Tibetan snow glasses woven Yak hair. Beautiful Chinese spectacle cases from Central Asia — also from Kermit Roosevelt.

Better than a million words, such a display emphasizes that man has been interested in improving his sight as long as he could see: for eons and eons of time.

At the present time on the clinical staff of Wilmer is a full-time professor who is one of the world's authorities on ocular motility and strabismus; in any country, from which any of the displays in these cases came, when he lectures on dimness or deprivation of vision ophthalmologists come from the far reaches of the land to hear him.

Incidentally, in the way that "then" plays into "now," it is interesting to know that Wilmer is involved in an innovative collaborative study with the physicists and engineers of the Applied Physics Laboratory at Silver Springs, which is a branch of Johns Hopkins. They have done very exciting things with our Navy and with the space program. (Dr. Boggs was right: space medicine is a speciality now.) The Wilmer Director states: "About four years ago we began close collaboration with these gentlemen in a number of areas and they have contributed an aspect of research that has hitherto been unavailable to biological research, at least in ophthalmology, in the world."

Some of their most productive work has been with the Wilmer physiologist in the study of aqueous humor dynamics; with the Wilmer Assistant Professor of Pathology and of Ophthalmology in the study of the transparency of the cornea, and the Wilmer Associate Professor of Ophthalmology in the influence of oxygen on retinal vasculature, and on the development of an Argon laser. Also they have been very active in producing a new type of fundus camera for the taking of rapid sequence pictures to demonstrate the flow of the dye flourescein through the retinal vessels.

In line with this latter work, the photography department of Wilmer has expanded in the last 10 years from a budget of approximately $10,000 to $75,000 a year. It was here, at Wilmer, that the use of intravenous fluorescein to study the retinal vasculature was begun. Now it is one of the most useful tools for study of retinal lesions in diabetes, macular degeneration, and many other vascular abnormalities in the fundus. Observations from these experimental studies have been the

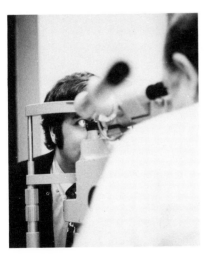

A Wilmer ophthalmologist prepares a patient for a treatment with a newly-developed lazer machine. He aims the machine with a beam of light before turning on the powerful lazer.

subject of many papers from the Wilmer Institute in these 10 years, too.

A principal reason for the existence of the Wilmer Institute is to train ophthalmologists. In the last 10 years 7 Professors of Ophthalmology have gone out from Wilmer: 1 to Yale; 1 to Baylor; 1 to the University of Illinois; 1 to the University of Kentucky; 1 to the University of San Antonio and 2 to the University of Miami.

If you never read the first edition of this book, you've been asking yourself all along, how did Wilmer start? Who was Dr. Wilmer?

One question which recurs repeatedly in the minds of persons interested in The Johns Hopkins Hospital is, "Where would the place have been if Dr. Welch hadn't remained a bachelor?" He bore the institution the same sort of hovering love which many a mother lavishes upon her children, and due to his influences the Wilmer Institute also came to Hopkins.

A member of the family of Mrs. Henry Breckenridge was kicked in the eye by a horse and taken to Dr. William Holland Wilmer, who practiced in Washington on Eye Street, for treatment. The patient's eye was saved and Mrs. Breckenridge, in gratitude, asked Dr. Wilmer what she could do for him. He replied, "Build me a hospital in which to teach, and operate."

Mrs. Breckenridge, a highly practical lady, in 1944 also established the eye-banks throughout the country. After her conversation with Dr. Wilmer, though, she set about raising the money among her friends to build his hospital. Her conversation with Dr. Wilmer took place in 1920; two years later the foundation was incorporated and Dr. Welch, in 1924 and 1925, with the help of the General Education Board, lured Dr. Wilmer to bring his hospital to Hopkins. In one morning, Dr. Welch raised $600,000 from a series of interviews with rich men. The General Education Board had agreed to give $1.5 million toward the Institute, if the amount was matched. Thanks to Dr. Welch and Mrs. Breckenridge this was accomplished in about one month's time.

As you already know, Dr. Samuel Theobald, a native of Baltimore, had functioned as the Clinical Professor of Ophthalmology at Hopkins until 1912; and from the beginning there had been ophthalmologists practicing at Hopkins.

To make way for the new clinic, but still maintain the three cupola front of the hospital, Ward B, in the original plan called "the woman's pay ward" was reconstructed and became part of the 6 story building, now known as the Wilmer Institute, begun in 1927 and dedicated in 1929. The Woods Building is a wing of the Wilmer Institute, which was opened in 1964.

Ever since it opened, the Wilmer Ophthalmological Institute has been one of the great eye hospitals of the world. It didn't have to "grow up"; it started "full grown." From the time the first patient occupied a bed in it, toward the end of 1928, it has ever attracted renowned professors, who considered excellence in one's performance as important as the air in one's lungs. In the 45 years of its existence it has had 3 Ophthalmologists-in-Chief, who also bear the title of Director of the Department of Ophthalmology and Professor of Ophthalmology. They are always referred to as *The* Professor. From the doors of Wilmer have gone out to serve the world in all 9 full professors, 15 associate professors, and 8 assistant professors, as well as many practicing ophthalmologists. At the 30th meeting of the Wilmer Residents Association, which lasts for 3 days in April each year, 800 to 1,000 ophthalmologists were present.

As you already know, in its laboratories much has been accomplished which has helped the sight of many millions of people. In the original Wilmer Building, the late Dr. Alan C. Woods, a native of Baltimore, and the second Professor, clarified many mechanisms and increased ophthalmological understanding of endogenous uveitis, which is responsible for 20% of the blindness in people today. In the building which bears Dr. Woods name, the Associate Professor of Ophthalmology continues work upon this problem, and also upon the neuro-ophthalmological difficulties which brought the present Professor Emeritus his international fame.

The late Dr. Jonas S. Friedenwald's monumental work on glaucoma — he spent every afternoon of his life in his laboratory at Wilmer — has more than half-way built the foundation upon which other men may solve the disease. Dr. Friedenwald also wrote 140 technical papers.

Here, too, "live men stand on dead men's shoulders" and the physiologist, already mentioned, is widening man's understanding of glaucoma.

One question which has arisen in the minds of all OHH who have read this far in this chapter is "It is all very well to talk about research, but what about the patient NOW?"

Wilmer ran 72% of its occupancy 1970-71, the year after it was air-conditioned and renovated. Inpatients numbered 2,088. There were 273 active staff private patients; 1,014 active staff semi-private patients; 801 resident staff patients.

Private patients may know their operating fees, if they request to do so, as may semi-private patients. In neither case are the fees limited beforehand.

The cost to resident staff patients, in many cases, is lessened through Medicaid or Medicare; all groups, of course, are subject to Blue Cross or Blue Shield or other "third party payers" if they care to pay the premiums.

During 1970-71 there were a total of 2,974 operations performed and they break down as follows: 972 of these were residents staff and 274 of the 810 were cataracts. There were 462 active staff cataract operations, and 1,540 other operations. In other words, 736 of all the operations were for cataracts. Also, in the Private Outpatient Department there were 459 operations and the Resident Outpatient Department did 153.

Some extremely interesting Wilmer figures for 1970-71 are that there were 16,727 inpatients days on which they had a profit of $6,096.96; however their over-all loss for the year was $155,619. It cost $3.55 more per patient to see a

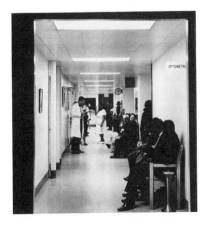

A busy day in the
Wilmer general clinic.

patient in the general outpatient clinic than the patient paid, and there were 27,036 such patient visits. There was a net revenue of $1.19 per visit in the private outpatient clinics, but 95 more visits were made there than in 1970, whereas the general outpatient clinic had 1,258 fewer visits.

There is no longer an admitting office in Wilmer, and all admissions are made through the central admitting office in CMSC building.

The eye clinics in the Wilmer basement still handle their tremendous load though, as witness that 27,036 visits, and they are open Monday through Friday, every morning and afternoon. The strabismus clinic is Monday afternoon, Tuesday, Wednesday, and Friday mornings; the glaucoma clinic Monday and Thursday afternoons.

The Wilmer Emergency Room is still open ALL TIMES in the Wilmer basement.

To handle this terrific patient load, there are a total of 17 house staff, 5 of whom are new each year, and all are kept 3 years and some 4 years. One man each year is picked to go on for the 5 year residency; there is one man always in the 4th year of service and one always in the fifth.

All sorts of pathetic and interesting things are seen in the Wilmer outpatient clinic, for while much of the work is refraction, much of it is terrible tragedy, too.

Such a case was the washerwoman who didn't bring her child the day the stick was stuck in his eye, because the woman for whom she worked hadn't paid her, when she took the wash back. Therefore, she didn't get the bus fare to go to the hospital until she was paid, two days later. The child's eye had to be removed.

A Baltimore optical company has facilities in the Wilmer basement, near the general eye clinic, and prescriptions may be filled and glasses purchased there before leaving the hospital.

In this age when medicine is so busy "going out into the community," Wilmer holds "meaningful" clinics, too. One such was to Walkersville, Maryland, where most of the Wilmer resident staff, many full-time staff doctors, 32 volunteer nurses, several School of Hygiene men and 150 local volunteers from the Lions Club did a full day of mass screening of eye problems with special emphasis on a fungus disease called histoplasmosis carried by dust particles. The Wilmer doctors believe it may affect the central vision area of the retina. They gave a routine eye examination and skin sensitivity test to 1,200 people — about 70% of the town's population. Of them 81 have ocular histoplasmosis and will be routinely followed by the Wilmer Clinic. Every person they saw came back to learn the result of his or her skin sensitivity test.

Preventive ophthalmology is being emphasized and followed up by Wilmer men, everywhere. All ophthalmologists in Maryland have in their waiting rooms now Give The Gift Of Sight brochures, which contain the legal portion one fills out to leave one's eyes to the Medical Eye Bank of Maryland. Any patient in Wilmer can obtain such forms, too.

As already indicated, Wilmer has had a complete renovation. The operating suite occupies the entire 4th floor, and there are now 3 beautifully equipped operating rooms, with an induction room for each and a Recovery Room, for patients who have had general anesthesia. Also, there is a room for the photocoagulator and examining children under general anesthesia. Minor operative procedures are done here. The space where the operating suite and research used to be (OHH) has been extended out over the corridor to make way for these changes.

Wilmer V is now used by the research team in microsurgery and they have developed some interesting instruments which are now extremely valuable in the diagnosis and treatment of ocular disease.

All Wilmer surgery is done in Wilmer; that is all eye surgery is done on this 4th floor of Wilmer. And the best description of this probably ever written for the layman was that given by Mr. Mencken in that magnificent set of articles he wrote on The Johns Hopkins Hospital in 1937.

> "They are outfitted with instruments so delicate that ordinary surgical instruments, by comparison, seem almost like icetongs and garden rakes. Some of the knives, at first glance, appear to be pins. In order to use them in the narrow area of the eye, with its crowded mass of delicate tissues, an ophthalmological surgeon has to wear magnifying goggles."

These instruments are vastly more refined now than they ever were then, and the men who use them now are using them for corneal transplantation, and glaucoma procedures, as well as the familiar cataract of Mr. Mencken's day.

Speaking of which brings to mind one of the best stories about Wilmer, which is that of Dr. Alan C. Woods' retort after his own cataracts had been removed from both eyes. A colleague failed to recognize the name of the surgeon who performed the operation and in reply to his query, Dr. Woods said simply, "He's my resident." The colleague replied, "You wouldn't let your resident operate on you, would you?" The Professor snorted, "I can't imagine a better man to do it, and if I haven't taught him enough to remove my own cataracts, I ought to go blind."

Needless to say, he came out of the operation with "two beautiful, round pupil, 20/15 eyes." At the conclusion of the second operation, the resident was overjoyed to be able to tell him, "Professor, you are again symmetrical."

Speaking of cataracts, it is jolting — and wonderful, too — to see two little twin brothers, aged 5 who have had their congenital cataracts removed aiding each other to get their contact lenses in correctly.

The "new" Wilmer has 79 beds. (OHH, it lost 1 bed). The patient area on both the 2nd and 3rd floors has been completely modernized into active staff rooms, rooms for 2 patients, and on occasion 3 patients. Many have private tubs and showers; all have private toilet facilities.

Since all are air-conditioned, this will greatly reduce "outside" noises, which

Two patients enjoy each other's company in a recently remodeled room in Wilmer.

The Wilmer Parlor with portraits of Dr. Alan C. Woods (1889-1962) after a portrait by Jaques Maroger, Dr. Alfred E. Maumenee after a portrait by Henry Cooper and Dr. Frank B. Walsh after a portrait by Jaques Maroger. Over the mantle is a portrait of Dr. William H. Wilmer by Frank O. Salisbury.

are so trying to one lying in bed with bandaged eyes. Incidentally the average length of stay in Wilmer now is 8.66 days.

The Wilmer parlor, off the Main Corridor of the hospital, which also has been completely renovated, now holds the most impressive single display of portraits in the entire hospital. Over the fireplace is the portrait of Dr. William Holland Wilmer the first Director and Ophthalmologist-in-Chief of The Wilmer Institute; on the wall directly opposite is the portrait of Dr. Alan Churchill Woods, the second Director and Ophthalmologist-in-Chief. As one stands in the parlor, one sees on the wall abutting on the Main Corridor of the hospital, the portraits of the two living Wilmer Greats. To the right is the portrait of the present Director and Ophthalmologist-in-Chief. To the left is that of the Professor Emeritus.

Because of the esprit de corps existing among Wilmer men there is a feeling which is difficult to describe but instantly felt, as soon as one enters the building. You are in a hospital: a serious, frightening hospital, where doctors work tremendously hard and are always in the presence of silently frightened, or joyously happy people. Nothing is casual regarding the eye, and never let the sun set on an eye injury or other eye difficulties if you have them.

Terrible tragedy can walk into the door of such a hospital, any minute, anywhere. Here are two examples: A boy of 23, wheeled into the private patient examining room at 11:30 A.M., on a stretcher manned by volunteer firemen. He was an industrial accident with metal in and behind his eye. The accident happened at 7:30 A.M. and the case had been refused by 3 hospitals before finally arriving at Wilmer. After the ophthalomologist examined him, he was wheeled off for X-rays, the operation was scheduled for 2:30, and by 5:00 he was in bed, with the metal removed and a very good chance of saving some of the vision in the eye.

The 6 patients who had been waiting for that doctor forgot their whines, and while the X-rays were being taken and the patient readied, he saw all of them and took care of their difficulties with knowledge and dispatch.

Again, in that same waiting room, a group of patients were waiting including a father, from mid-New York State, and a 15-year-old son. They had been sent to Wilmer by a local doctor in his home town who thought the son could have a corneal transplant in his bad eye.

The eye turned out to have insufficient circulation; in fact it was in such bad

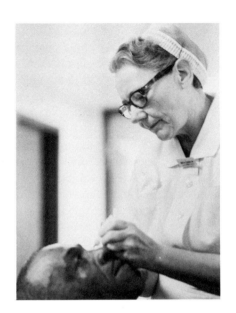

Eye drops are carefully
administered by a Hopkins nurse.

condition that two Wilmer surgeons, in consultation, felt that it should be removed, immediately, if the vision in the other eye was to be saved. The father said he had to think it over. They walked out of the waiting room and never returned.

Eyes are reality and many people can't face reality. Four year medical students go into ophthalmology in their 2nd, 3rd and 4th years, and learn this. Five year students follow these footsteps a year later.

In the 2nd year, the 4 year students learn surgical diagnostic methods. In the 3rd year they attend clinics, lectures and work in the dispensary and are permitted to go on ward rounds; while in the 4th year the entire class goes to 12 lectures on ophthalmology; and they, too, then have the privilege of going on ward rounds.

Some years ago a Wilmer social worker asked a farmer patient when he was going home. He blinked his "renewed" eyes and replied, "Soon as the surgeon-doctor comes over to 'zamine me. You see I was the furst brain job ever done in Hopkins." The excited worker inquired, "Who did it? Halsted?" The farmer replied, "Nome, Doctor Heuer done it. He was Dr. Halsted's helper. It was an amurism." She inquired if he had been given a general anaesthesia before they operated on his aneurysm. He answered, "No ma'am. They jes' give me a little cocaine and then hit felt like they was cuttin' me with a can opener, which weren't none too sharp, a pullin' my right eye right out behindst this ear."

He ceased speaking a moment, and returning to the present continued, "I don't spect no good to cum to me frum the visit. But I seys ef I kin do somethin' to help science I aims to do hit, when you thinks what science done for me! Seems like he's comin' to close up my history, the nurse seys, which I takes to mean jes' to see if I kin still git around and take in what I sees. The nurse seys them papers 'bout me will stay here long as the hospital does. Hit's mos' as gratifying as a tombstone to think 'bout."

At present, they are very interested in the computerization of the outpatient histories and the development of clinical neurophysiology in Wilmer, but — alas —

this man was an inpatient.

Whatever they are, though, the propensity of Wilmer patients to regard the Institute with gratitude is phenomenal, for although Dr. Wilmer retired in 1934 and Dr. Woods in 1956, between those dates many bequests were given; among them $13,273, for research in connection with "glaucoma and related matter"; $5,304 to establish a lectureship in ophthalmology, this being left by Dr. Clyde A. Clapp, an ophthalmologist who served there; the biggest bequest is a memorial to Robert Weeks Kelley and amounts to $374,218.62 to be used to maintain, "free beds, board, accommodations, treatment and attendance for patients unable to pay, or if not so needed to establish one or more scholarships or fellowships either in the Department of Ophthalmology or for the benefit of Graduates of the Department." Another large bequest came from the late Ella LeClair Roten, who left $354,517.14 to be used in the treatment of the "eyes and of tuberculosis of unmarried girls and women who are unable to pay for the same."

In 1968, they received $566,513 from the will of Isabelle M. Bailey, as a memorial to her stepfather and mother "for use in research into the causes and cure of blindness."

Wilmer has been the repository of some very colorful characters and, consequently, good stories, one of the funniest concerning an old jalopy. Dr. Winford Smith ran a "tight" hospital and *nobody* was ever allowed to park on the brick roadway in front of the hospital.

This jalopy in question was owned by a now famous and then resident surgeon in Halsted, at the time this story occurred. He lived, of course, on one of the upper floors of the Administration Building, and he used to park the jalopy outside of Wilmer, in order to take advantage of the incline downhill toward Broadway, as he was always faced with a reluctant battery.

When the King of Siam was to visit Wilmer prior to becoming a patient there, the Proper People, of whom there were several, requested that this eyesore be expunged from the hospital landscape. It was so ordered and when the parade of cars, replete with august personages, made its dignified entrance into the hospital driveway, bringing up the rear was the faithful old jalopy.

As the assembled crowd, many of whom were its permanent riders, saw their favorite, they broke into a mighty cheer, whereupon the Little King bowed right and left and considered himself honored in a grand manner.

And Dr. Wilmer, who had practiced on Eye Street in Washington, formerly, and knew protocol, whatever his inward thoughts, smiled, too. Whereupon the amazed interns cheered louder than ever!

The jalopy owner had to go and perform an operation and didn't have time to fool around with front yard behavior; after all he had complied with what was requested, "Get that thing put where the King won't see it."

The third Director of Wilmer, as was the first, was raised in Alabama. He graduated from Cornell Medical School, and gave up the professorship at Stanford University to return to the Institute where he had trained. He and Dr. Woods were both sons of ophthalmologists, born in the tradition of service to the blind.

Dr. William Holland Wilmer for whom the clinic was named was a suave, elegant, infinitely polite man. He was also the son of Alabama's great Civil War Bishop, who was a fine fund raiser in the North, for Southern causes after the war. Perhaps Dr. Wilmer learned by osmosis how to get people to give him money for the benefit of other people.

During the Bishop's final illness, the Doctor Wilmer went from Washington to Mobile on a special car of the Southern Railroad, and the whole South knew he was making the trip. When he arrived at his father's bedside, he leaned over and asked the old gentleman gravely, "Father, are you dying?" The Bishop looked up with a twinkle in his eye and replied, "I don't know, Willie. I never died before."

A person with the Bishop's humor would have enjoyed seeing this sight, as through the wide iron gateway of The Johns Hopkins Hospital, over the cobblestones, past the sundial, a man and a woman walked up the roadway to the Wilmer Institute. The man moved with the swift, long steps of a person who is always trying to get out of sight, with the hidden haste of a ridge walker. His store clothes hung limply on his long body, his wide brimmed, black felt hat was weary and his jaw set with a grimness which accentuated the high, gaunt bones of his face.

(There are still hundreds of men like him in the mountains and they feel about the Hopkins Hospital just as he did.)

Hung from his arm, like a small semicolon in his life-sentence, was a meager little woman. The white flower springs in her best black calico and her matching sunbonnet were emphasized by the April sun. They gave to her sombre outfit and the grey little face, from which she was struggling to erase great fright, a child-like quality.

Long years had accommodated her movements to his, she floated along, her feet scarcely touching the ground. They walked wordlessly and without any noticeable change in gait, the man opened the heavy door, wafted his wife up the inside steps and said to the nurse seated at the desk in the hallway.

"I'm Goldie and this is She. Old Docta Abernathy up to Mills Gap, Wes' Virginny saunt us. The sights is po' in her eyes. He sed the Hopkins Hospital mought re-aim 'em. Then, agin, they moughtn't. But I took a chance and brung her."

She was a hymn-singing Christian, full of old-time-religion, who shouted now and then. For several weeks the authorities sat upon her as one might upon a loud mouthed puppy. Little or nothing could be done for her glaucoma and she desired to "git back in the mountains to some good truck patch", so the hospital sent for Goldie.

He arrived Sunday morning at 3:00 A.M. (before Amtrak), stepped from the B. & O. Station over to the hospital and appeared, tobacco cud included, upon the corridor of the third floor of Wilmer at 3:25 A.M. shouting, "She! Git ep. Yo heer me, woman! Git ep! This is Goldie, cummon, us is goin' home! The B. & O. don't wait on nobody!"

You can't get very far in medicine if you can't see and, therefore, it is fitting and proper that the Wilmer Eye Institute be the ONLY clinic opening upon the front yard of the hospital. For if you can't see, you can't find your way around, either, and need, as soon as possible, to get where you are going.

* * * FINIS * * *

Dusk.

THE SUN for April 30, 1939, in the excellent article written by Amy Greif entitled "Johns Hopkins Hospital Celebrates Half Century," lists the additions to medical knowledge made by Johns Hopkins as follows:

"The tremendous additions to the share of medical knowledge which have been contributed by Johns Hopkins cannot be counted. Only a few may be mentioned here, such as:

Discovery of Flexner dysentery bacillus

Diabetes effects, which led to the discovery of insulin as a potent agent for treatment

Recognition of value of silk as a suture material

Introduction of rubber gloves in aseptic surgery

New demonstration of radical operations for the cure of malignant growths

Introduction of buried plate and screw method for treatment of fractures

Demonstrations of effect of iodine on thyroid gland

Development of improved operation for removal of lung

Discovery that lead can be detected in blood by means of spectroscope

Introduction of operation for radical removal of prostate, resulting in the cure of a large percent of cases

Development of special operations for restoration of function to immobilized joints

Study of deafness and its prevention, which has led to the revision of some old criteria of diagnosis, and which, it is felt, will by a simple operation, prevent many cases of deafness in children

Introduction of sulfanilamide and its application to the treatment of infections

Introduction of a distinctive approach to the study of patients with mental disorders, which has influenced psychiatric thought and practice in this country

A senior staff member of The Johns Hopkins Hospital was asked by the author to up-date this list by noting some of the advances made more recently. He has kindly done so, as follows:

Pathogenesis of fever

Treatment of staphylococcal infections

Mechanism of thyroid hormone action

Studies in poliomyelitis

Excretory function of kidneys

Mechanism action of insulin

Conduction of nerve impulses

Culture of cancer cells in artificial media

Surgical treatment of congenital and acquired heart abnormalities

Studies of coronary artery disease

Genetic aspects of disease in children and adults

Virus infections of the eye

Mechanism and frequency of drug reactions

Immune disorders

Fine structure anatomy

Diagnostic and therapeutic uses of radoisotopes

Pharmacotherapy, especially of psychiatric disorders and glaucoma of the eyes

Control of fertility and sterility by hormones

Application of engineering advancements both in medical research and in care of patients

Authors without whom it would have been difficult to write this book:

Articles on The Johns Hopkins Hospital — H. L. Mencken in the *Sunpapers*

The Life of Sir William Osler — Harvey Cushing, M.D.

John Shaw Billings — Fielding H. Garrison, M.D.

Autobiography of a Surgeon — Hugh H. Young, M.D.

A Surgeon's Life — J. M. T. Finney, M.D.

Halsted of Johns Hopkins — Samuel James Crowe, M.D.

Osler and Other Papers — W. S. Thayer, M.D.

William Henry Welch — S. and T. J. Flexner

The John Hopkins Hospital and
The Johns Hopkins University School of Medicine — Alan M. Chesney, M.D.

William Steward Halsted — W. G. MacCallum, M.D.

Johns Hopkins — H. H. Thom

The Johns Hopkins Hospital — J. S. Billings, M.D.

Book of Plans for The Johns Hopkins Hospital — Drs. Billings, Folsom, Jones, Morris and Smith

When the Hopkins Came to Baltimore — A. K. Bond, M.D.

The Sunpapers of Baltimore — Mencken, Johnson, Kent, and Owens

Files of the Sunpapers — The Staff

William H. Welch and the Rise of Modern Medicine — Donald Fleming

The Johns Hopkins Hospital School of Nursing — Johns and Pfefferkorn

Time and the Physician — Lewellys F. Barker, M.D.

William Sydney Thayer — Edith Gittings Reid

Pithotomy Club Programs — The Members

Turtle Derby Programs — The Interns

L.O.D. Yes — R. Carmichael Tilghman, M.D.

Dr. Kelly of Hopkins — Audrey W. Davis

Accounting of a Stewardship — Thomas B. Turner, M.D.

History of Blockley — J. W. Croskey

The Use of Silk in Surgery — W. S. Halsted, M.D.

Mr. Guy's Hospital — H. C. Cameron, M.D.

Woman's Surgeon — Seale Harris, M.D.

S. Weir Mitchell — Ernest Earnest

People, Places, and Books — Gilbert Highet

Memories of Eighty Years — James B. Herrick, M.D.

Bodine: A Legend in His Time — Harold A. Williams

The Precursors of Essential Hypertension and Coronary Artery Disease —
Volumes I, II, III — Caroline Bedell Thomas, M.D. and others

Brochures

Hugh Hampton Young	Ormond S. Culp, M.D.
Howard Atwood Kelly	R. W. TeLinde, M.D.
Hugh Hampton Young	Miley B. Wesson, M.D.
Recollections of John Whitridge Williams	Alan F. Guttmacher, M.D.

Mr. Thomas Guy of London and Mr. Johns Hopkins of Baltimore
Samuel P. Asper, M.D.

William Osler and Howard A. Kelly	Willard E. Goodwin, M.D.
Guide to Interviewing and Clinical Personality Study	John C. Whitehorn, M.D.
American Journal of Ophthalmology, Alan C. Woods Issue	The Wilmer Staff
Aviation Medicine in the A.E.F.	Colonel William H. Wilmer and others
JAMA — William Osler Commemorative Issue	The Osler Faithful
JHMJ — The Inner History of The Johns Hopkins Hospital	William Osler, M.D.

Remarks on the Occasion of the Dedication of the Miles Seminar Room
J. Paul Higgins, M.D.

JHMJ, February, October, 1971, April, May, 1972

William Barry Wood   Drs. Tilghman, Bunting, McDermott, Eisenhower

Dedication of The Thomas B. Turner Auditorium   Drs. Rogers, Gordon, Turner, Heard

The Division of Clinical Pharmacology at Johns Hopkins and The Alan Bernstein Memorial Laboratories   Drs. Tilghman, Genecin

The Presentation of A Portrait of Vivien Thomas   Drs. Zuidema, Hanlon, Nelson, Rogers, Haller, Mr. Thomas

FORM OF BEQUEST

I give and bequeath to The Johns Hopkins Hospital, a corporation established under the laws of the State of Maryland, the sum of_____ dollars, the same to be used for the furtherance of its charitable and educational work.

_____
Signature

_____
Address

_____
Date

Witnessed this_____day of

_____, 19_____.

1. _____   _____
   Witness   Address

2. _____   _____
   Witness   Address

THE JOHNS HOPKINS HOSPITAL

Certificate of Authorization for Removal
of Tissue or Organs From Living Donor

History No.:

Patient's Name:

I, _____, hereby authorize and give permission to
           Donor

Dr. _____ and such assistants as he may designate
         Operating Surgeon

to perform an operation upon myself for the removal of _____
         Specify Organ or Tissue

from my person for donation and transplantation to my _____
         Relationship

_____
    Name of Recipient

The operation is to include such procedures as may be necessary in the judgement of the operating surgeon for the purpose of attempting to transplant said organ and tissue, and I hereby authorize the use of such anesthetics as he may deem advisable.

I make this request and give my permission for this procedure with full knowledge that this attempt to graft the above described organ and tissue may not be successful. The risks and uncertainties involved have been fully explained to me by Dr._____

_____
    Operating Surgeon

Nevertheless, I make this request and grant the authority set forth above voluntarily and upon my own initiative and with no assurances from anyone as to the results that may be obtained, either in respect to myself or the recipient.

WITNESSED this_____day of

_____, 19_____.

Signed:

1. _____   _____
    Witness   Donor

2. _____   _____
    Witness   Spouse

SPECIAL TISSUE PERMISSION

THE JOHNS HOPKINS HOSPITAL

Certificate of Authorization for Removal of
Tissue or Organs from Deceased Donor.

History No.:

Patient's Name:

For the benefit of other patients, permission is given to the Johns Hopkins Hospital and the doctors of its staff to remove.

Type of tissue or organ

from the body of

name of deceased

for transplantation to a patient in need of such tissue or organ, or for special examination.

Signature	Relationship

Date	Witnesses (2) (1) (2)

Instruction: *To be signed by next-of-kin, witnessed, and forwarded to the Admitting Office*

_____

Authorized Administrative Officer

_____

(NOTE: This form can be used for donation of corneas of eyes, kidneys and other tissues to persons in need of such transplants and also for temporal bones for ear research — A.T.)